Table of Contents

MW00609381

Contributors

1900s

<u>Stephen A. Forbes</u> – Born in 1844 in Silver Creek, Illinois (near Freeport), Stephen A. Forbes led an amazing life. After being held prisoner by the Confederate Army during the Civil War, he earned his Ph.D. from Indiana University, became the dean of the College of Science at the University of Illinois, was the first Director of the State Laboratory of Natural History (now the Illinois Natural History Survey), and eventually was elected to the National Academy of Sciences. In 1906, Dr. Forbes recruited Alfred O. Gross and Howard A. Ray to census birds throughout Illinois. While Dr. Forbes was not an ornithologist, he appreciated the value of birds as a part of nature and for the ecological services they provided to farmers by removing insects. The attention the survey received appears to have surprised Dr. Forbes, and he noted "the census work on the birds of the state has attracted wide attention throughout the country" (Forbes 1910). Dr. Forbes died in Urbana in 1930.

<u>Alfred O. Gross</u> – Born in 1883 in Atwood, Illinois, Alfred O. Gross worked at what is now the Illinois Natural History Survey from 1902 to 1909. From the Survey, he went to Harvard University for his Ph.D. (1912). After Harvard, Dr. Gross joined the faculty of Bowdoin College where he stayed through 1953. He was a fellow of the American Ornithologists' Union, and he authored 265 scientific articles and books. Dr. Gross died in 1970 in Greenwich, Connecticut.

<u>Howard A. Ray</u> – Born in 1882 in Libertyville, Illinois, Howard Ray worked at the Illinois Natural History Survey from 1905 through 1909. The only other information that we were able to gather is that he moved to Peabody, Kansas, and worked at a bank where he was held hostage by bank robbers in the mid-1930s.

1950s

<u>Richard R. Graber</u> – Born in 1924 in Kingman County, Kansas, Richard "Dick" Graber received his B.S. from Washburn University (1948), M.A. from the University of Michigan (1949), and Ph.D. from the University of Oklahoma (1955). After a short stint at Southwest Texas State Teachers College, Dick moved to the Illinois Natural History Survey where he worked from 1956 through 1983, producing several important books and publications over the course of his career, many co-authored with his wife, Jean. He and Jean published the first repeat of this survey "A Comparative Study of Bird Populations in Illinois, 1906-1909 and 1956-1958." Dr. Dick Graber passed away in 1997.

<u>Jean W. Graber</u> – Born in 1924 near Cedar Point, Kansas, Jean Graber received her B.S. from Washburn University (1945), her M.S. at the University of Michigan (1949), and her Ph.D. from the University of Oklahoma (1957). Although Jean was an active researcher at the Illinois Natural History Survey with her husband, she was not officially hired until 1972, when she worked as an "honorary" wildlife specialist for $1 per year. Jean and Dick Graber conducted early research on birds in Mexico and Central America, and her dissertation on Black-capped Vireos made an important contribution to our knowledge of this now federally-threatened species. Dr. Jean Graber lives along the Ohio River in Golconda.

2000s

Jeffery W. Walk – Born in 1972 in Effingham, Jeff Walk attained his B.S. at Eastern Illinois University (1994), and M.S. (1997) and Ph.D. (2001) from the University of Illinois, Urbana-Champaign. Dr. Walk is the Director of Science for the Illinois Chapter of The Nature Conservancy. Jeff initiated the most recent survey, and led project development, fieldwork, and reporting with Mike Ward.

Michael P. Ward – Born in 1973 in Jacksonville, Mike Ward attained his B.S. at Truman State University (1995), and M.S. (1999) and Ph.D. (2004) from the University of Illinois, Urbana-Champaign. Dr. Ward is the director of the Critical Trends Assessment Program at the Illinois Natural History Survey, and a Visiting Professor in the Department of Natural Resources and Environmental Sciences at the University of Illinois. Mike led the project's development, fieldwork, and reporting with Jeff Walk.

Thomas J. Benson – Born in 1978 in Des Moines, Iowa, Thomas "T.J." Benson received his B.S. at the University of Iowa (2000), M.S. from Iowa State University (2003), and Ph.D. from Arkansas State University (2008). T.J. is an avian ecologist at the Illinois Natural History Survey, and conducted most of the analyses for this research.

Jill L. Deppe – Born in 1974 in Allentown, Pennsylvania, Jill Deppe received her B.S. from Indiana University of Pennsylvania (1996) and Ph.D. from the University of California, Riverside (2005). Jill is an avian ecologist at the Illinois Natural History Survey. Dr. Deppe contributed the landcover classification, spatial analyses, and orthorectification of historic images for the project.

Stacy A. Lischka - Born in 1980 in Kewaunee, Wisconsin, Stacy Lischka received her B.S. from the University of Wisconsin (2003) and M.S. from Michigan State University (2006). Stacy is a human dimensions specialist at the Illinois Natural History Survey. Stacy developed and carried out the human dimensions survey for the project.

Steven D. Bailey - Born in 1959 in Danville, Illinois, Steve received an Associates Degree from Danville Area Community College (1979). He is an avian ecologist with the Critical Trends Assessment Program at the Illinois Natural History Survey. Steve helped conduct much of the fieldwork.

Jeffrey D. Brawn – Born in 1953 in Massachusetts, Jeff Brawn received his B.S. from University of Massachusetts-Amherst (1975), M.S. from the University of Missouri-Columbia (1979), and Ph.D. from the University of Northern Arizona (1985). Jeff is currently the head of the Department of Natural Resources and Environmental Sciences at the University of Illinois at Urbana-Champaign. Dr. Brawn helped develop the sampling design for the study and participated in fieldwork.

ACKNOWLEDGMENTS

We thank Jean Graber for writing the foreword and providing information about the 1950s survey. We are grateful to Marilyn Campbell, Illinois Audubon Society, for early support of the project and to Richard Day-Daybreak Imagery, Mary Kay Rubey, Ivan Petrov, Robert Randall, Greg Spyreas, and Nick Anich who provided many of the images of birds for this publication. Mark Alessi, John Bergstrom, Tara Beveroth, Joseph Merkelbach, Kevin Sierzega, David Thomas, Regina Walk, and Lee Witkowski assisted in the field. GIS mapping and digitizing of aerial photos for analysis was performed by Misty Barron, Tara Beveroth, Jessica Cochran, Heather Fraser, Kevin Sierzega, and Stephanie Wheeler. Courtney McCusker scanned historical aerial images and analyzed point count data. Diane Szafoni, Tari Tweddale, and Deete Lund provided GIS support. Linda Campbell and Mallory Eschbach assisted with human dimensions surveys. David Thomas, Jeff Levengood, Lisa Sheppard, and Jeffery Hoover provided helpful comments on this book. Charlie Warwick and Carolyn Nixon were instrumental in proofing and laying out the book.

Finally, we owe special thanks to the several hundred landowners who granted us access to their property for these surveys.

Tara Beveroth, on the left, was a key contributer to this survey. Also in the picture, from left to right, are Jean Graber, Jill Deppe, and T.J. Benson.

FUNDING

Support for this project was provided by the State Wildlife Grant Program, Project T-16-P-1, with John Buhnerkempe, Illinois Department of Natural Resources, and Michael Vanderford, U. S. Fish & Wildlife Service, administering the grant. The human dimensions surveys were supported by Federal Aid in Fish & Wildlife Restoration Project, W-112-R.

DEDICATION

This volume is dedicated to the past and present scientists who have contributed to a better understanding of the birds of Illinois and the world. It is our hope that this volume contributes to a greater appreciation of the avian diversity in Illinois and an understanding of the factors limiting their populations. We hope that this survey is conducted again in 50 years and hopefully that study will document the recovery of many of Illinois's birds.

FOREWORD

The Illinois Natural History Survey (INHS) is unique in the scope of its activities, sponsoring the collection and study of data on non-game species very early in its history. In 1906 the Director of the INHS (Stephen A. Forbes) asked two young men (Alfred O. Gross and Howard A. Ray) to conduct a census of Illinois birds (all species, all over the state).

This was done using random transects, walking at a steady rate through all habitats and counting birds seen within designated parameters of the transects. At that time (early 1900's) it was possible to walk with little interruption (except for natural barriers – streams, lakes, etc.) and at the end of the day to camp or receive lodging at hospitable farmhouses near the end of the transect. Fifty years later (1957), it was still possible to walk across properties though permission was sometimes acquired prior to the census period. We (the Grabers) were once stopped by an armed posse pursuing escaped convicts from a nearby prison. Presently, with the increase in human population, it is more difficult to walk cross-country transects without interruption. Most landowners just want to talk, but this takes precious censusing time. Because of seasonal migration, there is a very limited period of the year for censusing breeding or wintering birds. Every daylight hour (holidays and Sundays included), weather permitting, is used to census. One cannot allow acquaintances to participate as one cannot count with distractions. Censusing requires alert concentration at all times. Birds are difficult to census accurately. The transect method is considered one of the best ways to count birds over large areas (Bibby, Burgess, and Hill 1992). Point counts are not considered accurate (Efford and Dawson 2009). Transect counts are at best an estimate and a record of most of the species present. If a bird is sitting quietly in the upper canopy of a tree, it is probably not counted. At times identification is not possible because of a limited view. It is possible that a single bird might cross the transect more than once and be counted more than once. It is not possible to be exact in a count of large flocks encountered in winter. The best that censuses can show are the trends of populations and the presence of species.

It is important to census at the present date. There have been many changes since 1958. There was scarcely any pesticides or herbicides applied to crops in the 1950s and crops were grown less densely (see Fig. 11 in Graber and Graber 1963).

Jean Graber

Today, fences and fencerow trees and shrubs have been largely eliminated. The acreage of row crops has increased while grassland (hay and fallow fields), shrubs, older forests, and wetlands have decreased. Habitats are much more disturbed by human recreation. Space occupied by housing and roadways has greatly increased. Tract size of natural habitats has decreased and been fragmented. Some serious predators (raccoons) have increased. While change is part of the natural world, in recent times it has accelerated allowing little time for adaptation.

We need to know what we have at present and take steps to try to preserve and protect diversity and prevent extinction. It is especially important to preserve old growth forest as it requires a very long time to acquire it. Mitigation is not satisfactory as we do not know enough to adequately replace destroyed habitats. Large tracts of forest are needed because natural forest is not homogeneous. Timber stand improvement creates tree farms but destroys natural forest. We need to guard against exotics which compete and/or can destroy native species.

Lastly, we must educate people to know and treasure what we have. Ecology and biology ought to be required subjects in grade school. While these are not considered "cutting edge of science," they are important. Many of our problems arise because politicians who control the management of our resources have not had education grounded in biology and ecology and an appreciation of the natural world. We cannot increase indefinitely without destroying all other species, and, in the end, ourselves.

— Jean W. Graber

Stephen A. Forbes recruited Alfred O. Gross (right) and Howard A. Ray (left), both recent graduates of the Univesity of Illinois, to conduct the 1900s survey.

Section I
INTRODUCTION

[That species of birds are not equally abundant] is obvious to every one, and it must be equally obvious, consequently, that until we know how abundant, on an average, the various species are in the various parts of the country and throughout the country at large, we can make little definite application, either scientific or strictly practical, of the knowledge we now have. Our present information in this field is like a chain, one of the links of which is missing and has been replaced by a piece of twine. To substitute iron for cotton at this point is the object of the studies now in progress in Illinois on the distribution, average numbers, and ecological preferences of the various species of Illinois birds.

— Stephen A. Forbes (1907)

The fauna that we study now is an ever-changing heritage from the past. Though in a broad sense evolution has no beginning and no end, it has directions that are affected by factors untold in numbers… The value of systematic bird censuses increases as the years pass, for without some reference to the past we cannot see the trends of evolution; we can see neither the magnitude nor the direction of change. In terms of quantitative data on bird populations in North America, we have few reference points before 1915. In view of the paucity of quantitative data, and the habitat changes that have occurred in the past half century, the efforts of Stephen A. Forbes and Alfred O. Gross to provide detailed information on the bird life of 1906-1909 in virtually every habitat in Illinois appear particularly farseeing and commendable.

— Dick & Jean Graber (1963)

A project that began with two young men walking across rural Illinois toting shotguns and field glasses evolved into the first systematic bird survey in North America (Hickey 1981). When Stephen A. Forbes, Director of the Illinois Natural History Survey from its creation until 1930, directed Alfred Gross and Howard Ray to travel the state in 1906, no one in the country had yet attempted to count all the species of birds they observed across habitats, with a specific and repeatable method. Through 1909, Gross and Ray crisscrossed the state in all seasons, by foot, horseback, train, and steamboat, while counting and collecting the birds they saw.

In the mid-1950s, Richard and Jean Graber were newly hired ornithologists at the Illinois Natural History Survey. Among the first projects they undertook was to repeat the 50-year-old surveys during the summer and winter months of 1956-1958. The Grabers' 1963 publication, "A Comparative Study of the Bird Populations of Illinois, 1906-1909 and 1956-1958," remains the standard for assessing changes in bird populations of the state for the first half of the 20th century. With the exception of two obscure summer bird censuses by the U. S. Biological Survey (Cooke 1915, 1916), data on bird populations are scarce for most of North America until the Breeding Bird Survey began in the mid-1960s (Peterjohn et al. 1995).

From 2007-2009 we collected additional data that provide a bookend to what is now a 100-year bird survey. We present a summary of the changes to the summer bird populations and habitats across the state over the past century. Whereas our use of air-conditioned vehicles on interstate highways, use of Global Positioning System satellites to record our movements, and analysis of data on laptop computers would have been pure fantasy to our predecessors, their methods for counting birds in the field have been essentially retained. The Grabers benefited from their communications with Alfred Gross during their work, and we are especially grateful to Jean Graber for her helpful insights about this study, as well as the detailed notes and photographs compiled by her and her late husband Dick Graber.

As the Grabers noted, "The value of systematic bird censuses increases as the years pass." Long-term data provide the best benchmarks to assess changes in the distributions and abundance of birds we observe today. Most bird conservation priorities in North America are driven by trends recorded over the past 40 years by the Breeding Bird Survey. The Breeding Bird Survey has become the pre-eminent bird monitoring program for the continent, providing annual data on more than 400 bird species collected by volunteers from some 4,100 routes located across the U.S. and Canada. Yet, the Breeding Bird Survey was not designed to evaluate changes in bird populations within specific habitats (Sauer 2000).

With habitat-specific bird survey information reaching back 100 years, Illinoisans have the unique opportunity to better answer important questions. Are abundances and recent trends of bird populations within the "normal" range of variation and therefore "acceptable," or are abundances and trends outside of what's been recorded over the long term and a cause for concern? How do changing bird distributions relate to factors such as land use and climate?

This study provides three snapshots spanning a century. Important changes in the avifauna undoubtedly occurred within these windows, such as those documented by Charles Kendeigh at Trelease Woods near Urbana from 1922 to 1976. Kendeigh (1982) reported a spike in the abundance of arthropods and the forest birds that feed on them in the 1950s, when Dutch elm disease eliminated a common canopy tree and there was a surge of plant growth from the understory. The unique span of time and geographic scale are this study's strengths. In Illinois, where land cover and land use have changed dramatically owing to agricultural practices and development, insights into the dynamics of bird communities and populations over a diverse suite of habitats are crucial to understanding the past, present, and future sustainability of the avifauna across Illinois and the Midwest.

Birds are among the most visible, popular, and economically important types of wildlife. But how well do peoples' perceptions of changes in bird populations and habitat match what has happened over time? As a part of the third iteration of this study, we asked residents near our bird-survey locations about their knowledge and opinions of bird populations and habitats in their local areas. The human component of sustaining biodiversity is essential, and we must be able to work with landowners and bird enthusiasts around the state in order to conserve bird populations valued by Illinois residents.

Our goal for this book is to summarize the results of surveys conducted across all three time periods. We direct our findings to a broad audience under four major headings:

The Changing Illinois Landscape. The types of habitats that birds use and their extent and distribution continue to shift. Understanding changes in the abundance and distribution of birds is not possible without first understanding how their habitat has changed. Using information from many sources, we have summarized how the amount and distribution of forest, grassland, wetland, and cropland have changed in Illinois from 1820 to the present. With aerial photos, we have a direct "bird's-eye view" of how the landscape has changed in the places surveyed for birds in the 1950s and 2000s. At ground level, many sites were photographed by Gross in the 1900s, by the Grabers in the 1950s, and again by us in the 2000s. These series also illustrate the changing Illinois landscape.

Bird Communities Through Time. Looking within habitat types, we examine how the kinds of birds and their relative abundances have shifted across the three survey periods. We consider how land use has changed over time to the benefit of some species and detriment of others. In certain habitats, the species seen by Alfred Gross 100 years ago are similar to what we found there today. In other places, Gross would likely be surprised – and perplexed – by the birds in those habitats now. We were also surprised by the changes that have occurred in many of the bird communities.

Species Accounts. Every species has a unique life history based on traits that range from their preferred habitat, diet, and nesting behavior, to the timing and distance of their migration. Because of land use change, competition with introduced species, and climate change, some of these strategies work better than others in the modern Illinois landscape. Forty-four bird species illustrate the successes and failures of these strategies in a landscape that has been fundamentally altered by human activities. Some species are new to Illinois whereas others have been nearly eliminated. Others have apparently adapted and developed behaviors that have led to increases or major changes in their north-south distributions.

Looking Back, Moving Forward. We conclude with a section that considers all that we have learned about birds in Illinois to shed light on what the future might hold. The human population and the footprint of developed lands will grow; almost certainly, urban, suburban, and cropland will be the dominant land uses in the 2050s. But what will those developed areas look like? Will corn and soybeans still be the most common crops, or will feedstocks grown for biofuels dominate the rural landscape? How will the bird communities in forests, savannas, shrublands, grasslands, and wetlands change?

Another large unknown is how much and how quickly climate will change in the region. Several scenarios on future climate change have been derived, and even the most optimistic models indicate that there will indeed be some change in annual temperature and precipitation patterns. How climate change will affect the distribution of plants and other components of bird habitat in Illinois will likely be a major topic of discussion among our scientific descendents.

The practice of conservation has made significant progress in the past century, but the century ahead is likely to be even more challenging with more and more species dependent on our interventions to avoid becoming endangered or extinct. We hope that the insights gleaned from this study will set the stage for the continuation of this fascinating and important project in 2056 and help ensure the richness of bird life in Illinois and the region for future generations.

New Books
from a
Restaurant

1.1. Jean and Dick Graber in the field.

Section II
OVERVIEW OF METHODS

From the field notes and publications of Forbes, Gross, and the Grabers (Forbes 1907, 1908, 1913; Forbes and Gross 1921, 1922; Graber and Graber 1963), we have good descriptions of where they sampled, how birds were sampled, and how these data were analyzed. Nonetheless, we were uncertain about a number of details about the previous surveys. For example, Gross used terms like "grove" and "meadow" to identify habitat types in his field notes, but nowhere did we find his description of those areas. Was a "grove" planted with trees like an orchard? Did it have an open, savanna-like canopy, or was it an upland forest? Was a "meadow" hayed, grazed, or idle? Thus, we cannot be sure how certain habitats align with today's methods for classifying habitats and ecosystems. Accordingly, we are explicit and use words and images in defining our habitat classifications. What seems obvious to us today may not be so apparent in 50, 100, or 150 years. Documents and images from this project in the 1900s, 1950s, and 2000s are all archived at the University of Illinois Archives and the Illinois Natural History Survey library in Champaign, Illinois.

WHERE WE COUNTED BIRDS

Selecting Avian Sampling Areas. In the 1900s surveys, Gross and Ray traveled routes they selected between various towns and other landmarks (Fig. 2.1). Many of their starting points were locations they could reach by train, and they would walk towards another rail stop for the trip back to the Illinois Natural History Survey on the University of Illinois campus in Urbana-Champaign. Gross and Ray sampled habitats as they encountered them, and thus covered these habitats in proportion to their occurrence. They began their surveys each morning and often continued them, with interruptions, through the afternoon. At night, they camped or slept in barns, the homes of families who took them in overnight, and hotels when in larger towns.

The Grabers visited many of the same counties as Gross and Ray and "deliberately chose a starting point in an area that seemed to represent the region" (Graber and Graber 1963). Ultimately, the Grabers surveyed 96 locations, 32 in each of the northern, central, and southern regions of Illinois (Fig. 2.2). From these starting points, the Grabers also surveyed habitats as they were encountered, ideally walking a giant square, 1.5 to 2 miles on a side, until they returned to their car. In practice, about half of their survey routes were less than two miles in total length.

While a few of the Grabers' study sites were easily found (e.g., "Apple River State Park"), descriptions of many starting points were somewhat imprecise, described by a distance and direction from the nearest town (e.g., "3 ½ miles northwest of Macomb"). The Grabers recorded the distance they traveled through each habitat type sequentially from these starting points but did not note their direction of travel or when they changed directions. We are confident we know most of the Grabers' starting locations to within 1 mile, but the routes they surveyed from those points are often unknown.

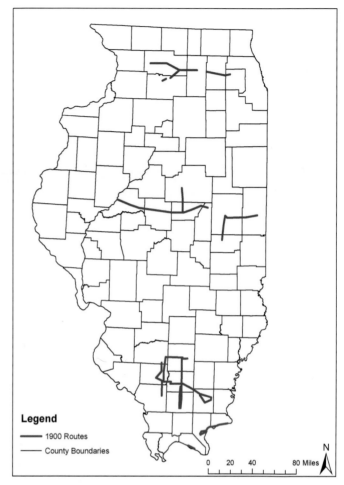

Legend
— 1900 Routes
— County Boundaries

0   20   40   80 Miles

N

2.1. Approximate routes surveyed by Alfred Gross and Howard Ray, 1907 and 1909.

We used the 96 starting locations described by the Grabers as the basis for our avian sampling locations. In cases where two or more of the Grabers' starting points were less than 5 miles apart, we combined those points into one central point. We also surveyed two areas near the 1900s survey locations that were not surveyed in the 1950s. Ultimately, we surveyed birds at 73 sites: 24 in northern Illinois, 24 in central Illinois, and 25 in southern Illinois (Fig. 2.3; see also Appendix I).

Selecting Landscape and Resident Sampling Areas. Seven sites in each region (North, Central, South) were randomly selected to examine land use changes in a 13.9-square mile area based on aerial photographs taken near the time of the 1950s and 2000s surveys. To learn about residents' familiarity with birds and changes they had observed that might affect birds, we contacted individuals living within a 20-mile radius of the avian sampling locations and asked them to complete a mail-back survey about observations in their home county.

Classifying Habitat Types. In the field, we categorized the areas we surveyed for birds into one of 22 habitat types (Table 2.1). The definitions of these habitat types largely follow the 1999-2000 Land Cover of Illinois classifications and are primarily based on *land cover*, although for grasslands (idle, grazed, hayed) and soybeans (no-till or conventional tillage), we further partitioned these by *land use*. In total, the habitat types we sampled represent more than 99% of the state's current land cover and use. Each of these habitat types is described and pictured in Section IV.

For our analysis of aerial photographs, we used a set of 11 habitat (land cover) types to describe the landscape, rather than the full set of 22 habitat types used to classify bird survey areas. We restricted the number of land cover types at this scale for two reasons. First, less information was available for identifying land cover types from the photographs than in the field. Vegetation height and color of plants and soil were generally unavailable or unreliable because of differences in light conditions, time of day, or the angle of the plane at the time when photographs were taken. An observer conducting a bird survey in a field could readily identify the crop type planted there because he/she could examine plant height, color, and other characteristics. On the other hand, a person looking at that same field in an aerial photograph could identify it as cropland based on its shape and pattern, or texture, but could not reliably identify whether the field was planted with corn, soybeans, or some other crop type. Second, aerial photographs from the 1950s and 2000s differed in color (black-and-white vs. color) and quality, which influenced our ability to identify particular land cover types. To be consistent between the two time periods, we limited our classification to land cover types that we could reliably identify from both sets of photos. A detailed technical account of the analysis of aerial photos can be found in Appendix II.

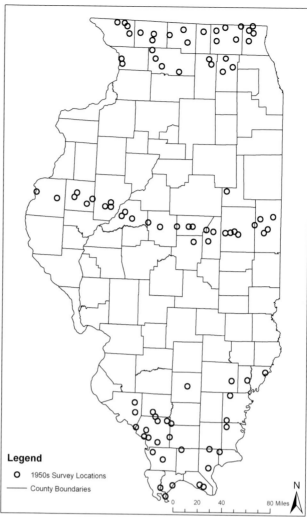

Legend

○ 1950s Survey Locations
— County Boundaries

0   20   40   80 Miles

N

2.2. Approximate starting locations of surveys by Dick and Jean Graber, 1957 to 1958.

Table 2.1. Habitat types assigned to all areas surveyed for birds in the field and identified from aerial photographs.

Observed in the Field	Identified from Aerial Photographs
Idle grassland	Grassland
Grazed grassland	Linear grassland (43.5 yards wide)
Mowed or hayed grassland	Forest
Linear grassland (<30 yards wide)	Linear forest (43.5 yards wide)
Upland forest	Shrubland
Floodplain forest	Cropland
Coniferous forest	Orchard and nursery
Linear forest (<30 yards wide)	Developed area
Savannas-Open woodland	Barren area (quarries, construction sites)
Shrubland	Wetland
Corn	Open water
Soybean (no-till or conventional tillage)	
Wheat	
Oats	
Alfalfa	
Unplanted cropland	
Orchards and other crops	
High-density developed	
Low-density developed	
Developed open space (parks, cemeteries, golf courses)	
Marsh/wetland	
Open water	

HOW WE COUNTED BIRDS

We recorded birds with two types of surveys – transects and point counts. Transect surveys are conducted by one or more people traversing a designated route and counting birds as they move along. This commonly-used technique is flexible and can be used in different habitats (Bibby et al. 2000). Transect surveys were the only method used in the 1900s and 1950s surveys. Transects allow observers to cover more area, and birds will be seen or flushed at times when they may otherwise have been inactive. In contrast, a moving observer might inhibit singing or movement of other birds.

Because point counts are the most common method in modern bird surveys, we added point counts to the 2000s surveys. Point counts are a stationary survey (Bibby et al. 2000) in which an observer remains in one location and records all of the birds seen or heard within a defined period of time. Depending upon when they are conducted, point counts are a good method for surveying birds that advertise their presence by singing often. The North American Breeding Bird Survey is based on a series of 3-minute point counts conducted 0.5 miles apart along roadsides.

The Transect Method. New methods for counting birds and estimating their abundances are routinely developed. But, when repeating historic biological surveys, it is essential to maintain a consistent methodology among time periods to ensure that comparisons are valid (Igl and Johnson 2005). Differences in how the locations for the 1900s, 1950s, and 2000s surveys were selected were inevitable, but the methods used in the field to observe and record birds remained consistent (Fig. 2.4). The transect method for sampling birds developed by Stephen Forbes has some features that are peculiar to us today, but to which we remained faithful.

Forbes (1907) gives this brief summary of his method:

Two acute and thoroughly reliable ornithological observers…were sent into the field under instructions to traverse the state in various directions, traveling always in straight lines and always thirty yards apart, and noting and recording the species, numbers, and exact situation of all birds flushed by them on a strip fifty yards in width, including also those crossing this strip within one hundred yards to their front. No attention is paid by them, for this purpose, to any other birds.

Legend

— County Boundaries

▨ Survey Area for Illinois Residents

○ 2000s Bird Survey Locations

● Bird Surveys and Aerial Photograph Analysis

2.3. Approximate locations of bird surveys in the 2000s (solid and open circles). Residents were surveyed about birds and bird habitat within 20 miles of these points (gray area), and aerial photos from the 1950s and 2000s were analyzed at 21 sites (solid circles).

2.4. Dick and Jean Graber conducting a transect survey.

Thus, birds that were seen or heard behind the observers, or outside the designated transect, were not counted. Gross and Ray modified the technique slightly in dense habitats, where they walked 20 yards apart and counted birds in a transect 30 yards wide and 100 yards long. Similarly, we walked narrower transects in shrublands, forests, and orchards. The Grabers transects were also performed in a manner consistent with that of Gross and Ray.

In all three time periods, paired observers moved at a pace of 40-50 minutes per mile (about 10-12 minutes to traverse 0.25 miles across a typical 40-acre field). One observer recorded all the birds seen (by both workers), made notes on the habitat, and recorded the distance traveled within each patch of habitat. The transect method was unusual in that the observers were constantly talking to relay sightings and avoid double-counting birds. During our surveys, we recorded all of this information directly into a hand-held computer with a Global Positioning System (GPS) that recorded our location and distance traveled.

To minimize variation among observers, we used as few observers as possible throughout the study. Either Jeff Walk or Mike Ward recorded data on every transect; together, they surveyed several sites at the beginning of each field season to ensure consistency in methods. On about 80% of transects, Steve Bailey was the second observer.

<u>Timing of Surveys.</u> In the 1900s and 1950s, surveys typically began early in the morning, usually before 8:30 a.m. but in some cases as early as 4:30 a.m., and often continued throughout the afternoon. Nonetheless, in the 2000s we limited our transect surveys to the morning hours, beginning at sunrise and typically ending by 10 a.m. but occasionally as late as 11 a.m. (Fig. 2.5). This was necessary for two reasons. First, we conducted point counts during breaks from our transect counts (points counts will be discussed later in the chapter). Observers rely heavily on vocalizations to detect birds during point counts, and bird song tapers off dramatically after mid-morning. Second, we spent most afternoons making contacts with landowners to get permission to access areas we wanted to survey the following morning.

Gross and Ray conducted transects in all seasons from 1906 to 1909, but did summer surveys only in 1907 and 1909 (Forbes and Gross 1923). The Grabers surveyed in both the winter and summer. We conducted surveys only during the summer months of 2006, 2007, and 2008. During the 1900s and 1950s, the dates of summer bird surveys ranged from May 22nd through July 15th. We restricted our fieldwork to the period from May 22nd to July 14th. Our earliest surveys were in the southern zone, with fieldwork beginning in the next zone northward one week later. Similarly, we stopped sampling in southern Illinois in late June and by mid-July in northern Illinois (Table 2.2).

2.5. The 2000s surveys were conducted only between sunrise and about 10 a.m . Sunrise at Chain O' Lakes State Park, McHenry County.

<u>Sampling Habitats.</u> Gross and Ray and the Grabers intended to sample different habitat types as they encountered them along their chosen routes (Fig. 2.6). With this type of haphazard sampling, both teams hoped to generate a representative sample of habitats across the entire state, and habitats should have been sampled roughly in proportion to their occurrence. For example, if an area was covered by 50% corn, 30% forest, 15% grassland, and 5% development, the distance traveled on surveys should have been about 50% through corn, 30% through forest, 15% through grassland, and 5% through developed areas. When land cover types were either very common or scarce, this created problems. In an area 90% dominated by corn and soybeans, observers over-sampled those common habitats. Uncommon habitats, such as marshes and shrublands, were encountered too infrequently on these "random" transects and too little data were collected to make robust inferences. To correct this problem, in 1958 the Grabers did supplementary sampling of several scarce habitats they had encountered in small acreages.

Because the landscape of Illinois is dominated by a few land cover types, if we had surveyed habitats as we haphazardly encountered them, the problem of over-sampling common habitats and under-sampling scarce habitats would have been even more severe than that faced by the Grabers. Since the 1950s, the Illinois landscape has become more and more homogeneous, and encountering only one or two types of habitat at a site was likely, even on a long transect. To counter this problem and avoid a bias associated with seeking out scarce habitats for supplemental sampling, we used a different approach.

Table 2.2. Range of dates of bird surveys in each region (North, Central, South) of Illinois in 1900s, 1950s, and 2000s.

Region	1900s	1950s	2000s
North	30 June - 8 July	25 June - 15 July	3 June - 14 July
Central	22 May - 15 July	15 June - 12 July	28 May - 3 July
South	4 June - 15 July	11 June - 10 July	22 May - 27 June

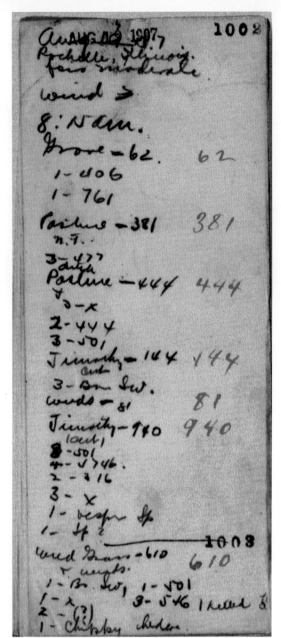

2.6. Original data sheets used by Gross and Ray in the 1900s. They recorded the number of birds seen (species were given a numeric code) and the number of paces walked in each habitat.

the day before our surveys. We typically arrived at a survey area in the afternoon and began mapping habitat types and securing permission to conduct surveys. This process sometimes took several hours. Fortunately, the landowners we met were cooperative. In only three instances throughout the study did landowners decline our requests to count birds in specific areas: two pastures where bulls might present a danger to us, and one wheat field that was ready to harvest where we may have scattered ripe grain. In all three cases, we were allowed to sample other areas on those farms. Most landowners were very interested in our study, and all of them indicated this was the first time they had ever been asked for permission to count birds on their land.

Since the starting points were selected 50 years ago, we avoided the temptation to 'cherry-pick' locations to work. With a few exceptions, we surveyed birds in any patch of habitat we could access, regardless of perceived value as bird habitat (e.g., recently mowed alfalfa fields, overgrazed pastures) or convenience (e.g., dense shrublands of thorny vegetation, steep hillsides). We avoided patches too small to accommodate transects at least 100 yards in length and did not survey corn fields that were eye-level or taller, as it was pointless to conduct a visual survey where visibility was so limited.

The length of transects depended upon the size of each patch, and transects were oriented along the patch's longest axis, or to minimize the need to cross wide streams and interstate highways. We started a new transect each time we crossed from one habitat type to another. Transitions between most habitat types were obvious (e.g., corn to soybeans), whereas others occurred along a gradient (such as from forest to savanna, and from savanna to grassland). We considered the character of habitat within 50 yards to determine when to end a transect in one habitat type and begin another transect in a second habitat type.

Our method for selecting habitats to sample proved to be effective, in that the transects allowed us to visit all major habitats in roughly even proportions. Our sampling of different habitats therefore contrasted with their availability across the landscape (Fig. 2.9). Available habitat was dominated by corn and soybeans, but the sampled areas included similar amounts of forest, developed areas, and grasslands. When compared to land cover of the 1900s, Gross and Ray appeared to favor grassland habitats and avoid wooded and residential areas on their transect surveys. With supplemental sampling, the Grabers achieved a relatively even proportion of habitat types among transects.

In their field notes and major publication (Graber and Graber 1963), the Grabers were not explicit about how they handled the common situation of hearing but not seeing a bird. They did remark that "reduced visibility in woodlands and dense shrub habitat undoubtedly affected the accuracy of the method" and "the strip census is not well adapted to woodland areas." At

At each survey area, our intent was to sample birds in as many different habitat types as possible within three miles of the starting point. For especially uncommon habitats (e.g., marshes), we surveyed patches located up to four miles from the origination points. A cost of this strategy was that it required time for scouting habitat types and making landowner contacts

Table 2.3. Number of birds and species recorded and acres covered on transect surveys (all habitat types combined) in each time period.

Time period	Acres	Birds	Species
1900s	7,604	8,980	93
1950s	6,707	16,818	128
2000s	2,975	18,123	133
Total	17,286	43,921	162

Table 2.4. Sampling effort and response to a survey of Illinois residents about birds and bird habitats in each zone.

Region	Sites	Residents contacted	Surveys returned	Response rate (%)
North	27	540	245	47
Central	28	534	207	38
South	27	522	200	37
Total	83	1596	652	41

the beginning of our project, we consulted with Jean Graber, and she confirmed their understanding that Gross and Ray had only counted birds seen, and that she and Dick had done the same. Therefore, we repeated this method and only recorded birds detected visually.

Across all three time periods, nearly 44,000 birds were counted on more than 17,000 acres. In large part due to sampling only during morning hours, the 2000s surveys covered less than one-half as much area as the 1900s or 1950s surveys. However, we recorded more birds during the recent surveys than were seen in either of the two previous periods (Table 2.3).

Why did we count more birds when we sampled a smaller area? One possibility is our deliberate sampling strategy to survey habitat types relatively evenly. As a result, we spent less time walking through bird-poor habitats such as soybeans and corn, and considerably more time in bird-dense habitats, such as developed areas. Gross, Ray, and the Grabers may have over-estimated the distance traveled by counting paces, and it is possible that we were "better" at spotting birds. Undoubtedly, we have better optics and field guides than were available 50 or 100 years ago. An intriguing explanation is that a few species have become much more abundant over the past 50 years. Four

2.7. Alfred Gross, Howard Ray, and an assistant camping near Running Lake, Union County. This location is within what is now Union County State Conservation Area.

2.8. Every effort was made to return to the same location as previous surveys. In some cases pictures from the 1900s or 1950s helped assure we were at the exact location. The circles highlight Tower Rock (1907, top; 2009, bottom) in the Mississippi River near Grand Tower, Jackson County.

species – Red-winged Blackbird, European Starling, Common Grackle, and American Robin – made up nearly half of all the birds we saw.

Point Counts. Approximately every 400 yards we interrupted our transect surveys, but no more frequently than every 400 yards, to conduct point counts. Both observers independently completed 5-minute point counts, during which they remained in their same positions (i.e., 20 or 30 yards apart, depending on habitat type) and counted all birds. Each observer recorded his/her results separately, recording all birds seen or heard and estimating the distance to each bird detected. The point counts and transects were separate surveys in the sense that a bird first seen during a transect could be counted on a point count, and a bird first detected on a point count could be recorded on a transect. Many birds that were "uncountable" on transects (e.g., heard but not seen or outside the sweep area) were "countable" on point counts.

HOW WE SURVEYED THE KNOWLEDGE AND VALUES OF LOCAL RESIDENTS

From May to August 2007, we visited residences within 20 miles of each bird survey area until 15 to 20 individuals accepted a questionnaire. The initial survey was either delivered in person or left at an obvious location near the main entrance to the residence; it included a questionnaire, cover letter, and postage-paid return envelope. At the time of delivery of the initial survey, we recorded participants' addresses for follow-up mailings. Approximately 2-3 weeks after delivery, a reminder postcard was sent to individuals who had not responded. In September 2007, identical replacement questionnaires, cover letters, and return envelopes were mailed to those who had not responded to the first two mailings. A third mailing of the survey, a cover letter, and postage-paid envelope were mailed to remaining non-respondents in October 2007. Due to a lower than desired response rate, a shortened survey was mailed in January 2008 to measure differences between people who had responded to the full-length survey and those who had not. In total, we gave the survey to 1,596 residents, and ultimately received completed surveys from 652, for an overall response rate of 41% (Table 2.4). Response rates to similar surveys of less than 30% are considered suspect, and responses rated greater than 65% are exceptional (Dillman 2000).

Individuals were asked to respond to questions in several categories:
• participation in wildlife-related activities
• whether they own land or manage their property in any way to attract wildlife
• their perceptions of changes in bird populations, bird habitat, and land use in their home county over the past 5 to 10 years
• preference for changes in bird populations and habitats in the future
• motivations for managing wildlife on their own land
• demographic information such as age, gender, and education level.

Participants were also given the opportunity to comment on any other issues affecting bird populations in their area that were not otherwise addressed in the survey. The complete questionnaire can be seen in Appendix III.

HOW WE ANALYZED DATA

When trying to characterize the dynamics of bird populations, there are always factors that can confound analyses and apparent population trends. Fortunately, there are techniques to account for some of these sources of variation. Nonetheless, we emphasize that comparisons across the three time periods must be done thoughtfully. A simple method we use in Section IV for describing the bird communities observed in different habitat types across time periods is to report the relative abundances of each species (% of all birds seen). We assumed this metric is less prone, although not immune, to error than the estimates of density for each species (e.g., birds/100 acres) because of problems such as variation in bird activity with time of day, difficultly judging distances to birds, and in estimating the distance traveled (and, therefore, the area surveyed). This is not a perfect solution, because if only one bird species changes abundance, the relative abundances of all the other species change by default.

Perhaps the most serious source of potential bias in bird survey data is detection probability, the chance of seeing a bird when it is present within the transect area. This quantity is typically less than 100% and varies by bird species, day of year, time of day, habitat type, and observer. Forbes (1907) did not think detection was an issue for his transect method, and he was confident in the abilities of Gross and Ray:

Their movement is like that of a gigantic sweep-net 150 feet wide and 300 feet deep, so drawn across the country day by day as to capture every bird which comes in its way; with this difference, that the birds are not actually caught or even inconvenienced, and that nothing can escape the meshes of their well-trained observation.

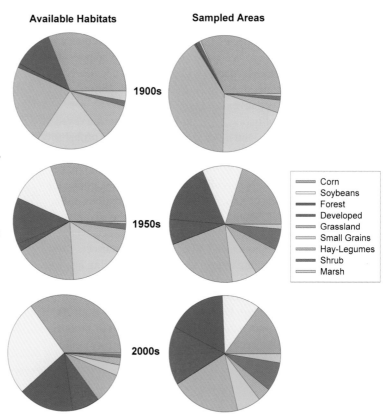

2.9. Comparison of available habitats (proportion of statewide land cover) and areas sampled for birds in the 1900s, 1950s, and 2000s surveys (proportion of transects in each habitat type). Forests were under-represented and grasslands over-represented in the 1900s sample. The latter samples are well-balanced, in part due to supplemental sampling in the 1950s and a revised sampling scheme in the 2000s.

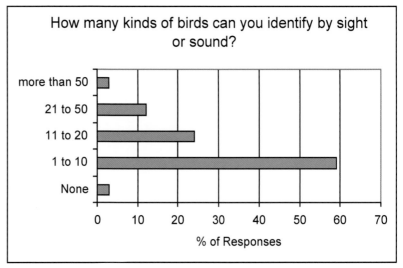

2.10. Responses by Illinois residents to the question "How many kinds of birds can you identify by sight or sound?"

We now have the means to adjust counts based on estimates of detection probability. For this study, we made heavy use of occupancy modeling which is a new technique to account for imperfect detection probabilities (MacKenzie et al. 2006) and is the basis for the species summaries found in Section V. The primary objective of occupancy modeling is to help resolve the problem of whether a species was present but undetected or was truly absent; in other words, we wanted to minimize the effect of "false negatives." This technique allowed us to account for effects of habitat type, amount of habitat surveyed at a location, time of day, and other factors on detection probability of each species and evaluate differences in the probability that transects were occupied by that species. Thus, we could make meaningful comparisons in probability of occupancy among the different time periods (1900s, 1950s, 2000s) and regions of the state (North, Central, South). As an example of the advantages, consider the issue that some 1900s and 1950s transects were done in the afternoon hours, and all of the 2000s transects were conducted during morning hours. Occupancy modeling helps to resolve the problem that most birds are less active later in the day and less likely to be detected.

We used Program DISTANCE 5.0 (Thomas et al. 2006) to model the point count data and estimate densities of birds (birds per acre) within each site. With DISTANCE, we could also adjust for variation in detectability with distance from the observer. Due to sample size requirements, we could not derive detection functions (i.e., functions describing how the probability of detecting a bird changes with distance from the observer) and density estimates for all species.

At the 21 sites where we analyzed aerial photographs, we calculated the average size and number of habitat patches and the percent of the landscape covered by each of the 11 land cover classes. We compared these habitat attributes among the north, central, and southern regions of the state and between the 1950s and 2000s.

For the human dimensions surveys, we summarized the frequency of participant responses to our questions and compared them among the three regions of the state. Respondents were characterized by several factors. They were nearly evenly split between women and men, and their average age was 56 years old. The average respondent had lived in the area for 35 years, and most respondents lived on a farm (30%) or in a rural area but not a farm (40%). More than 75% of survey respondents had closely observed and tried to identify birds in the past three years, and 67% reported that they feed birds near their homes. Additionally, most people reported that they could identify 1-10 species of birds by sight or sound (Fig. 2.10).

2.11. Alfred Gross (right), Howard Ray (center), and an assistant (left) at Running Lake, Union County. In the 1900s, optics were poor and there were no field guides, thus collecting specimens was a common method for identifying and cataloguing bird species. The five guns in this photograph would have been used to collect both specimens and dinner.

Section III
CHANGES IN THE ILLINOIS LANDSCAPE

*Natural cataclysms may alter habitats quickly but not widely,
or widely but not quickly. It is man who combines the two, who
changes the face of the earth not in millennia but in decades.*

-Dick & Jean Graber (1963)

The Illinois that birds live in today is far different from
what birds experienced in Illinois 100 years ago. One difference
is that there are far more people—13 million residents now
compared to roughly 5 million in 1900. Now there are about 4.5
million fewer acres of pastures, hayfields, and other grassland
habitats, but surprisingly, nearly two million more acres of
forest. Even land use familiar to us today has undergone
striking changes. For example, there was roughly the same
amount of corn planted in the state in 1900 as in 2000, but yield
increased from about 35 to 175 bushels per acre. Birds have
responded to these changes in land use in various ways: some
dramatic, others subtle, some expected, and others surprising. In
this section, we describe changes in the Illinois landscape and
some of the notable effects they have had on birds in the state.

Land cover—the vegetation, human-made structures,
and waters that occupy the state's surface—has been a dynamic
feature of Illinois for the past 200 years (Fig. 3.1). At the time of
the General Land Office Survey of the state, conducted around
1820, about two-thirds of Illinois was covered by tallgrass
prairie with most of the rest in forest (Anderson 1970). Several
hundred thousand acres of prairie would probably be considered
wetland or marsh today, but nonetheless, little land was in
cultivation or permanent settlements.

Change came fast to Illinois soon after John Deere's
1837 invention of the self-scouring steel plow that allowed
wholesale conversion of native prairie to cropland. Prairie-
chickens thrived with the interspersion of cropland and prairies;
by some estimates, as many as 10 million birds were in Illinois
around 1860 (Westemeier 1985). Market hunters took advantage
of this abundance in the mid-1850s, shipping hundreds of
thousands of birds each year to Chicago, St. Louis, and New
York. The boom was short lived, however, and by 1870, numbers
were so diminished that hunting was no longer profitable in
Illinois (Merritt 1904). Wetter areas, initially spared from
cultivation, were quickly drained and tilled when clay tiles came
into widespread use by the 1850s. Upland forests in southern
Illinois were the first wooded areas to be cleared for agriculture.
As the need for farmland, fuel, and lumber grew during the
1800s, the amount of forested land rapidly decreased.

When Gross and Ray conducted their surveys, the
Illinois landscape was already dominated by agriculture, though
it looked considerably different than it does today. More than
90% of Illinois was in farms, and over 40% or more of the state's
residents lived in rural areas. Farms averaged about 130 acres
in size. Although corn was the dominant crop, about half of the
farmland was devoted to hay, small grains (primarily oats), and
pasture. Horses and cattle were present on 94% and 92%
of farms, respectively. This landscape was ideal for House
Sparrows, which became the most common bird in Illinois after
first arriving in the state around 1870 (Lowther and Cink 2006). It
has been hypothesized that aggressive competition for nest
cavities by House Sparrows contributed to sharp declines in

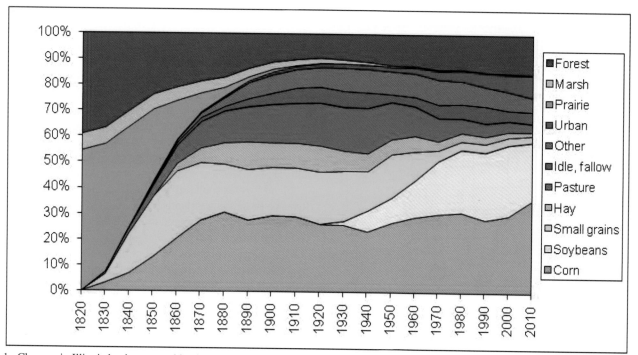

3.1. Changes in Illinois land cover and land use, 1820 to present. All values are approximate and are derived from several sources, in-
cluding periodic Censuses of Agriculture from 1850 to 2007, Telford 1926, U.S. Forest Service 1949, Graber and Graber 1963, Essex and
Gansner 1965, Anderson 1970, Hahn 1987, Luman et al. 1996, Schmidt et al. 2000, Land Cover of Illinois 1999-2000, Bretthauer and
Edgington 2002, and Crocker et al. 2006.

Eastern Bluebird populations. Approximately 300,000 acres of native prairie likely remained in the state at the beginning of the century (less than 2% of the amount present in 1820), and wetlands were being drained at a rapid pace. Virtually all of the state's forests had been logged for building materials and fuel (Telford 1926), and Field Sparrows and Brown Thrashers were among the most common birds in the cut-over scrub that had previously been forest.

The period when the Grabers were doing their field work was a time of rapid change for agriculture in Illinois, with increasing efficiency, mechanization, and use of synthetic pesticides, herbicides, and fertilizers. Average farm size had increased to about 200 acres, but only 20% of the state's residents were then living in rural areas. The acreage planted to soybeans, which emerged as an important crop after the 1930s, increased by roughly 50% between 1950 and 1960, to nearly 5 million acres. Alternate growing of corn and soybeans displaced a corn-oats-alfalfa rotation. The European Starling, first seen in Champaign, Illinois in 1922 (Ford 1956), had become "the new House Sparrow," further displacing Eastern Bluebirds, Red-headed Woodpeckers and other native cavity-nesting birds.

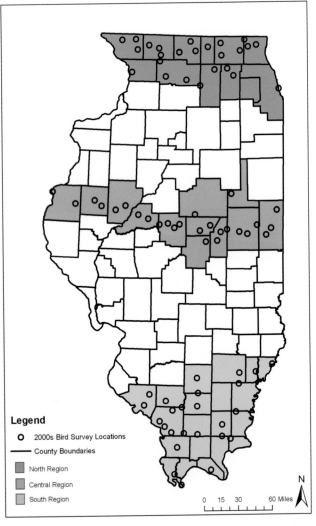

Legend
○ 2000s Bird Survey Locations
── County Boundaries
▨ North Region
▧ Central Region
▤ South Region

0   15   30   60 Miles

N

3.2. Counties surveyed for birds and considered for land use change between 1950s and 2000s.

Today, the state's land cover falls into three primary categories: corn-soybean row crop, forest, and developed areas (Fig. 3.1). Urban areas, where more than 85% of residents now live, are still a relatively small proportion of the land area of Illinois, but represent the fastest-growing land-use category. Urbanization bodes well for American Robins, House Finches, and other birds that thrive in developed environments. With human population growth in urban areas, the percentage of the population living in rural areas has diminished significantly. Since the 1950s, half of Illinois' counties have experienced declines in their population. The change is most profound in southern Illinois, where two-thirds of counties are less populous today than a century ago. Owing to natural regeneration and abandonment of marginal cropland, the amount of forest in Illinois has steadily increased for more than 80 years.

Because of urbanization and the regrowth of forests, the amount of land in farms has declined by about 10% over the past 50 years. Nevertheless, acreage devoted to the two principal crops—corn and soybeans—has increased by roughly 48%. The expansion of row crops has come at the expense of small grains, hay, and pasture. In effect, the agricultural grasslands preferred by meadowlarks have become the row crop fields preferred by Horned Larks. The number of cattle in the state has dropped from about 4 million in 1957 to 1.2 million in 2007. Average farm size has increased to 370 acres, and there are less than one-third as many farms today as in 1900 (about 76,000 compared to 264,000).

REGIONAL CHANGES IN LAND COVER BETWEEN THE 1950s AND 2000s

When considering changes in land cover between the 1950s and 2000s in the counties where we surveyed birds in the three regions (Fig. 3.2), interesting patterns and contrasts emerged among northern, central, and southern Illinois (Table 3.1). The abundance of hay and number of cattle (and presumably acres of pasture) declined substantially in each region, especially in the 13 central Illinois counties. Ironically, the counties in southern Illinois, which were historically forested, today contain 200,000 more acres of Conservation Reserve Program grasslands than either the central or northern regions, which were historically prairie. The Conservation Reserve Program, administered by the USDA Farm Service Agency, is a program in which agricultural landowners voluntarily replace crops with land cover types that promote the conservation of natural resources and wildlife in exchange for annual payments; cropland is often replaced by grassland. Hay and Conservation Reserve Program grasslands cover about 9% of the area of southern counties, compared to 6% in the northern region and 3% in central Illinois.

Corn acreage in the 12 northern-most counties dropped by 27%, whereas it increased in the central (+71%) and southern regions (+30%). Soybeans have become more common statewide, particularly in the southern 21 counties where their cultivation has jumped by nearly 800,000 acres since the 1950s. Wheat production remains most common in the southern counties and scarce in northern Illinois. The central Illinois counties are by far the most intensively cultivated (nearly 85% of the land area), whereas cropland occupies 50 to 55% of the southern and northern regions.

The southern counties, which were the most forested in the 1950s and remain so today (about 32% of the land area), experienced the smallest percentage increase in forest acreage. In contrast, the northern counties, which were the least forested in the 1950s, had the largest increase in forest cover (now approximately 13% of the land area). Central Illinois has the least forest cover (about 8% of the land area), although forest increased modestly in this region from the 1950s. The steady increase in forested land in Illinois since the 1920s (Bretthauer and Edgington 2002) bodes well for forest birds such as woodpeckers and chickadees.

The human population increased most in the northern counties, which are now about 28% covered by developed areas. These counties were also the most populous in the 1950s. If not for growth in the Bloomington-Normal, Champaign-Urbana, and Carbondale-Marion areas, populations in the central and southern regions would have declined between the 1950s and 2000s. Development covers about 4% of the counties in both central and southern Illinois today.

Table 3.1. Summary of land cover (in acres), number of cattle, human population, and their % change in (A) northern, (B) central, and (C) southern Illinois in the 1950s and 2000s. Values rounded to the nearest thousand. Values in red indicate a net percent loss, and values in black indicate a net gain. Unless otherwise referenced, agricultural statistics are from the U.S. Department of Agriculture, National Agricultural Statistics Service; human population statistics are from the U.S. Census Bureau.

Land Cover			
A. North	**1950s**	**2000s**	**% Change**
Corn	1,757,000	1,283,000	- 27
Soybeans	136,000	472,000	+ 247
Wheat	24,000	45,000	+ 88
Oats	505,000	9,000	- 98
Hay	476,000	110,000	- 77
Conservation Reserve Program	n/a	78,000	n/a
Forest	237,000	398,000	+ 68
Developed	n/a	929,000	n/a
Cattle (head)	853,000	283,000	- 67
People (#)	6,437,000	8,337,000	+ 30

B. Central	**1950s**	**2000s**	**% Change**
Corn	1,473,000	2,512,000	+ 71
Soybeans	1,141,000	1,608,000	+ 41
Wheat	275,000	61,000	- 87
Oats	482,000	0	- 100
Hay	338,000	46,000	- 86
Conservation Reserve Program	n/a	114,000	n/a
Forest	301,000	367,000	+ 22
Developed	n/a	205,000	n/a
Cattle (head)	556,000	132,000	- 76
People (#)	624,000	724,000	+ 16

C. South	**1950s**	**2000s**	**% Change**
Corn	662,000	862,000	+ 30
Soybeans	488,000	1,279,000	+ 162
Wheat	320,000	309,000	- 3
Oats	34,000	0	- 100
Hay	303,000	91,000	-70
Conservation Reserve Program	n/a	320,000	n/a
Forest	1,361,000	1,431,000	+ 5
Developed	n/a	160,000	n/a
Cattle (head)	341,000	183,000	- 46
People (#)	402,000	434,000	+ 8

PERCEPTION OF LAND COVER CHANGE

While changes in the landscape were easily detected by examining aerial photographs from different years, we wanted to understand how residents' perceptions of recent land use change in their area (county of residence over the past 10 years) compared with the actual longer-term, broader-scale changes. A mismatch between the public's perception of landscape changes and actual events could lead to misguided conservation priorities and affect the public's resistance or support for managing certain habitats.

We asked residents of each region about land cover/land use changes they had observed in their home county over the past 10 years, and we compared their responses to actual longer-term trends in land cover change in northern, central, and southern Illinois. In all regions, a majority of residents reported that the amount of forest was decreasing, whereas forest is actually increasing (Fig. 3.3). On the other hand, a majority of residents thought the number of homes and buildings was increasing in each region, a pattern that is consistent with land cover data. New development tends to occur near existing development, where most residents live, and it generally takes place quickly. Forest regeneration, however, is a slower process that occurs, on average, farther away from where most residents live. Thus, it is likely that changes in development were more noticeable to respondents than changes in forest, causing them to have a more accurate perception of the former.

Hay and pasture have declined precipitously in all three regions, and most residents in northern and central Illinois thought that pasture was in fact becoming less common. The majority of southern Illinois respondents believed pasture had stayed about the same (Fig. 3.3). Most northern Illinois residents thought corn and soybeans had decreased (they have slightly), whereas residents of central and southern Illinois believed corn and soybeans had remained somewhat constant in central and southern Illinois (where they have increased).

Whereas residents broadly agreed that the number of homes and buildings had increased and that forests and pastures had decreased in their home county over the past 10 years (Fig. 3.3), perceptions were more mixed on whether cropland, conservation programs, orchards, or wetlands and ponds had increased, decreased, or stayed the same. Clearly gradual, long-term changes in land cover are not as readily noticed and may not be reflected in what people see and remember from their home area. We may conclude from these data that residents would rank conserving forests as a priority for habitat managers. However, our examination of land use statistics indicates that grasslands are at far greater risk of conversion than forests. This mismatch tells us that education is necessary, otherwise the conservation of critical bird habitats such as grasslands could be complicated by lack of support.

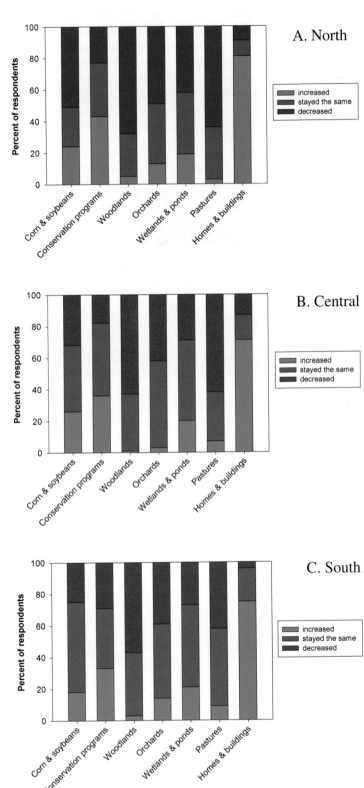

3.3. Respondents' perceived changes in land use in their home county over the past 10 years for (A) northern, (B) central, and (C) southern Illinois.

A BIRD'S EYE VIEW OF LANDSCAPE CHANGE: COMPARING 1950s AND 2000s AERIAL PHOTOGRAPHS

To understand how the landscape has changed over the past 50 years beyond statewide and county land use statistics, we compared aerial photos taken near the time of the 1950s bird surveys and again in 2007. From the land cover types identifiable in the aerial photos (Table 2.1), we summarized changes in the six most common land cover classes over 21 sites (seven sites in each region; each site is nearly 14 square miles, or 36 square km). We feature the paired 1950s and 2000s aerial photographs and case histories of 8 of the 21 sites that illustrate the most dramatic and important changes to the Illinois landscape. These photos are shaded with colors representing different land cover types. Throughout our discussion of landscape changes, we highlight how these shifts have impacted bird species and communities in the state since the Grabers' surveys in the 1950s.

Similar to the previously discussed statewide and regional summaries, our analysis of aerial photographs indicates that grassland decreased at sites throughout the state, whereas developed and forested areas increased (Table 3.2). While the amount of cropland decreased significantly in northern Illinois and by small amounts at sites in the central and southern regions, county-level data (Table 3.1) show cropland actually increased in central and southern Illinois between the 1950s and 2000s. In general, the biggest changes in the six land cover types occurred in northern Illinois.

In addition, we revisited several locations that were photographed by Gross in the 1900s and the Grabers in the 1950s. These series of photographs illustrate how specific locations have changed over time (e.g., Fig. 3.4).

3.4. Landscape 1.5 miles northwest of Golconda, Pope County in 1907 and 2009. Much of southern Illinois has become reforested over the past century.

Table 3.2. Average change in six land cover classes (as % of landscape) between the 1950s and 2000s at seven sites in each of the three regions of Illinois. For reference, a 1% change in a 14-square mile site equals the net gain/loss of about 90 acres. Values in red indicate a net loss in percent land cover, and values in black indicate a net gain.

Region	Cropland	Developed	Forest	Grassland	Shrubland	Wetland
North	- 13.1	+ 11.5	+ 4.3	- 6.0	+ 0.3	+ 0.8
Central	- 2.4	+ 4.0	+ 3.8	- 4.7	- 1.7	- 0.03
South	- 0.8	+ 4.5	+ 1.9	- 2.8	+ 0.1	+ 1.2

Cropland. Cropland decreased substantially in the 7 sites in northern Illinois over the past 50 years, while the southern and central sites experienced much smaller reductions (Table 3.2, 3.3). Most cropland loss in the north was due to expanding development. At Lake Villa (Fig. 3.11) 22% of the landscape was converted from cropland to development. Interestingly, although we sampled corn and soybean fields at Lake Villa, we found no Horned Larks, which are the most characteristic cropland bird in Illinois. In other northern sites, cropland-to-development conversion ranged from 1% to 5%. A substantial proportion of the landscape at some northern sites was also converted from cropland to grassland.

The smaller losses in cropland acreage in the southern and central regions were caused primarily by conversion to development and forest, although transitions to grassland also contributed to cropland loss. At Goreville in southern Illinois (Fig. 3.13), enrollment of marginal cropland into the Conservation Reserve Program drove a 9% shift from cropland to grassland and a reduction in cropland. A 5% cropland-to-grassland conversion took place at Crab Orchard in the same region (Fig. 3.14), occurring mostly on and near Crab Orchard National Wildlife Refuge.

Across the 21 sites, the number of crop fields decreased while average field size increased by 80% to 92% (Table 3.3). The move to a smaller number of larger fields was accompanied by a shift to a corn-soybean dominated system. Birds that use grassy or shrubby field borders, such as Vesper Sparrows and Brown Thrashers, have become less common as a result of these changes in the agricultural landscape, which are best depicted in the paired photos near Flagg Center (Fig. 3.15, 3.16) and Havana (Fig. 3.20, 3.24).

3.5. Most of Illinois's wetlands were drained prior to 1907 and the by-product of this is drainage ditches. The biggest difference in these is the addition of grass filter strips as seen in these photographs. This ditch is two miles west of Champaign, Champaign County.

3.6. Corn has been the dominant habitat in Illinois for 100 years and in some areas the landscape has not changed. These three pictures were taken 1mile north of Buffalo Hart in Sangamon County. Elkhart Hill is visible in the distance.

Table 3.3. Average percent cover of cropland in the landscape and average number and size of crop fields at seven sites in each of the three regions of Illinois. For reference, a 1% change at a 14-square mile site equals the net gain/loss of about 90 acres.

	% Cover		Number of Crop Fields		Average size (acres)	
Region	1950s	2000s	1950s	2000s	1950s	2000s
North	61.5	48.4	344.1	139.6	16.3	31.6
Central	62.0	59.6	313.3	165.9	18.3	34.1
South	45.3	40.4	316.6	150.1	12.8	23.0

Grassland. The largest net reduction in grassland cover occurred at sites in northern Illinois, but this change was less pronounced than the loss of cropland in that region (Table 3.4). Most grassland in the North was converted to development (e.g., 9.3% of the Lake Villa area, Fig. 3.11), spurred by a large increase in population growth there over the past 50 years (Table 3.1). Conversion to forest and cropland also contributed to the reduction of grassland cover at some northern sites. Three to five percent of the Flagg Center and Lake Villa landscapes were converted from grassland to forest (Figs. 3.15 and 3.11, respectively), while at Apple River, 4% of the area shifted from grassland to cropland (Fig. 3.12). The average size of grassland patches decreased considerably at the northern sites (Table 3.4). Bobolinks and Savannah Sparrows, grassland birds which are largely restricted to northern Illinois, have become much less common since the 1960s (Sauer et al. 2008), likely reflecting the loss of this habitat type. The widespread loss of grasslands is concerning because birds that depend on grasslands have experienced the most consistent, widespread, and severe population declines of any group of birds in North America (Peterjohn and Sauer 1999).

Net losses in grassland cover in central and southern Illinois sites were primarily caused by conversion to forest. For example, 11% of the landscape near Goreville (southern Illinois) shifted from grassland to forest since the 1950s (Fig. 3.13). Although there are fewer grassland patches today, the remaining grasslands in southern Illinois are larger on average than grasslands 50 years ago. For Henslow's Sparrows, a bird that prefers larger grasslands and denser vegetation, the larger fields enrolled in the Conservation Reserve Program (Fig. 3.7) in the southern part of the state since the late 1980s have fueled the recovery of this species (Herkert 2007), despite declines in the total amount of grassland in the region. In 2009, the Henslow's Sparrow was removed from the Illinois list of threatened species.

3.7. This field 1 mile southwest of Bluford, Illinois, (Jefferson County) represents how rural grasslands have changed. In 1907 this field was probably grazed by cattle, whereas in 2008 this field was enrolled in the Conservation Reserve Program.

3.8. Prairie grasses and rushes in southern Winnebago County. Nearly all prairies were gone by 1907, however, in recent years efforts have been made to restore prairies in certain areas.

Table 3.4. Average percent grassland cover and average number and size of grasslands at sites in northern, central, and southern Illinois. For reference, a 1% change at a 14-square mile site equals the net gain/loss of about 90 acres.

Region	% Cover		Number of Grasslands		Average size (acres)	
	1950s	2000s	1950s	2000s	1950s	2000s
North	17.3	11.3	126.9	110.4	12.4	9.4
Central	11.4	6.7	127.4	82.0	8.6	7.7
South	14.7	11.9	180.0	97.7	7.2	11.4

Forest. Forest cover increased across Illinois between the 1950s and 2000s, with the largest change in the northern region (Table 3.5). Interestingly, we measured the largest increase in forest area at the site that also became the most heavily developed—Lake Villa in Lake County (Fig. 3.11). Northern sites tended to have more and larger forest patches in 2007 compared with 50 years ago (Table 3.5). Mirroring county-level data, sites in southern Illinois, where forests are a more dominant landscape component, experienced the smallest increase in forest cover over the same 50-year time period. Several of our southern sites were in the Shawnee National Forest, which was established in the early 1930s. As these forests matured over time (Figs. 3.13, 3.26), we observed a notable increase in canopy closure, best exemplified at Cora (Fig. 3.30). Because of this trend, Red-headed Woodpeckers, Eastern Towhees, and other birds that prefer open-canopy type woodlands with shrubby openings have been displaced to the benefit of bird species better suited to closed-canopy forests. The statewide increase in forest cover is promising for many birds, including Acadian Flycatchers, Kentucky Warblers, Carolina Wrens, Blue-gray Gnatcatchers, and Red-eyed Vireos.

3.9. This hillside near Shelterville (Hardin County) represents how forests in southern Illinois have matured over the past century. Also the crop field in the foreground has been abandoned and is now shrubland.

3.10. These images, taken on a bluff just northeast of Brownfield (Pope County), represent some of the most dramatic changes documented via the three studies. This floodplain area was in agriculture in 1907; by 1963 the area had succeeded into second-growth forest, only to be cleared again before 2008 for corn and soybean production.

Region	% Cover		Number of Forest Patches		Average size (acres)	
	1950s	2000s	1950s	2000s	1950s	2000s
North	4.2	8.5	46.4	74.0	9.6	13.1
Central	12.4	16.2	55.0	55.1	23.0	31.9
South	27.1	29.0	70.7	68.1	49.6	50.4

Developed. Development increased across Illinois over the past 50 years, and sites in the northern region changed the most. By 2007, developed land cover had increased by 135% in the north, largely due to conversion from cropland and grassland (see Cropland and Grassland previously). The average number of developed areas in the three regions changed little, but on average they became much larger (Table 3.6). Average patch size increased by 1,015% at the northern sites, 112% at the central sites, and 160% in the southern areas (Table 3.6). The enormous expansion of developed areas was most pronounced at Lake Villa in northern Illinois (Fig. 3.11), where suburban and urban centers engulfed surrounding cropland, grassland, and forest. In the northern sites, most development occurred in relatively few urban and suburban centers. At central and southern sites, most development took place in many smaller patches in rural areas or small towns, as illustrated in the Crab Orchard area in the south (Fig. 3.14).

Table 3.6. Average percent developed cover and average number and size of developed areas at sites in northern, central, and southern Illinois. For reference, a 1% change at a 14-square mile site equals the net gain/loss of about 90 acres.

	% Cover		Number of Developed Areas		Average size (acres)	
Region	1950s	2000s	1950s	2000s	1950s	2000s
North	7.9	19.4	28.7	29.1	35.8	399.4
Central	4.6	8.5	50.0	42.4	8.2	17.3
South	4.5	9.0	65.0	56.0	6.9	18.0

Shrubland. Shrubland is not an abundant land cover type in Illinois and it comprised less than 3% of the total landscape at the 21 sites we considered (Table 3.7). Only wetlands in central Illinois sites were less common than shrublands in the 2007 aerial photos. Because of the general rarity of shrublands in Illinois, a number of shrubland birds are of conservation concern, including Yellow-breasted Chats, Bell's Vireos, Willow Flycatchers, Northern Bobwhites, Brown Thrashers, and Field Sparrows. Shrublands are ephemeral by nature since they represent a transitional stage between grassland or cropland and forest, and where they are found in the landscape changes over time. Allerton Park (Figs. 3.28, 3.29) illustrates the successional change from shrubland to forest. Other land cover types, such as cropland, developed areas, and forests tended to be more stable than shrublands.

Table 3.7. Average percent shrubland cover and average number and size of shrublands at sites in northern, central, and southern Illinois. For reference, a 1% change at a 14-square mile site equals the net gain/loss of about 90 acres.

	% Cover		Number of Shrublands		Average size (acres)	
Region	1950s	2000s	1950s	2000s	1950s	2000s
North	0.7	1.0	11.1	19.7	4.7	4.7
Central	2.2	0.5	22.3	10.1	8.4	4.9
South	1.3	1.4	30.0	16.0	4.2	7.2

Wetland. Over time, wetland cover slightly increased at the northern and southern sites and remained essentially unchanged at central sites (Table 3.8). The slight increase in the northern sites may reflect mitigation for urban and suburban development. As with shrublands, wetlands are a minor component of the landscapes we examined but are most prevalent at northern sites. Marshes and other wetlands are an important habitat for several familiar birds, including Canada Geese, Great Blue Herons, Mallards, and Wood Ducks, as well as less familiar birds, such as Virginia Rails and Least Bitterns. A disproportionate number of the state's threatened and endangered species are dependent on wetland habitat.

Table 3.8. Average percent cover of wetlands and average number and size of wetlands at seven sites in each of the three regions of Illinois. For reference, a 1% change at a 14-square mile site equals the net gain/loss of about 90 acres.

	% Cover		Number of Wetlands		Average size (acres)	
Region	1950s	2000s	1950s	2000s	1950s	2000s
North	3.3	4.1	27.8	27.7	9.9	15.1
Central	0.1	0.1	2.3	6.0	4.7	1.0
South	0.3	1.5	3.8	6.5	6.4	15.8

Lake Villa 1954

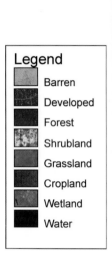

Legend
- Barren
- Developed
- Forest
- Shrubland
- Grassland
- Cropland
- Wetland
- Water

N   0   0.5   1   Miles

3.11. Aerial view of Lake Villa in Lake County, 1954 and 2007. Lake Villa experienced a dramatic increase in urbanization over the past 50 years, covering an additional 32% of the landscape in 2007 than in 1954. In the 1954 aerial image, several areas have been subdivided but not yet built up. Between 1960 and 2007, the population of Lake County more than doubled, from about 294,000 to 710,000 residents. As development sprawled across the landscape, it engulfed surrounding cropland and grassland (34% and 11% less of the landscape, respectively). Ring-necked Pheasants, Horned Larks, Bobolinks, and Eastern Meadowlarks were among the open-habitat birds found in this area by the Grabers in 1957, but not detected on transects in 2008.

Although wetlands and forests were not dominant land cover types in the Lake Villa area in either time period, both habitat types increased over the past 53 years. Several grassland areas were converted to marshes. Some wetlands were restored as mitigation for damage to other wetlands, and others have expanded due to increased or redirected stormwater runoff from developed areas. We found marsh-dependent birds such as Virginia Rails, Marsh Wrens, and Swamp Sparrows in these wetlands. The increase in forest cover reflects attempts to protect remaining natural areas in the county. The Lake County Forest Preserve District, established in 1958, now includes more than 27,000 acres of forest, prairie, wetlands, and lakes in Lake County. Conservation lands in Lake County sustain populations of many state-endangered birds, including Common Moorhens, Black Terns, and Yellow-headed Blackbirds.

Lake Villa 2007

Table 3.9. Changes in dominant land cover classes in Lake Villa from 1954 to 2007.

Land cover type	% Cover		Number of patches		Average size (acres)	
	1954	2007	1954	2007	1954	2007
Developed	25.0	57.0	15	2	148.2	2537.0
Cropland	37.1	3.4	248	26	13.3	11.8
Grassland	21.0	9.9	146	87	12.8	10.1
Wetland	3.5	8.2	47	81	6.7	8.9
Forest	2.4	6.4	56	79	3.7	7.2

Apple River 1958

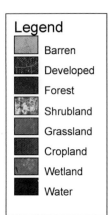

Legend
- Barren
- Developed
- Forest
- Shrubland
- Grassland
- Cropland
- Wetland
- Water

N

0   0.5   1
Miles

3.12. Aerial view of the Apple River, slightly south of the town of Apple River (located along northern edge of the images) in JoDaviess County, 1958 and 2007. Among the sites we considered, the Apple River area best demonstrates the loss of grasslands. In 1958, about 30% of the area was grassland, and JoDaviess County had nearly 57,000 acres of hay. When Dick and Jean Graber surveyed the area in early July 1958, Bobolinks and Western Meadowlarks were the most common birds in the pastures and hay fields they sampled, and they found Upland Sandpipers in pastures and alfalfa fields.

By 2007, only about one-half as much grassland remained in the Apple River area (16%), with the lost grasslands transitioning about equally to forest and cropland. Hay acreage throughout JoDaviess County was less than 35,000 acres. The most common birds we found in the pastures and hayfields of JoDaviess County were Red-winged Blackbirds and European Starlings, and we did not record Upland Sandpipers on any transects across the state in the 2000s. On average, grasslands that remained in the Apple River area were about half the size of grasslands in 1958. Bobolinks and Western Meadowlarks were infrequently seen in the Apple River area in 2007, and like several other grassland-nesting birds, are known to prefer larger grasslands (Herkert et al. 1993).

Apple River 2007

Table 3.10. Changes in dominant landscape characteristics along Apple River from 1958 to 2007.

	% Cover		Number of patches		Average size (acres)	
Land cover type	1958	2007	1958	2007	1958	2007
Grassland	30.8	16.2	163	170	16.8	8.4
Forest	10.1	18.3	70	108	12.8	15.1

Goreville 1959

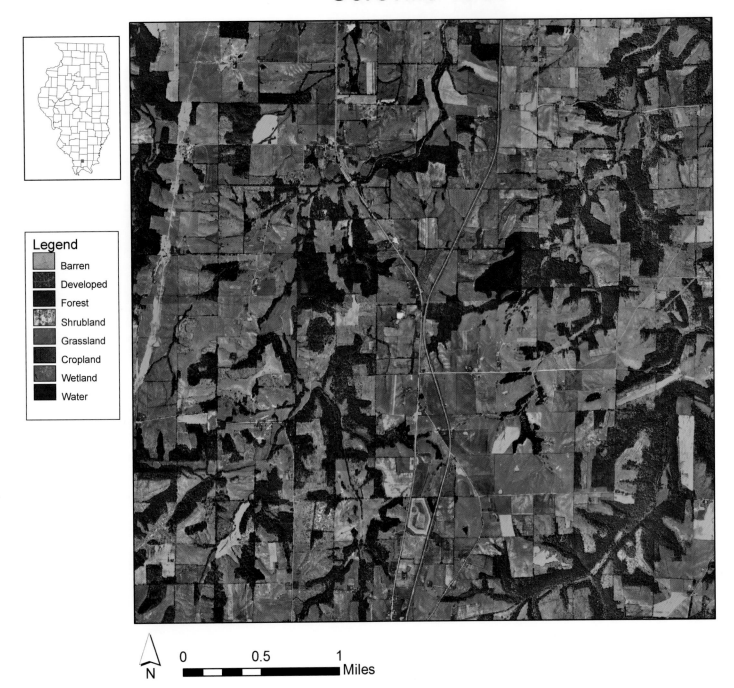

Legend
- Barren
- Developed
- Forest
- Shrubland
- Grassland
- Cropland
- Wetland
- Water

0   0.5   1
Miles
N

3.13. Aerial view near Goreville, Johnson County, 1959 and 2007. The area experienced a large shift in land cover over the past 48 years; 54% of the landscape changed from one land cover type to another. As at many sites we analyzed, forest and developed areas increased at the expense of cropland and grasslands. The increase in forest near Goreville was unmatched; an additional 13% of the landscape grew into forest between 1959 and 2007, to just over 40% of the area. We expected the expansion of forested areas to relate to population increases for Acadian Flycatchers, Red-eyed Vireos, Scarlet Tanagers, and other birds typical of southern Illinois forests.

Interestingly, a lot of the areas that were grassland in the 1950s (probably mostly hay fields and pastures) grew up into forest, and large areas of cropland were converted to grassland

through the Conservation Reserve Program. As a result, the amount of cropland in the area is greatly reduced, but only modestly so for grasslands (Table 3.11). Hayed and grazed grasslands are now more scarce, and idle grasslands are more common. On our surveys, we encountered just two Eastern Meadowlarks, which prefer the shorter, more open structure of grazed grasslands. In idle grasslands, we flushed several Henslow's Sparrows, a bird of tall, dense grasses that the Grabers only saw on two transects anywhere in Illinois in the 1950s.

The growth of municipal areas accounts for only a small portion of the expansion of developed areas. In the 1959 photograph, the initial construction of Interstate 57 is visible on the left (west) side of the area; in 2007, Interstates 57 and 24 and their intersection in the upper left (northwest) are obvious. The corridor

Goreville 2007

Table 3.11. Changes in dominant land cover classes near Goreville from 1959 to 2007.

Land cover type	% Cover		Number of patches		Average size (acres)	
	1959	2007	1959	2007	1959	2007
Cropland	25.2	7.3	310	71	7.2	9.1
Forest	27.6	40.4	109	136	22.5	26.4
Developed	2.8	13.3	79	116	3.2	10.1
Grassland	35.7	28.8	343	201	9.1	12.8

along Illinois Route 37, which runs north-south in the center of the pictures, shows considerable exurban development between Goreville to the south and the small community of Pulley's Mill to the north. Lastly, part of the Lake of Egypt is captured in the upper right (northeast) corner of the 2007 photograph (see detail in Fig. 3.17). Southern Illinois Power Cooperative dammed the Saline River in 1962 to create Lake of Egypt, and since that time the shoreline has become progressively more developed.

Crab Orchard 1959

Legend

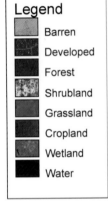

- Barren
- Developed
- Forest
- Shrubland
- Grassland
- Cropland
- Wetland
- Water

0   0.5   1

N   Miles

3.14. View of Crab Orchard Lake near Carbondale, Jackson and Williamson Counties, 1959 and 2007. Over the 48-year period between 1959 and 2007, the area around Crab Orchard Lake and Carbondale experienced a loss of cropland and gain of developed areas and forests. Although those changes are consistent with trends throughout Illinois, the size of the changes was particularly large. Today, much more development is visible on the west side of the photo, near Carbondale, and along the Illinois Route 13 corridor (center of images) in locations that formerly were cropland.

An increase in forest cover was concentrated around Crab Orchard Lake and within the Crab Orchard National Wildlife Refuge, established in 1947. This area was occupied by rural homesteads and used for agriculture and logging until 1939 when the Resettlement Administration purchased land along Crab Orchard Creek and created the reservoir for recreational uses. The growth in forested areas around the lake between 1959 and 2007 is due primarily to the abandonment of agricultural land. The area in the upper-left of the image, along Crab Orchard Creek, was a forested block in 1950, and now is a reclaimed strip mine dominated by grassland and lakes (Fig. 3.19).

Crab Orchard 2007

Table 3.12. Changes in dominant land cover classes near Crab Orchard Lake and Carbondale between 1959 and 2007.

Land cover type	% Cover		Number of patches		Average size (acres)	
	1954	2007	1954	2007	1954	2007
Cropland	36.6	15.0	278	86	11.6	15.6
Developed	6.9	21.1	40	40	15.3	46.9

Flagg Center 1958

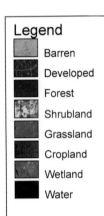

Legend
- Barren
- Developed
- Forest
- Shrubland
- Grassland
- Cropland
- Wetland
- Water

0   0.5   1
Miles

N

3.15. Aerial view near Flagg Center, Ogle County in 1958 and 2007. From 1958 to 2007, the amount of cropland near Flagg Center did not change much, but the composition and configuration of fields changed substantially. Over time, the size of farming equipment has become progressively larger. In 1958, a 4-row corn planter would have been fairly typical, whereas 24-row corn planters were widespread by 2007. Accompanying these changes, cropland near Flagg Center and throughout the state was consolidated into fewer but larger fields. Field edge habitats – grassy borders and shrubby fence lines – that provide nesting sites for Northern Bobwhites, Brown Thrashers, Vesper Sparrows, and other birds that often feed in cropland were removed to make way for the large equipment. In the 1950s, variation in soil moisture – apparent as light and dark areas within individual fields – was a common characteristic of the agricultural landscape. Drainage

improvements due to tiling have eliminated much of this variation in soil moisture, a common pattern observed in agricultural areas throughout Illinois over the past 50 years.

The crops grown on farms have shifted, too. In the late 1950s, small grains, hay, and cattle were considerably more common on the landscape than in the 2000s (Table 3.1). On their haphazard transects near Flagg Center, the Grabers encountered eight different types of crops, including alfalfa, red clover, yellow sweet clover, oats, and wheat. Besides corn and soybeans, we were only able to locate single examples of wheat and alfalfa in the area. Grasslands no longer used for haying or grazing have largely been converted to corn and soybeans in areas that can be tilled. Several grassland areas along the Kyte River were abandoned and have grown up into forests.

Flagg Center 2007

Table 3.13. Changes in dominant land cover types near Flagg Center from 1958 to 2007.

Land cover type	% Cover		Number of patches		Average size (acres)	
	1958	2007	1958	2007	1958	2007
Cropland	80.1	77.3	347	159	20.5	43.2
Grassland	12.5	6.5	73	66	15.3	8.6

3.16. This pair of images from Flagg Center illustrates how the size of crop fields has increased from 1958 (left image) to 2007 (right image).

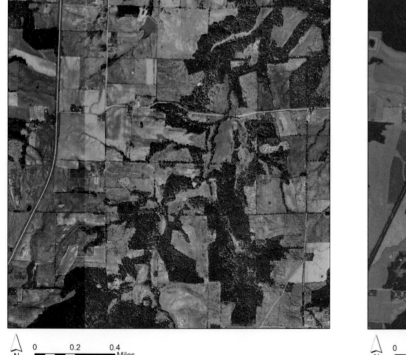

3.17. This pair of images from Goreville illustrates the increase in forest cover, as well as the appearance of Lake Egypt and the developed areas that sprung up along the margins of the reservoir.

3.18. This pair of images taken in 1959 (left) and 2007 (right) illustrate how forests along Crab Orchard Lake and development along Route 13 have increased over the 48-year period.

3.19. The forested block near Crab Orchard in 1959 (left) was a reclaimed strip mine characterized by grasslands and lakes in 2007 (right).

Havana 1957

Legend

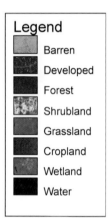

   Barren

   Developed

   Forest

   Shrubland

   Grassland

   Cropland

   Wetland

   Water

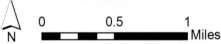

N   0   0.5   1   Miles

3.20. Aerial view of an area east of Havana, Mason County, 1957 and 2007. This was the most stable site we assessed in our study; 79% of the landscape did not change land cover classes from 1957 to 2007. Interestingly, the site showed almost no change in development. Despite this general lack of change in land cover between 1957 and 2007, Havana is an excellent example of how agricultural land use practices have changed over the past 50 years. Consistent with the statewide trends, cropland near Havana shifted from several, smaller fields of diverse crop types to fewer, larger fields cultivated primarily for corn and soybeans. In addition to this shift, farmers near Havana implemented center-pivot irrigation (circular field shapes in the 2007 image).

      The first center-pivot method of irrigation was built in 1947-48 by Frank Zyback, but it was only after many years of refinement that the systems finally took off in the 1960s. About a quarter of a century later, more than 10,000 center pivot systems were in use across the Midwest.

      Most cropland in Illinois receives sufficient rainfall and has soils with enough water-holding capacity that irrigation is not necessary. But in areas with sandy soils, including much of Mason and Tazewell counties east of the Illinois River in central Illinois, center-pivot irrigation is a common practice. A picture taken in 1907 near Havana shows sandy soils supporting only sparse vegetation (Fig. 3.24). In 2007, the same location is irrigated and growing corn. The triangular corners of fields, beyond the reach of center-pivot irrigation systems, are often left as patches of idle grass and shrubs, providing some small pieces of habitat for Ring-necked Pheasants, Northern Bobwhites, Lark Sparrows, and Dickcissels that are often lacking in more intensively cultivated landscapes.

Havana 2007

0   0.5   1
Miles

N

3.21. Havana fish market was the western-most area surveyed by Gross and Ray. While no censuses were conducted at the location of this photograph, this area is now a popular area to watch birds, as it is just south of Chautauqua National Wildlife Refuge, Mason County.

3.22. Aerial view near Poplar City, Mason County. Notice the large increase in trees between 1954 (left) and 2007 (right). Conifers were planted to reduce erosion in the 1950s and these trees are still present. Ground-level photographs were taken at three points in this area: (1) a forested area (Fig. 3.23); (2) a sand blowout that is now irrigated cropland (Fig 3.24); and (3) sand prairie that has degraded through time (Fig 3.25).

3.23. The forest that remains in the sand areas of Mason County does not receive the periodic fire it did historically. A spring burn in May of 1907 blackened these oaks. By contrast fire suppression has resulted in the forest being invaded by invasive plants such as honeysuckle by 2008.

3.24. Irrigation in Mason County has resulted in the ability to farm very sandy soil. These pictures taken approximately 3 miles southeast of Havana illustrate how this landscape has changed. Notice the man to the right of the tree in 1907.

3.25. Landscape ½ mile east of Poplar City, Mason County. Significant sand mining had occurred since 1963.

Cora 1959

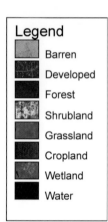

Legend
- Barren
- Developed
- Forest
- Shrubland
- Grassland
- Cropland
- Wetland
- Water

N

0   0.5   1
Miles

3.26. Aerial view near Cora in the northwestern Shawnee National Forest, Jackson and Randolph counties in 1959 and 2007. Of the 21 sites we analyzed, the area near Cora was the least changed from 1959 to 2007: 79% of the landscape remained in the same land cover type. Pictured in the lower left of the images is the Mississippi River. To the northeast, the floodplain of the river has continually been cropland. Farther from the river, the Ozark Hills rise abruptly from the floodplain and are extensively covered by forest. Despite the stability of land cover types, subtle but important changes are evident.

The upland areas, historically forested, had been cleared for agriculture by the early 1900s. But because of severe soil erosion on the rough terrain, the land quickly lost its value as farmland and was being abandoned. The Shawnee National Forest was established in 1933 to reforest the former cropland, prevent soil erosion, eventually produce timber, and provide economic opportunities for local citizens via recreational activities on the forest. Additionally, most of the wooded, non-farmed areas in the region had been logged at least once, and the existing vegetation when the Shawnee National Forest was begun was secondary forest.

As these forests have matured over time, a notable change has been canopy closure. The forested areas in the 1950s aerial photo look blotchy and uneven, and the topography of the ground surface is readily apparent (Fig. 3.30). This was because the trees were different heights and there were many open spaces between trees interspersed with young trees and shrubs nearer the ground (i.e., an open canopy). By the time of the 2007 photo, the forest had matured into a closed canopy and looks more like a continuous blanket that obscures the steep-sided ravines of the forest floor.

Cora 2007

N
0   0.5   1
Miles

3.27. Gross considered this forest in Union County
among some of the highest quality sampled in the 1900s.

A.O. Gross June, 1907.

Allerton Park 1955

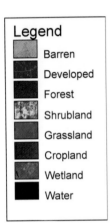

Legend

	Barren
	Developed
	Forest
	Shrubland
	Grassland
	Cropland
	Wetland
	Water

N

0   0.5   1
Miles

3.28. Aerial view of Allerton Park near Monticello, Piatt County, 1955 and 2007. In 1946, Robert Allerton donated Allerton Park to the University of Illinois for use in education and research, and as a forest preserve and public park. The notable changes that have occurred in and near Allerton Park since 1955 are similar to trends across Illinois: an increase in forested and developed areas at the expense of shrublands and grasslands. Over the 52-year period, forest cover increased by 10%, covering 28% of the landscape in 2007.

A large shrubland area south of the Sangamon River, as illustrated in Fig. 3.29, has become almost entirely forested. In the early 1970s, this area was the site of a study by Louis Best on the nesting biology of Field Sparrows (Best 1974), the most common and characteristic bird of shrub areas. The transition of shrublands to forests throughout Illinois has been detrimental to Field Sparrows, Brown Thrashers, Yellow-breasted Chats, and many other shrubland birds. The birds we encountered most frequently on transects at Allerton Park were Great Blue Herons, House Wrens, and Indigo Buntings in the floodplain forests.

Allerton Park 2007

Table 3.14. Changes in dominant land cover classes in Allerton Park from 1955 to 2007.

Land cover type	% Cover		Number of patches		Average size (acres)	
	1955	2007	1955	2007	1955	2007
Forest	17.8	28.0	25	26	63.2	95.8
Shrubland	6.7	0.6	22	6	27.2	8.4
Grassland	14.4	8.3	99	64	12.8	11.6

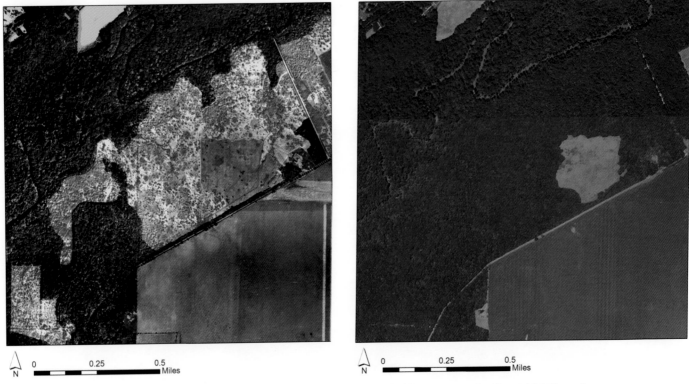

3.29. Left image (1955) shows large area of shrubland at Allerton Park that by 2007 had been converted to forest (right image).

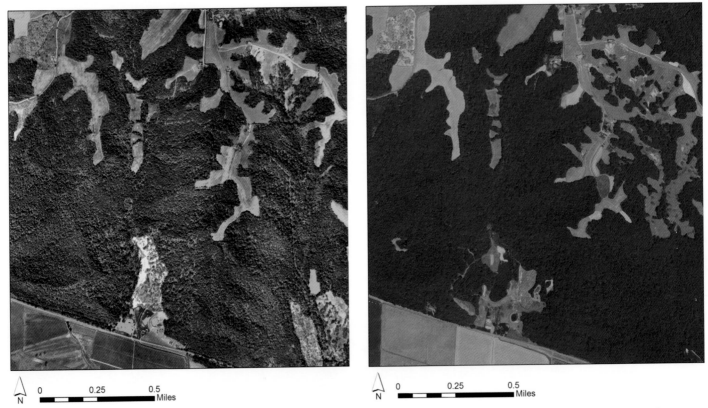

3.30. Shift from open-canopy forest in 1959 (left image) to closed-canopy, mature forest in 2007 (right image) in the northwestern region of Shawnee National Forest, near Cora. In the left image, the topography is clearly evident, whereas in the right image, little topographic variation can be seen.

Section IV
BIRD COMMUNITIES THROUGH TIME

In the previous section we characterized changes in the overall landscape of Illinois. In this section we summarize changes within specific land cover types. For each land cover type we consider how the extent, regional abundance, and character have changed from the early 1900s to the present.

We also emphasize how the bird communities of each land cover or habitat type have varied over the past century. The bird species commonly seen in each habitat type (representing a total of 95% of the birds seen) are presented in order of their relative abundance for each time period. Forbes and Gross often referred to the species that combine to make up 85% of all birds seen as the "most important species" in each habitat type. This is a quick way of describing the smaller set of birds that are characteristic of a given habitat type. It also provides insight into how the diversity of the bird community in a habitat has changed over time. Some habitats are dominated by a few abundant species, and others host many different species, each having a low relative abundance.

We summarized our results in this section in a manner consistent with the earlier survey periods. In the following sections we examine changes in bird species using analytical techniques not available in the 1900s or 1950s, such as occupancy modeling. In addition to a table summarizing relative bird abundances for the three time periods, we include graphs of the estimated densities of the most important bird species in each region (north, central, and south) in each habitat for the 2000s survey period. We have organized this section into treatments of each dominant land cover type (e.g., grassland) and then subdivided them into finer land cover types.

GRASSLAND

Native prairies were once the dominant ecosystem in Illinois, but by the time of the 1900s surveys, they were almost entirely converted to agriculture. Several million acres of substitute grasslands (hay fields and pastures dominated by Eurasian grasses), provided suitable habitat for many grassland species. Over time, the extent of these grasslands has been reduced. The 1999-2000 Land Cover of Illinois estimated that grasslands covered just over 4 million acres, or about 11% of the state. U.S. Department of Agriculture statistics account for about 2.1 million acres among the state's pastures, hay fields, and Conservation Reserve Program enrollments. The remaining grassland is primarily found along roadsides, waterways, field borders, and other similar small and/or narrow patches.

Most of the state's fertile prairie soils have been converted to cropland, and grasslands are now more common on soils that formerly supported forests. This accounts for the concentrations of grasslands found in northwestern, western, and southern Illinois. Many of these grasslands are near riparian corridors and on sloping lands not suitable for cultivation. Because of their evolutionary history, grassland birds appear to prefer large, open prairies with few trees, avoiding

small grasslands and areas near woody vegetation (Herkert et al. 1993). Although there may be 4 million acres of grassland in Illinois, most of it is in a landscape context that is intrinsically unattractive to prairie birds such as Bobolinks and Upland Sandpipers.

Moreover, the height and density of grassland vegetation has a profound effect on their suitability for different birds. We considered four types of grasslands in our surveys: idle grasslands, or those that had been left undisturbed throughout the growing season; grazed grasslands, or pastures with few or no trees; grasslands that had been hayed or mowed during the growing season; and linear grasslands that were narrower than 30 yards wide.

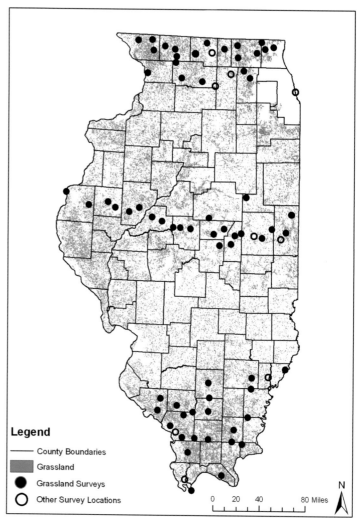

4.1. Distribution of grasslands in Illinois. The filled circles are sites where the surveys included grasslands.

Idle grasslands. Idle grasslands were those that had not been grazed, hayed, or mowed in the year of the survey (Fig. 4.2). Some areas probably were mixed hay that had not yet been harvested, but most were publicly-owned conservation areas, private lands enrolled in the Conservation Reserve Program, or abandoned pastures. Vegetation in idle grasslands was generally 24 to 36 inches tall and dense. Stands of cool-season grasses (e.g., tall fescue, smooth brome, orchard grass) with variable amounts of legumes and other forbs were the most common, although we visited some areas planted to native warm-season grasses (e.g., big bluestem, switchgrass, Indian grass, little bluestem). Areas with scattered shrubs and saplings, comprising <10% of the overall cover, were common in idle grasslands that had remained undisturbed for several years.

Table 4.1. Summary of survey effort in idle grasslands in the three survey periods.

	Time Period		
	1900s	1950s	2000s
Acres surveyed			
North	39	205	91
Central	23	101	102
South	359	348	93
Sites surveyed			
North	6	17	14
Central	14	14	15
South	26	19	17

Comparisons among time periods are difficult to make because of differences in definitions and changes in Census of Agriculture reporting, but the amount of idle grassland habitat likely has declined over the past century. Graber and Graber (1963) estimated that about 1.8 million acres of fallow and ungrazed grasses plus an unknown amount of unharvested mixed hay in 1907 have declined to 1.2 million acres of fallow and ungrazed grassland plus an unknown amount of unharvested mixed hay in 1957. In 2007 about 800,000 acres were enrolled in grassland practices of the Conservation Reserve Program. We

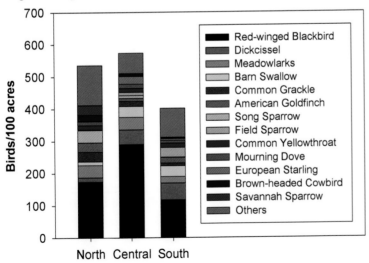

4.3. Densities of the 13 most abundant species observed in idle grasslands in Illinois by region, 2000s.

4.2. Idle grassland near the La Moine River in Hancock County.

judged that some of these older fields better fit our definition of shrublands because of the growth of woody vegetation. Other idle grasslands, such as those on reclaimed mines and public and private conservation areas, and not managed with haying or grazing, may total another few hundred thousand acres.

As in the 1950s, Red-winged Blackbirds were the most frequently seen bird species in idle grasslands in the 2000s, comprising nearly 40% of the overall bird community (Table 4.2). Blackbirds comprised only 5.8% of the birds seen in the 1900s. The proportion of meadowlarks seen in idle grasslands, however, has become smaller in each successive time period. Other species were observed only during a single time period. A flock of 14 Sandhill Cranes – a species not recorded in the 1900s or 1950s in any habitat – was encountered at a single idle grassland site in the 2000s. Henslow's Sparrows were also seen at several idle grasslands in the 2000s but not in the other time periods. The idle grasslands of the Conservation Reserve Program played a key role in the rapid population growth of Henslow's Sparrows over the past few decades (Herkert 2007), culminating in its removal from the Illinois threatened species list in 2009.

During the 2000s surveys, Red-winged Blackbirds, the most common species in this habitat type, were particularly concentrated in central Illinois, whereas Dickcissels generally decreased in density from the south to north (Fig. 4.3). Field Sparrows were densest in the southern region, while Savannah Sparrows were only seen in northern Illinois.

Table 4.2. Relative abundance of birds (% of all birds recorded in a specific survey period) observed in idle grasslands in Illinois, 1900s, 1950s, and 2000s. Species are listed in order of decreasing abundance in each survey period. Boldfaced text indicates species totaling 85% of birds recorded within each time period; only species totaling 95% of all birds seen are listed.

1900s		1950s		2000s	
Species	%	Species	%	Species	%
Meadowlarks	**21.0**	**Red-winged Blackbird**	**25.2**	**Red-winged Blackbird**	**39.4**
House Sparrow	**17.1**	**Meadowlarks**	**14.7**	**Dickcissel**	**7.4**
Mourning Dove	**6.7**	**Mourning Dove**	**11.2**	**Eastern Meadowlark** [A]	**6.5**
Red-winged Blackbird	**5.8**	**Dickcissel**	**8.2**	**Barn Swallow**	**5.3**
Field Sparrow	**4.2**	**Horned Lark**	**5.6**	**Common Grackle**	**3.6**
Common Grackle	**3.4**	**Common Grackle**	**5.0**	**American Goldfinch**	**3.4**
Dickcissel	**3.1**	**Bobolink**	**3.6**	**Song Sparrow**	**3.0**
Eastern Kingbird	**2.8**	**Field Sparrow**	**3.0**	**Field Sparrow**	**2.7**
Red-headed Woodpecker	**2.4**	**Barn Swallow**	**2.5**	**Common Yellowthroat**	**2.5**
American Goldfinch	**2.2**	**House Sparrow**	**2.5**	**Mourning Dove**	**2.2**
American Robin	**2.2**	**American Goldfinch**	**2.0**	**European Starling**	**2.2**
Northern Mockingbird	**1.9**	**Grasshopper Sparrow**	**1.7**	**Brown-headed Cowbird**	**2.0**
Northern Flicker	**1.8**	Savannah Sparrow	1.5	**Savannah Sparrow**	**1.8**
Eastern Bluebird	**1.8**	Brown-headed Cowbird	1.1	**American Robin**	**1.7**
Brown-headed Cowbird	**1.5**	Northern Bobwhite	0.9	**Cedar Waxwing**	**1.7**
Orchard Oriole	**1.5**	Common Yellowthroat	0.8	Indigo Bunting	1.6
Northern Bobwhite	**1.5**	Northern Cardinal	0.6	Bobolink	1.3
Brown Thrasher	**1.5**	European Starling	0.4	Grasshopper Sparrow	1.0
Blue Jay	**1.5**	Eastern Kingbird	0.4	Sandhill Crane	1.0
Common Yellowthroat	**1.3**	Brown Thrasher	0.4	Henslow's Sparrow	0.9
Bobolink	**1.3**	Swamp Sparrow	0.4	Tree Swallow	0.8
Lark Sparrow	**1.3**	Chimney Swift	0.3	Chimney Swift	0.7
Barn Swallow	1.0	Northern Flicker	0.3	Sedge Wren	0.7
American Crow	1.0	American Crow	0.3	Canada Goose	0.7
Bewick's Wren	0.9	Eastern Bluebird	0.3	N. Rough-winged Swallow	0.4
Grasshopper Sparrow	0.7	Upland Sandpiper	0.3	Eastern Kingbird	0.4
Chimney Swift	0.7	Blue Jay	0.2	Northern Flicker	0.4
Savannah Sparrow	0.6	Lark Sparrow	0.2	Cliff Swallow	0.4
Purple Martin	0.6	Killdeer	0.2	Baltimore Oriole	0.4
Song Sparrow	0.4	Orchard Oriole	0.1		
Indigo Bunting	0.4	Song Sparrow	0.1		
Killdeer	0.4	Bachman's Sparrow	0.1		
Northern Cardinal	0.4	Common Nighthawk	0.1		
American Kestrel	0.4	Sedge Wren	0.1		
Loggerhead Shrike	0.4	Yellow-headed Blackbird	0.1		
Number of birds	**672**		**1418**		**1382**
Number of species	**45**		**47**		**59**

[A] No Western Meadowlarks were recorded in idle grassland in 2000s, whereas Eastern Meadowlarks were seen in all three regions during the latest survey.

Grazed Grasslands. "Pasture" is another term for this habitat, but this section specifically considers perennial grasslands used by grazing animals (cattle, horses, sheep, or goats) during the same growing season as our surveys with less than 20% coverage by trees and shrubs (Fig. 4.4, Table 4.3). Therefore, we excluded the 266,000 acres of pastured woodland and 308,000 acres of cropland used only for pasture or grazing estimated by the U.S. Department of Agriculture. Grazed savanna-like areas, with >20% coverage by trees, were sometimes within the same pastures we surveyed. We compiled bird data separately for these areas and report the results with "Savanna-Open Woodland"(page 62).

The extent of grazed grassland has decreased from 6.1 million acres in 1907, to 2.0 million acres in 1957, and to 887,000 acres in 2007. Conversion of pastures, hay, and small grain acreage to corn and soybean production has resulted in an increase in area devoted to row crops, while total farm acreage has shrunk. Grazed grasslands largely persist in areas unsuitable for cropland, such as erodible land, flood-prone areas, or reclaimed strip mines.

4.4. Grazed grassland 2 miles east of Adair, McDonough County.

Table 4.3. Summary of survey effort in grazed grasslands in the three survey periods.

	Time Period		
	1900s	1950s	2000s
Acres surveyed			
North	218	285	69
Central	441	171	63
South	882	120	63
Sites surveyed			
North	8	17	10
Central	17	16	8
South	28	17	9

Graber and Graber wrote, "The characteristics of bluegrass pastures as bird habitats probably have not greatly changed in the present century." Though agricultural statistics are lacking, it is generally believed that modern grazed grasslands are smaller and more heavily grazed than their historical counterparts. Unlike the Grabers, we sampled few areas dominated by bluegrass; the grazed grasslands we visited were generally dominated by tall fescue in southern Illinois and smooth brome in northern Illinois. Near farmsteads, grazed grasslands sometimes approached barren feedlots in character, with patches of bare soil, abundant thistle, and other unpalatable weeds. Grazing reduced the height and density of pasture grasses to 6 inches or less; grasses taller than 12 inches were exceptional.

For the first time, meadowlarks were not the most common species in grazed grasslands, being outnumbered by Red-winged Blackbirds, Barn Swallows, and European Starlings (Table 4.4). The low relative abundance of Savannah Sparrows in the 1900s surveys is probably a result of Gross and Ray sampling grazed grasslands mostly in southern Illinois, which lies outside the breeding range of this species. House Sparrows were far less prevalent among birds in grazed grasslands during the most recent surveys than in the 1900s and 1950s. Regionally, European Starlings and Savannah Sparrows were densest in northern Illinois in the 2000s, Grasshopper Sparrows and Bobolinks reached their highest densities in central Illinois, and Barn Swallows and Eastern Bluebirds were densest in southern Illinois (Fig. 4.5).

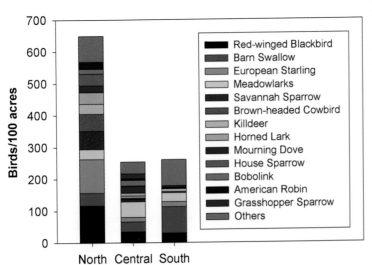

Legend:
- Red-winged Blackbird
- Barn Swallow
- European Starling
- Meadowlarks
- Savannah Sparrow
- Brown-headed Cowbird
- Killdeer
- Horned Lark
- Mourning Dove
- House Sparrow
- Bobolink
- American Robin
- Grasshopper Sparrow
- Others

4.5. Densities of the 13 most abundant species observed in grazed grasslands in Illinois by region, 2000s.

Table 4.4. Relative abundance of birds (% of all birds recorded in a specific survey period) observed in grazed grasslands in Illinois, 1900s, 1950s, and 2000s. Species are listed in order of decreasing abundance in each survey period. Boldfaced text indicates species totaling 85% of birds recorded within each time period; only species totaling 95% of all birds seen are listed.

1900s		1950s		2000s	
Species	%	Species	%	Species	%
Meadowlarks	**14.9**	**Meadowlarks**	**19.9**	**Red-winged Blackbird**	**15.4**
House Sparrow	**13.7**	**House Sparrow**	**14.6**	**Barn Swallow**	**13.7**
Common Grackle	**8.4**	**Red-winged Blackbird**	**10.8**	**European Starling**	**11.1**
Brown-headed Cowbird	**5.3**	**Common Grackle**	**5.9**	**Meadowlarks** [A]	**9.7**
American Robin	**4.7**	**Field Sparrow**	**5.3**	**Savannah Sparrow**	**5.3**
Field Sparrow	**4.4**	**European Starling**	**4.7**	**Brown-headed Cowbird**	**5.1**
Northern Flicker	**4.4**	**Savannah Sparrow**	**4.7**	**Killdeer**	**4.0**
Red-winged Blackbird	**3.8**	**Barn Swallow**	**3.6**	**Horned Lark**	**3.9**
Mourning Dove	**3.4**	**Bobolink**	**3.1**	**Mourning Dove**	**3.7**
Brown Thrasher	**3.1**	**Grasshopper Sparrow**	**2.8**	**House Sparrow**	**3.6**
Northern Bobwhite	**2.4**	**Brown-headed Cowbird**	**2.5**	**Bobolink**	**2.9**
Red-headed Woodpecker	**2.2**	**American Goldfinch**	**2.5**	**Grasshopper Sparrow**	**2.3**
Horned Lark	**2.0**	**Dickcissel**	**1.5**	**American Robin**	**2.3**
Dickcissel	**1.9**	**Eastern Kingbird**	**1.5**	**Eastern Bluebird**	**2.1**
Eastern Kingbird	**1.9**	**Vesper Sparrow**	**1.3**	Common Grackle	1.7
Blue Jay	**1.6**	**Mourning Dove**	**1.2**	Dickcissel	1.6
Lark Sparrow	**1.6**	Eastern Bluebird	1.0	Eastern Kingbird	1.6
Orchard Oriole	**1.4**	Killdeer	0.9	Rock Pigeon	1.5
American Crow	**1.4**	American Robin	0.9	American Goldfinch	1.1
Grasshopper Sparrow	**1.3**	Song Sparrow	0.8	Song Sparrow	1.1
Eastern Bluebird	**1.3**	Northern Flicker	0.8	Cliff Swallow	0.8
Barn Swallow	1.1	Horned Lark	0.7		
Northern Mockingbird	1.1	Blue Jay	0.6		
Upland Sandpiper	0.8	Baltimore Oriole	0.6		
Killdeer	0.7	Northern Bobwhite	0.6		
Chimney Swift	0.7	Chimney Swift	0.6		
Savannah Sparrow	0.6	Indigo Bunting	0.5		
Bobolink	0.5	Brown Thrasher	0.5		
Chipping Sparrow	0.5	Orchard Oriole	0.4		
Common Yellowthroat	0.5	House Wren	0.4		
Turkey Vulture	0.5				
Gray Catbird	0.5				
Loggerhead Shrike	0.5				
American Goldfinch	0.4				
Purple Martin	0.4				
Bank Swallow	0.4				
Song Sparrow	0.3				
Indigo Bunting	0.3				
Yellow-billed Cuckoo	0.3				
Eastern Phoebe	0.3				
Green Heron	0.3				
Number of birds	**2386**		**1237**		**827**
Number of species	**72**		**53**		**46**

[A] Eastern Meadowlarks were seen in all three zones in the 2000s. Western Meadowlarks were seen in northern Illinois, where the ratio was 19 easterns:2 westerns.

Hayed and Mowed Grasslands. We use this category for grasslands that were hayed or mowed in the year of our surveys, excluding linear areas such as field borders, waterways, and terraces (Fig. 4.6, Table 4.5). Most areas were mixed hay fields, composed of combinations of cool-season grasses (smooth brome, orchard grass, timothy) and legumes (alfalfa, red clover), but also ungrazed (typically fescue) pastures and other areas that had been mowed but not harvested. The distinction between mixed hay and idle grassland was clear in the field, as we encountered very few examples of mixed grass-legumes that were either not already cut or obviously intended to remain unharvested (e.g., wildlife management or conservation lands). Vegetation in hayed or mowed grasslands varied in stages of re-growth from short stubble (3 inches or less) to dense cover 18 inches tall, though most was shorter than 12 inches. Areas that had been mowed but unharvested had abundant litter. Woody vegetation, other than an occasional small stump, was absent.

The amount of mixed hay in Illinois remained fairly constant, at about 2.5 million acres, from 1907 to 1957. Over the past 50 years, about 90% of that area has been converted to other land cover types, with the U.S. Department of Agriculture estimating approximately 275,000 acres of hay, excluding alfalfa,

4.6. Hayed grassland 1/2 mile west of West Jersey, Stark County.

in 2007. As with alfalfa, contemporary mixed hay fields are harvested earlier and more frequently than in the 1950s, and almost all nests and young birds are destroyed by haying or mowing operations (Warner and Etter 1989, Bollinger et al. 1990, Frawley and Best 1991, Warner 1994).

Because most of the hayed and mowed grasslands we surveyed had been previously cut, we saw relatively fewer meadowlarks, Bobolinks, Dickcissels, Grasshopper Sparrows, or other grassland-nesting birds in the 2000s compared to the 1900s and 1950s surveys (Table 4.6). We commonly saw European Starlings, Red-winged Blackbirds, Common Grackles, and Barn Swallows using these grasslands for foraging. We believe that the regional differences in the densities of grassland birds are an artifact of chance encounters with large flocks of feeding birds (Fig. 4.7). For example, the high densities of European Starlings in the central and southern regions and Common Grackles in the northern region reflect single encounters with large groups. All of the Horned Larks, Rock Pigeons, and all but one Cliff Swallow were seen in single groups of each species.

Table 4.5. Summary of survey effort in hayed and mowed grasslands in the three survey periods.

	Time Period		
	1900s	1950s	2000s
Acres surveyed			
North	175	115	31
Central	126	43	45
South	597	18	44
Sites surveyed			
North	8	16	5
Central	13	9	9
South	27	6	10

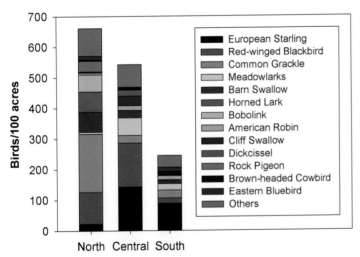

4.7. Densities of the 11 most abundant species observed in hayed and mowed grasslands in Illinois by region, 2000s.

Table 4.6. Relative abundance of birds (% of all birds recorded in a specific survey period) observed in hayed and mowed grasslands in Illinois, 1900s, 1950s, and 2000s. Species are listed in order of decreasing abundance in each survey period. Boldfaced text indicates species totaling 85% of birds recorded within each time period; only species totaling 95% of all birds seen are listed.

1900s		1950s		2000s	
Species	**%**	**Species**	**%**	**Species**	**%**
Meadowlarks	**27.2**	**Red-winged Blackbird**	**22.6**	**European Starling**	**19.7**
Dickcissel	**13.8**	**Meadowlarks**	**13.0**	**Red-winged Blackbird**	**18.9**
House Sparrow	**10.2**	**Dickcissel**	**11.4**	**Common Grackle**	**14.5**
Red-winged Blackbird	**8.3**	**European Starling**	**8.4**	**Eastern Meadowlark** [A]	**6.6**
Bobolink	**6.3**	**Bobolink**	**8.4**	**Barn Swallow**	**6.6**
Mourning Dove	**3.8**	**Grasshopper Sparrow**	**5.6**	**Horned Lark**	**3.8**
Grasshopper Sparrow	**3.5**	**Savannah Sparrow**	**5.3**	**Bobolink**	**3.1**
Common Grackle	**3.4**	**Horned Lark**	**5.1**	**American Robin**	**2.7**
Northern Flicker	**2.3**	**Common Grackle**	**4.2**	**Cliff Swallow**	**2.7**
Chimney Swift	**2.0**	**House Sparrow**	**3.9**	**Dickcissel**	**2.0**
Northern Bobwhite	**1.5**	Mourning Dove	2.3	**Rock Pigeon**	**2.0**
Field Sparrow	**1.4**	Vesper Sparrow	1.7	**Brown-headed Cowbird**	**1.8**
Brown Thrasher	**1.4**	American Robin	1.5	**Eastern Bluebird**	**1.8**
Eastern Kingbird	1.2	Barn Swallow	0.6	Savannah Sparrow	1.6
American Robin	1.1	Northern Flicker	0.5	Eastern Kingbird	1.4
Brown-headed Cowbird	0.9	Brown Thrasher	0.5	Grasshopper Sparrow	1.2
Greater Prairie-Chicken	0.9	Henslow's Sparrow	0.5	Purple Martin	1.1
Common Yellowthroat	0.8			House Sparrow	0.9
Barn Swallow	0.7			American Goldfinch	0.9
American Crow	0.7			Killdeer	0.9
Red-headed Woodpecker	0.7			Indigo Bunting	0.7
Upland Sandpiper	0.7			Canada Goose	0.7
Orchard Oriole	0.6				
Horned Lark	0.5				
American Goldfinch	0.5				
Song Sparrow	0.5				
Number of birds	**1476**		**665**		**557**
Number of species	**50**		**32**		**37**

[A] Western Meadowlarks were not encountered in hayed or mowed grasslands during the 2000s surveys.

Linear Grasslands. This category includes rural roadsides, drainage canals, waterways, field borders, terraces, and other linear habitats dominated by grasses with 20% or less coverage by trees and shrubs and too narrow to accommodate a typical transect (50 yards) (Fig, 4.8, Table 4.7). All of the linear grasslands we surveyed were between 3 to 30 yards wide, and many had been mowed or partially mowed during the current growing season. Some field borders and roadsides included fences, posts, or utility lines that birds used as perches.

    In intensively cultivated regions, linear grasslands are about the only potential bird habitat other than cropland. Not surprisingly, the birds observed in linear grasslands were quite similar to those seen in the adjacent corn and soybean fields. Generalist species, such as the Red-winged Blackbird, European Starling, and Common Grackle, dominated these small, heavily disturbed areas, whereas grassland birds, including Dickcissels and meadowlarks, were uncommon and present at lower relative abundances than in the 1950s (Table 4.8). There was little difference in bird density between linear grasslands in northern and central Illinois (there was not enough data from the southern portion of the state; Fig. 4.9).

    Conservation programs provide incentives to landowners to establish grassy buffers in riparian areas and, in recent years, field borders for wildlife. The Illinois Department of Natural Resources discourages the mowing of roadsides during the nesting season. Nonetheless, most studies examining the wildlife benefits of linear grasslands have found that they attract few grassland birds such as Bobolinks and Grasshopper Sparrows that typically only settle in larger grasslands (Bryan and Best 1991, Camp and Best 1993), and that the birds nesting in linear grasslands have poor nest success due to destruction by mowing and losses to predators using these travel corridors (Warner 1992, Bryan and Best 1994, Camp and Best 1994, Kammin 2003, Henningsen and Best 2005).

4.8. Linear grasslands included field borders, waterways, terraces, roadsides, and grassy access lanes such as this one photographed near Tilton, Vermillion County.

Table 4.7. Summary of survey effort in linear grasslands in the three survey periods.

	Time Period		
	1900s	1950s	2000s
Acres surveyed			
North	1	10	7
Central	1	14	6
South	0	11	1
Sites surveyed			
North	1	21	9
Central	2	18	9
South	0	17	2

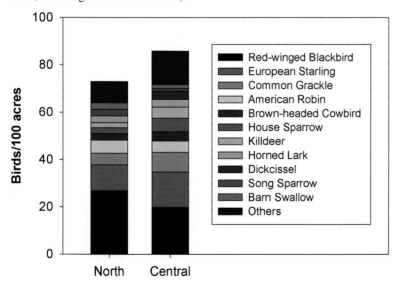

4.9. Densities of the 11 most abundant species observed in linear grasslands in Illinois by region, 2000s. Too few linear grasslands in the south were sampled for analysis.

Table 4.8. Relative abundance of birds (% of all birds recorded in a specific survey period) observed in linear grasslands in Illinois, 1950s and 2000s. Species are listed in order of decreasing abundance in each survey period. Boldfaced text indicates species totaling 85% of birds recorded within each time period; only species totaling 95% of all birds seen are listed.

1950s		2000s	
Species	%	Species	%
Red-winged Blackbird	**20.0**	**Red-winged Blackbird**	**33.7**
House Sparrow	**14.3**	**European Starling**	**13.3**
Common Grackle	**11.4**	**Common Grackle**	**9.6**
American Goldfinch	**9.0**	**American Robin**	**5.8**
Dickcissel	**8.1**	**Brown-headed Cowbird**	**4.2**
Meadowlarks	**4.4**	**House Sparrow**	**4.0**
Song Sparrow	**4.3**	**Killdeer**	**4.0**
Mourning Dove	**4.3**	**Horned Lark**	**3.4**
Indigo Bunting	**3.4**	**Dickcissel**	**3.0**
Common Yellowthroat	**2.3**	**Song Sparrow**	**2.9**
European Starling	**2.1**	**Barn Swallow**	**2.7**
Barn Swallow	**1.3**	Mourning Dove	1.8
Field Sparrow	**1.3**	Chipping Sparrow	1.8
Brown-headed Cowbird	1.2	American Goldfinch	1.4
Ring-necked Pheasant	1.2	Meadowlarks [A]	1.4
Brown Thrasher	1.1	Vesper Sparrow	0.8
Vesper Sparrow	1.0	House Finch	0.8
Northern Bobwhite	0.8	Brown Thrasher	0.6
American Robin	0.6	Mallard	0.6
Northern Cardinal	0.6		
Bobolink	0.6		
Horned Lark	0.5		
Red-headed Woodpecker	0.5		
Yellow-breasted Chat	0.5		
Loggerhead Shrike	0.4		
Number of birds	**946**		**623**
Number of species	**48**		**37**

[A] Western Meadowlarks (2 birds) were recorded in northern Illinois; Eastern Meadowlarks were found in all three zones.

FOREST

We use "forest" to describe habitats covered by trees taller than 20 feet and with a canopy closure of 80% or greater. We identified three types of forest in the 2000s surveys: upland, floodplain, and coniferous (Table 4.9). Upland and floodplain (bottomland) forests were dominated by deciduous trees and roughly divided by the 100-year floodplain. The coniferous forests we sampled were all plantations dominated by pines and spruces. Wooded and savanna habitats with less than 80% canopy coverage, areas dominated by short woody vegetation, and linear forests less than 30 yards wide are discussed in later sections. Previous surveys only rarely distinguished between upland and floodplain forests. Thus, for the 1900s and 1950s time periods, we summarize data in a single "forest" category to compare with recent data for upland and floodplain forests. The Grabers and Gross did not use the term forest in their field notes, but we include here habitats they described as "woods" and "timber."

The General Land Office surveys of 1820 showed more than one-third of Illinois was forested (Anderson 1970). All but about 22,000 acres were logged for building material and fuel, and most were cleared for agriculture until just 3 million acres of forest remained around 1920 (Telford 1926). Gross and Ray surveyed little forested land, and most of what they surveyed was in southern Illinois (Table 4.9). The most common bird they encountered, the Field Sparrow, suggests that many of these forests were relatively young and open from recent logging or grazing. The amount of forest in Illinois has continued to increase since that time. Graber and Graber estimated about 4 million acres of forest in 1957. At present, about 5.2 million acres are forested, including almost 3.5 million acres of upland forest, 1.1 million acres of floodplain forest, and about 80,000 acres of coniferous forest.

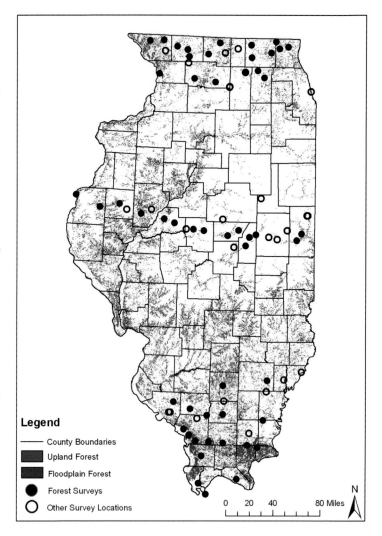

Fig. 4.10. Distribution of forests in Illinois. Approximately 4.7 million acres of forest are currently found in Illinois, covering about 13% of the state. Filled circles are sites where surveys included forests.

4.9. Summary of survey effort in forests during the three survey periods.

	1900s	1950s	2000s - Upland	2000s - Floodplain	2000s - Coniferous
Acres surveyed					
North	1	176	70	25	9
Central	11	216	40	48	9
South	58	339	56	46	25
Sites surveyed					
North	1	14	15	6	2
Central	5	10	9	7	3
South	20	21	15	9	6

Upland Forest. Oaks were the dominant trees, along with hickory, maple, and ash, in the upland forests we surveyed in the 2000s. The richness and density of the understory varied, but we could not characterize any upland forest as "without understory," as the Grabers did. Evidence of past grazing was apparent in many locations by the presence of plants such as honey locust and multiflora rose, but we did not sample any forests that were currently hosting livestock.

Although chestnut blight and Dutch elm disease altered the canopy of the state's forests, oaks and hickories have been the dominant canopy trees through the 1900s, 1950s, and 2000s surveys. Perhaps reflecting the continuity of the oak-hickory character of forests in Illinois over time, the birds found in upland forests in the 1950s and 2000s surveys were very similar. Twenty-seven of the 33 most important species (again, 85% of all birds seen) in modern forests were also among the most important species of forests in the 1950s (Table 4.10).

Significant changes in forest composition and bird communities are likely by 2057, however. Sugar maple dominance is estimated to have risen by 4,000% since the 1960s. The emerald ash borer is established in several counties and is likely to spread throughout the state. Mortality of infected ash trees is 100%. Invasive shrubs, especially bush honeysuckle and buckthorn, have infested many forests. Garlic mustard blankets the ground layer of many forests, especially in northern and central Illinois, and Japanese stilt grass has invaded some southern Illinois forests.

Regionally in the 2000 surveys, the birds of upland forests were similar (Fig. 4.12), with American Robins and House Wrens being denser in the north, and Tufted Titmice, Carolina Wrens, and Acadian Flycatchers denser in the south. Compared to the 1950s, American Robins, House Wrens, and Brown-headed Cowbirds are more abundant in today's upland forests (Table 4.10).

Brown-headed Cowbirds lay their eggs in other birds' nests, reducing or eliminating production of "host" young. Fragmented forests are well-suited to cowbirds and generalist nest predators such as raccoons, resulting in most of the state's forests being reproductive "sinks" (i.e., areas where recruitment falls short of the number of birds needed to compensate for adult mortality) for many birds, especially Neotropical migrants such as warblers (Robinson et al. 1995). Although Brown-headed Cowbirds have become relatively more abundant in the upland bird community since the 1900s and 1950s (Table 4.10), we do not see a clear decline in the relative abundances of common Neotropical migrant hosts of cowbird eggs and nestlings (e.g., Eastern Wood-Pewee, Acadian Flycatcher, Red-eyed Vireo, Kentucky Warbler), which would be expected if cowbirds were limiting their populations.

4.11. Upland forest at Copperhead Hollow Wildlife Area, Jersey County.

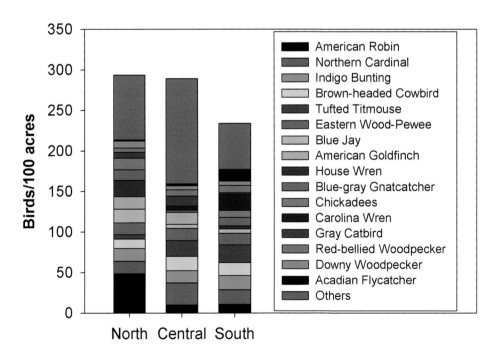

4.12. Densities of the 16 most abundant species observed in upland forest in Illinois by region, 2000s.

Floodplain Forest. Silver maple, cottonwood, sycamore, green ash, and black willow were the dominant tree species of floodplain forests, though oaks, pecan, hackberry, and other species were well-represented in some areas. Compared to the upland forests we surveyed, floodplain forests tended to have taller canopies and sparser understories. Poison ivy and garlic mustard were common ground-level plants.

Current programs to retire flood-prone areas from crop production (e.g., Wetlands Reserve Program, Conservation Reserve Enhancement Program) are resulting in the restoration of more floodplain forest. Due to levees, drainage improvements, and other modifications, floodplain forests in many areas are subject to relatively rapid changes in water levels, which favor silver maple and cottonwood dominance at the expense of hard mast trees, such as oaks and pecan.

As expected, floodplain forests differed from upland forests owing to few or no ground-nesting birds (e.g., Kentucky Warblers and Ovenbirds), and the presence of birds associated with standing water (Prothonotary Warblers, Great Blue Herons, and Wood Ducks). Regional variation in local densities of floodplain forest birds in the 2000s was substantial (Fig. 4.14). American Robins and House Wrens were common overall, but they were rarely seen in the southern zone. In contrast, Tufted Titmice, Blue-gray Gnatcatcher, and Acadian Flycatchers were scarcely seen in the northern or central regions' floodplain forests. Red-winged Blackbirds and Common Grackles reached their highest density in the northern region, and Gray Catbirds were densest in central Illinois floodplain forests.

4.13. Floodplain forest in Fort Massac State Park, Massac County.

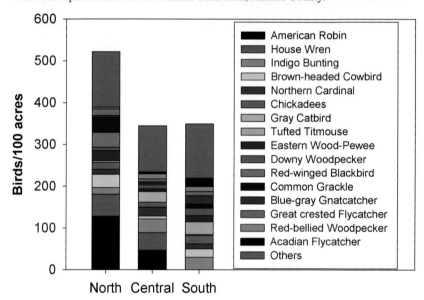

4.14. Densities of the 16 most abundant species observed in floodplain forest in Illinois by region, 2000s.

Coniferous Forest. Plantations of coniferous trees are an uncommon habitat type in Illinois, estimated at about 80,000 acres by the 1999-2000 Land Cover of Illinois. Roughly 4,000 acres of Christmas tree plantations occur in Illinois, but we did not survey any of these patches. The areas we encountered were all mature stands of pines mixed with some hardwoods on public lands, predominantly in southern Illinois.

One species, the Pine Warbler, is probably restricted to these artificial habitats in the state. Chipping Sparrows were especially abundant in the coniferous forest bird community; otherwise, the bird community was similar to other upland forests in southern Illinois (Table 4.10).

4.15. Coniferous forest 1 mile west of Lake of Egypt, Williamson County.

Table 4.10. Relative abundance of birds (% of all birds recorded in a specific time period) observed in forests in Illinois, 1900s, 1950s, and 2000s. Upland and floodplain forests were not differentiated and coniferous forests were not sampled in the 1900s and 1950s surveys. Species are listed in order of decreasing abundance in each survey period. Boldfaced text indicates species totaling 85% of birds recorded within each time period; only species totaling 95% of all birds seen are listed.

1900s		1950s		2000s – Upland		2000s – Floodplain		2000s – Coniferous	
Species	**%**	**Species**	**%**	**Species**	**%**	**Species**	**%**	**Species**	**%**
Field Sparrow	**9.2**	**Northern Cardinal**	**10.1**	**American Robin**	**9.8**	**American Robin**	**12.5**	**American Robin**	**13.8**
Blue Jay	**8.0**	**Common Grackle**	**8.4**	**Northern Cardinal**	**7.1**	**House Wren**	**7.4**	**Chipping Sparrow**	**12.1**
Indigo Bunting	**6.9**	**Tufted Titmouse**	**7.1**	**Indigo Bunting**	**6.0**	**Indigo Bunting**	**7.2**	**Northern Cardinal**	**11.2**
Great Cr Flycatcher	**6.1**	**Chickadees**	**5.7**	**Br-headed Cowbird**	**5.4**	**Br-headed Cowbird**	**4.6**	**Carolina Wren**	**6.9**
Northern Cardinal	**5.3**	**Indigo Bunting**	**5.0**	**Tufted Titmouse**	**5.4**	**Northern Cardinal**	**4.1**	**Blue Jay**	**5.2**
Brown Thrasher	**4.6**	**Red-eyed Vireo**	**3.7**	**E Wood-Pewee**	**5.4**	**Chickadees**	**4.1**	**Blu-gr Gnatcatcher**	**4.3**
American Robin	**3.8**	**E Wood-Pewee**	**3.4**	**Blue Jay**	**4.2**	**Gray Catbird**	**3.4**	**House Wren**	**4.3**
Northern Flicker	**3.4**	**Acadian Flycatcher**	**3.4**	**A Goldfinch**	**3.8**	**Tufted Titmouse**	**3.1**	**American Goldfinch**	**3.4**
Wood Thrush	**3.4**	**Blue Jay**	**3.1**	**House Wren**	**3.6**	**E Wood-Pewee**	**3.1**	**Chickadees**	**3.4**
Eastern Towhee	**3.4**	**Downy Woodpecker**	**2.8**	**Blu-gr Gnatcatcher**	**3.6**	**Downy Woodpecker**	**3.1**	**Kentucky Warbler**	**3.4**
Tufted Titmouse	**3.1**	**Br-headed Cowbird**	**2.6**	**Chickadees**	**3.3**	**Red-wing Blackbird**	**3.1**	**Acadian Flycatcher**	**2.6**
Common Grackle	**3.1**	**American Crow**	**2.5**	**Carolina Wren**	**2.9**	**Common Grackle**	**2.9**	**American Crow**	**2.6**
E Wood-Pewee	**2.7**	**Blu-gr Gnatcatcher**	**2.4**	**Gray Catbird**	**2.7**	**Bl-gray Gnatcatcher**	**2.6**	**Common Grackle**	**2.6**
Yellow-breast Chat	**2.7**	**Carolina Wren**	**2.4**	**Red-bel Woodpecker**	**2.7**	**Red-bel Woodpecker**	**2.6**	**Indigo Bunting**	**2.6**
C Yellowthroat	**2.6**	**Kentucky Warbler**	**2.4**	**Downy Woodpecker**	**2.5**	**Great Cr Flycatcher**	**2.6**	**Br-headed Cowbird**	**1.7**
Mourning Dove	**2.3**	**American Redstart**	**2.2**	**Acadian Flycatcher**	**2.2**	**Acadian Flycatcher**	**2.4**	**Cedar Waxwing**	**1.7**
Br-headed Cowbird	**1.9**	**Eastern Towhee**	**2.0**	**Red-eyed Vireo**	**1.8**	**European Starling**	**1.9**	**Eastern Towhee**	**1.7**
American Crow	**1.9**	**Red-bel Woodpecker**	**1.7**	**White-brst Nuthatch**	**1.8**	**American Redstart**	**1.9**	**R-thr Hummingbird**	**1.7**
Red-hd Woodpecker	**1.9**	**Mourning Dove**	**1.7**	**Kentucky Warbler**	**1.8**	**American Goldfinch**	**1.7**	**Tufted Titmouse**	**1.7**
Bewick's Wren	**1.9**	**Great Cr Flycatcher**	**1.7**	**Common Grackle**	**1.6**	**Blue Jay**	**1.4**	**Yellow-thr Warbler**	**1.7**
Downy Woodpecker	**1.5**	**American Robin**	**1.6**	**European Starling**	**1.3**	**Baltimore Oriole**	**1.4**	Baltimore Oriole	0.9
Red-eyed Vireo	**1.5**	**American Goldfinch**	**1.6**	**Baltimore Oriole**	**1.3**	**American Crow**	**1.4**	Brown Thrasher	0.9
Eastern Bluebird	**1.5**	**Field Sparrow**	**1.5**	**Mourning Dove**	**1.3**	**Orchard Oriole**	**1.4**	E Wood-Pewee	0.9
Northern Bobwhite	**1.5**	**White-eyed Vireo**	**1.5**	**Northern Flicker**	**1.1**	**Wood Duck**	**1.4**	Fish Crow	0.9
Red-bel Woodpecker	1.1	**Gray Catbird**	**1.4**	**R-thr Hummingbird**	**1.1**	Carolina Wren	1.2	Great Blue Heron	0.9
Prothonotary Warbler	1.1	**House Wren**	**1.3**	**Wild Turkey**	**1.1**	Northern Flicker	1.2	Orchard Oriole	0.9
American Kestrel	1.1	**Wood Thrush**	**1.2**	**Great Cr Flycatcher**	**0.9**	C Yellowthroat	1.2	Ovenbird	0.9
American Goldfinch	0.8	**Ovenbird**	**1.2**	**American Crow**	**0.9**	**Great Blue Heron**	**1.2**	Pine Warbler	0.9
Carolina Wren	0.8	Summer Tanager	1.1	**Wood Thrush**	**0.9**	**Prothonotary Warbler**	**1.2**	Pileated Woodpecker	0.9
Acadian Flycatcher	0.8	Red-hd Woodpecker	1.1	**Hairy Woodpecker**	**0.9**	Red-eyed Vireo	0.9	Red-bel Woodpecker	0.9
Chipping Sparrow	0.8	Northern Flicker	1.0	**Cedar Waxwing**	**0.9**	Song Sparrow	0.9	Red-eyed Vireo	0.9
Orchard Oriole	0.8	Hairy Woodpecker	1.0	**Eastern Towhee**	**0.9**	White-brst Nuthatch	0.7	Summer Tanager	0.9
Lark Sparrow	0.8	Brown Thrasher	1.0	Red-tailed Hawk	0.7	Mourning Dove	0.7	White-eyed Vireo	0.9
Belted Kingfisher	0.8	Worm-eating Warbler	0.9	Eastern Phoebe	0.7	Wood Thrush	0.7		
Baltimore Oriole	0.4	Song Sparrow	0.8	Scarlet Tanager	0.7	Red-tailed Hawk	0.7		
Barred Owl	0.4	Cerulean Warbler	0.8	Yellow-bill Cuckoo	0.7	Red-hd Woodpecker	0.7		
Chimney Swift	0.4	R-thr Humingbird	0.6	Red-wing Blackbird	0.4	Warbling Vireo	0.7		
Gray Catbird	0.4	Yellow-breasted Chat	0.6	Eastern Kingbird	0.4	Tree Swallow	0.5		
Summer Tanager	0.4	White-brst Nuthatch	0.5	Louisiana W.Thrush	0.4	R-thr Hummingbird	0.5		
R-thr Humngbird	0.4	Red-tailed Hawk	0.5	Ovenbird	0.4	Hairy Woodpecker	0.5		
Red-wing Blackbird	0.4	Red-wing Blackbird	0.5	Brown Thrasher	0.4	Eastern Phoebe	0.5		
Yellow-bill Cuckoo	0.4	Eastern Bluebird	0.5	Worm-eatng Warbler	0.4	Barred Owl	0.5		
House Sparrow	0.4			Eastern Bluebird	0.4	Rose-brst Grosbeak	0.5		
Eastern Kingbird	0.4			Chipping Sparrow	0.4	Chimney Swift	0.5		
Red-shoulder Hawk	0.4			Yellow-thr Vireo	0.4				
Number of birds	**300**		**1666**		**448**		**417**		**116**
Number of species	**46**		**72**		**60**		**54**		**34**

SHRUBLANDS, SAVANNA-OPEN WOODLANDS, AND LINEAR WOODED HABITATS

Shrublands. Shrubland areas constitute a range of conditions that vary from those similar to grasslands, to savanna-like areas, and forests, but share the characteristics of shrub and sapling coverage exceeding 20%, but with few or no canopy-level trees. This habitat does not include linear shrubby areas <30 yards wide, such as fencerows, riparian strips, or railroad rights-of-way. We found this habitat at former surface mines, abandoned pastures, and abandoned croplands that had not been cultivated for several years. For historical comparison, we include the areas Gross described as cleared land, clearings, deforested lands, and shrubs, and that the Grabers labeled as forest edge, pasture with shrubs, and shrubs (Table 4.11).

4.16. Shrubland on a reclaimed stripmine 2.5 miles southwest of Elkville, Jackson County.

The amount of shrub areas in the state has been consistently small. The Grabers estimated 500,000 acres of shrub habitat was present in the 1900s and 1950s. The 614,000 acres of "partial canopy/savanna upland" reported in the 1999-2000 Land Cover of Illinois includes an unknown amount of shrubland. Former surface mines were the only locations where we found extensive areas (i.e., more than about 10 acres) of shrubland. In all three time periods, shrublands were most often encountered in southern Illinois.

Whereas the vegetation structure of shrub-grown areas has likely been consistent over the past 100 years, these habitats are now dominated by invasive plant species. Common shrub and sapling species in these areas included bush honeysuckle, autumn olive, multiflora rose, osage orange, black locust, honey locust, and eastern red cedar, and typically vegetation was 4 to 10 feet tall. Dominant herbaceous plants in open spots were fescue, broom sedge, smooth brome, and sericea lespedeza.

American Goldfinches, Indigo Buntings, and Field Sparrows were among the most abundant birds in shrub habitat

during the three time periods (Table 4.14). By historical standards, the relative abundances of American Goldfinches, Common Grackles, and Brown-headed Cowbirds were higher in the 2000s than the 1900s and 1950s (Table 4.14). American Robins and Cedar Waxwings also were more common than in the past. Both species are fruit-eating birds that perhaps benefit from the fruits of honeysuckles and autumn olive that dominate present-day shrublands.

In light of the regional differences in species' densities observed during our 2000s surveys (Fig. 4.18), comparing our data with the 1900s and 1950s is complicated because of regional differences in sampling effort among the three time periods. Indigo Buntings were least dense in northern Illinois, whereas Mourning Doves and Yellow Warblers were denser in the northern region of the state than in the central or southern region. American Robins, Song Sparrows, Cedar Waxwings, and Gray Catbirds were denser in central and northern Illinois than in the south, but Yellow-breasted Chats were only detected in the south.

Table 4.11. Summary of survey effort in shrublands in the three survey periods.

	Time Period		
	1900s	1950s	2000s
Acres surveyed			
North	3	32	18
Central	1.0	50	14
South	85	128	33
Sites surveyed			
North	2	10	8
Central	1	8	6
South	24	17	11

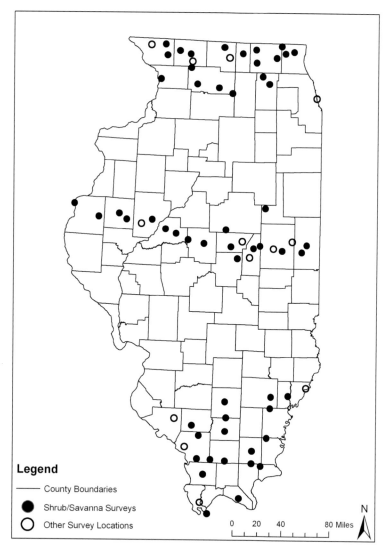

4.17. Distribution of shrublands and savannas-open woodlands was so sparse that it cannot be represented on the map. Filled circles indicate locations where surveys included shrubland, savanna-open woodland, or linear wooded habitats.

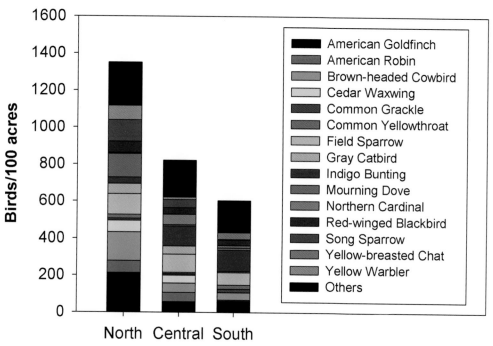

4.18. Densities of the 15 most abundant species observed in shrublands in Illinois by region, 2000s. One transect in northern Illinois, where 41 common grackles were encountered, was excluded from this graph.

Savannas – Open Woodlands. The terms savanna, barrens, and open woodlands have technical meanings as distinct natural communities, but we use the phrase savanna - open woodland to define a generic habitat structure that shares characteristics of grassland (a grassy ground layer) and forest (20 to 80% coverage by canopy-height trees). Only a few thousand acres of high-quality remnant savanna are known to exist in Illinois. The total amount of savanna-type habitat in Illinois – habitat with scattered trees and herbaceous ground cover – is unknown. The 1999-2000 Land Cover of Illinois estimated 615,000 acres of partial canopy/savanna upland, a category that also includes shrub-grown areas.

For savanna-open woodland habitats, it is impractical to make any historical comparison, because little of this habitat type was specified in either the 1900s or 1950s periods (Table 4.12). Gross describes a few areas as "groves," which based on the birds he recorded were probably savanna-like in structure. Graber and Graber (1963: Fig. 16, page 408), and likely Gross and Ray, included some grazed "savanna-like" areas with other grassland pastures. Open woodlands probably were not distinguished from other forest types.

Early in the 19th century, savannas and open woodlands were major habitats in Illinois (Nuzzo 1985). Most savanna was lost to timber harvest and conversion to agriculture, including the conversion of the native ground layer to introduced pasture grasses, by the early decades of the 20th century. Over the past 50 years, open woodland and savanna-type habitats have almost certainly declined due to development and trends towards closed-canopy forest (forest succession) through fire suppression.

Most of the savanna-open woodland we surveyed had a ground layer of non-native pasture grasses (bluegrass, orchard grass, timothy, fescue, brome) and had been or was being grazed. Mature burr, white, and black oaks were the dominant tree species, and surveyed areas typically had 10 to 30% coverage by shrubs, including multiflora rose, gooseberry, raspberry, blackberry, and young trees.

4.19. Savanna in Chain O' Lakes State Park, McHenry County.

The high dominance of European Starlings in the 2000s was skewed by the encounter of a large flock of 64 birds in a single savanna-like pasture in southern Illinois (Table 4.14). Excluding that observation, starlings dropped in rank to be the 4th most frequently seen bird, between Common Grackles and American Goldfinches, and the regional differences in bird communities were diminished (Fig. 4.20). European Starlings out-number and compete with native cavity-nesting species, including Eastern Bluebirds, Great Crested Flycatchers, and Northern Flickers, in savanna-like habitats; thus, they represent an important potential threat to native birds. American Robins were abundant in savanna-open woodland areas, as in upland and floodplain forests. The Red-headed Woodpecker is the signature bird of Midwestern oak savannas. Although we found Red-headed Woodpeckers more often in savanna-like areas than other habitats, in the 2000s very few were encountered across the state. In spite of sampling a relatively small amount of savanna-open woodland habitat, we observed more species (63) in these areas than any other habitat type in the 2000s (Table 4.14).

Table 4.12. Summary of survey effort in savanna and open woodlands in the three survey periods.

	Time Period		
	1900s	1950s	2000s
Acres surveyed			
North	2	15	30
Central	4	9	28
South	2	2	10
Sites surveyed			
North	2	6	10
Central	2	4	9
South	2	1	5

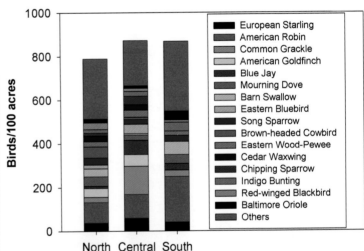

4.20. Densities of the 16 most abundant species observed in savannas-open woodlands in Illinois by region, 2000s. A flock of 64 European Starlings encountered in southern Illinois was excluded from this graph.

Linear Wooded Habitats. We combined fencerows, railroad rights-of-way, roadsides, and riparian areas that had at least 75% tree or shrub cover and were less than 30 yards wide under the heading of linear wooded habitats. We considered these areas to be more similar to shrublands than forests. The narrowest of these linear wooded areas were only 1-2 yards wide. Few linear wooded habitat patches were surveyed in the 1900s, but because of their importance as bird habitat in agricultural areas and their rapid elimination from those landscapes (Vance 1976), the Grabers surveyed many fencerows and hedgerows in the 1950s (Table 4.13)

The extent of these wooded corridors is now much less than it was in the 1950s, when the Grabers estimated 86,000 acres of edge shrub habitat and 13,000 acres of hedgerows in the state. Agricultural trends towards larger field size and fewer grazing animals have resulted in the removal of most fences and wooded field borders; these are especially scarce in the intensively-cropped east-central region.

The biggest change in relative bird abundance between the 1950s and the 2000s surveys is the ten-fold increase of American Robins (Table 4.15). In contrast, several species characteristic of low shrubs (e.g., Brown Thrasher, Common Yellowthroat, Field Sparrow, Northern Bobwhite) and grassland-associated birds (e.g., Dickcissels, meadowlarks) were relatively less abundant in the most recent surveys. This may be due to greater height or maturity of woody vegetation in these linear habitats, less available grassland habitat near these habitats, or both. In spite of these changes, linear wooded habitats had identical species richness (61 species) and a similar number of most important species (totaling 85% of birds seen) in the 1950s and 2000s periods (19 species and 18 species, respectively)

Among the three regions surveyed in the 2000s, American Robins, Song Sparrows, and Gray Catbirds had higher densities in northern and central Illinois than in the south (Fig. 4.12). Brown Thrashers were not recorded in northern Illinois, and Indigo Buntings were densest in the south. European Starlings and Red-winged Blackbirds reached their greatest densities in central Illinois linear wooded habitats.

Table 4.13. Summary of survey effort in linear woodlands in the three survey periods.

	Time Period		
	1900s	1950s	2000s
Acres surveyed			
North	0	4	3
Central	0	6	5
South	2	6	4
Sites surveyed			
North	0	15	9
Central	0	15	11
South	1	19	12

4.21. Linear wooded habitats included riparian areas, fence lines, railroad rights-of-way, and rural roadsides with at least 75% tree or shrub cover; (left) hedgerow 3/4 miles northwest of Illiopolis, Sangamon County, (right) linear woodlands 2 miles south of Marion, Williamson County.

Table 4.14. Relative abundance of birds (% of all birds recorded in a specific time period) observed in Illinois shrublands in 1900s, 1950s, and 2000s and savanna-open woodlands in 2000s. Species are listed in order of decreasing abundance in each survey period. Boldfaced text indicates species totaling 85% of birds recorded within each time period; only species totaling 95% of all birds seen are listed.

1900s – Shrub		1950s – Shrub		2000s – Shrub		2000s – Savanna	
Species	%	Species	%	Species	%	Species	%
Field Sparrow	**11.1**	**Field Sparrow**	**17.0**	**American Goldfinch**	**11.0**	**European Starling**	**15.0**
Indigo Bunting	**8.4**	**Indigo Bunting**	**9.6**	**Indigo Bunting**	**9.9**	**American Robin**	**12.8**
Northern Cardinal	**8.0**	**Red-winged Blackbird**	**6.8**	**Field Sparrow**	**9.4**	**Common Grackle**	**7.3**
Red-headed Woodpecker	**6.5**	**American Goldfinch**	**5.4**	**Common Grackle**	**8.4**	**American Goldfinch**	**4.3**
Common Yellowthroat	**6.1**	**Brown-headed Cowbird**	**5.4**	**Brown-headed Cowbird**	**8.0**	**Blue Jay**	**3.8**
American Goldfinch	**5.7**	**Yellow-breasted Chat**	**4.1**	**Mourning Dove**	**4.7**	**Mourning Dove**	**3.8**
Yellow-breasted Chat	**5.7**	**Northern Cardinal**	**3.8**	**Song Sparrow**	**4.7**	**Barn Swallow**	**3.0**
Mourning Dove	**4.6**	**Mourning Dove**	**3.1**	**Red-winged Blackbird**	**4.3**	**Eastern Bluebird**	**3.0**
Blue Jay	**4.2**	**Eastern Towhee**	**2.6**	**American Robin**	**3.5**	**Song Sparrow**	**3.0**
Brown-headed Cowbird	**3.4**	**Gray Catbird**	**2.5**	**Gray Catbird**	**3.0**	**Brown-headed Cowbird**	**2.8**
Yellow-billed Cuckoo	**2.3**	**Brown Thrasher**	**2.5**	**Yellow Warbler**	**2.8**	**Eastern Wood-Pewee**	**2.8**
Meadowlarks	**2.3**	**Common Yellowthroat**	**2.4**	**Cedar Waxwing**	**2.8**	**Cedar Waxwing**	**2.4**
Eastern Towhee	**1.9**	**Chickadees**	**2.4**	**Northern Cardinal**	**2.2**	**Chipping Sparrow**	**2.4**
Orchard Oriole	**1.9**	**Song Sparrow**	**2.2**	**Common Yellowthroat**	**2.2**	**Indigo Bunting**	**2.4**
Carolina Wren	**1.9**	**Bank Swallow**	**2.1**	**Yellow-breasted Chat**	**2.0**	**Red-winged Blackbird**	**2.2**
Red-winged Blackbird	**1.5**	**Common Grackle**	**2.0**	**Bell's Vireo**	**1.5**	**Baltimore Oriole**	**1.9**
Dickcissel	**1.5**	**Tufted Titmouse**	**2.0**	**European Starling**	**1.5**	**Northern Cardinal**	**1.9**
Northern Bobwhite	**1.5**	**Orchard Oriole**	**1.4**	**Ruby-thr Hummingbird**	**1.3**	**Eastern Kingbird**	**1.7**
American Robin	**1.1**	**Savannah Sparrow**	**1.3**	**Eastern Towhee**	**1.0**	**Gray Catbird**	**1.5**
American Crow	**1.1**	**Eastern Kingbird**	**1.2**	**Brown Thrasher**	**1.0**	**House Wren**	**1.4**
Eastern Phoebe	**1.1**	**Prairie Warbler**	**0.9**	**Purple Martin**	**1.0**	**Common Yellowthroat**	**1.3**
Tufted Titmouse	**1.1**	**Blue Jay**	**0.9**	**Willow Flycatcher**	**1.0**	**Blue-gray Gnatcatcher**	**1.1**
Wood Thrush	**1.1**	**Carolina Wren**	**0.9**	Dickcissel	0.8	**Red-bellied Woodpecker**	**1.1**
House Sparrow	**1.1**	**Bell's Vireo**	**0.8**	Downy Woodpecker	0.8	**Eastern Phoebe**	**0.9**
Great Crested Flycatcher	**1.1**	**Meadowlarks**	**0.8**	Barn Swallow	0.8	**Great Crested Flycatcher**	**0.9**
American Kestrel	**1.1**	**Wood Thrush**	**0.8**	Prairie Warbler	0.7	**Red-headed Woodpecker**	**0.9**
Ruby-throated Hummingbird	0.8	**Eastern Wood-Pewee**	**0.8**	Northern Bobwhite	0.7	**Wild Turkey**	**0.9**
Brown Thrasher	0.8	House Wren	0.7	American Crow	0.7	American Crow	0.8
Downy Woodpecker	0.8	House Sparrow	0.7	Cliff Swallow	0.7	Field Sparrow	0.8
White-eyed Vireo	0.8	Willow Flycatcher	0.5	Red-tailed Hawk	0.7	House Sparrow	0.8
Red-bellied Woodpecker	0.8	American Robin	0.5	Mallard	0.7	Northern Flicker	0.8
Turkey Vulture	0.8	Yellow Warbler	0.5	Blue Jay	0.5	Orchard Oriole	0.8
Lark Sparrow	0.8	Dickcissel	0.5	Yellow-billed Cuckoo	0.5	Rock Pigeon	0.8
Bewick's Wren	0.8	Northern Bobwhite	0.5	Northern Flicker	0.5	White-breasted Nuthatch	0.8
Summer Tanager	0.8	American Crow	0.5	House Finch	0.5	Brown Thrasher	0.6
Common Grackle	0.4	White-eyed Vireo	0.5			Eastern Towhee	0.6
Gray Catbird	0.4	American Redstart	0.5			N. Rough-winged Swallow	0.5
Purple Martin	0.4	Vesper Sparrow	0.5			Warbling Vireo	0.5
Eastern Kingbird	0.4	European Starling	0.4			Chimney Swift	0.3
Eastern Wood-Pewee	0.4	Downy Woodpecker	0.4			Cooper's Hawk	0.3
Northern Mockingbird	0.4	Yellow-billed Cuckoo	0.4			Double-crested Cormorant	0.3
Eastern Bluebird	0.4	Eastern Phoebe	0.4			Killdeer	0.3
Red-eyed Vireo	0.4	Warbling Vireo	0.4			Red-eyed Vireo	0.3
Scarlet Tanager	0.4	Ruby-throated Hummingbird	0.3			Red-tailed Hawk	0.3
Bachman's Sparrow	0.4	Barn Swallow	0.3			Summer Tanager	0.3
Hairy Woodpecker	0.4	Red-headed Woodpecker	0.3			Tufted Titmouse	0.3
Number of birds	**261**		**750**		**598**		**632**
Number of species	**48**		**74**		**51**		**63**

Table 4.15. Relative abundance of birds (% of all birds recorded in a specific time period) observed in linear woodlands in Illinois, 1950s and 2000s. Species are listed in order of decreasing abundance in each survey period. Boldfaced text indicates species totaling 85% of birds recorded within each time period; only species totaling 95% of all birds seen are listed.

1950s		2000s	
Species	%	Species	%
Red-winged Blackbird	**12.6**	**American Robin**	**16.7**
Common Grackle	**11.3**	**Red-winged Blackbird**	**16.0**
Indigo Bunting	**8.3**	**Indigo Bunting**	**6.6**
House Sparrow	**7.9**	**Common Grackle**	**5.4**
Dickcissel	**5.7**	**American Goldfinch**	**4.9**
Northern Cardinal	**5.1**	**Song Sparrow**	**4.9**
Field Sparrow	**5.0**	**European Starling**	**4.4**
Mourning Dove	**4.8**	**Mourning Dove**	**4.1**
Brown Thrasher	**3.8**	**Northern Cardinal**	**3.7**
Common Yellowthroat	**3.5**	**Brown-headed Cowbird**	**3.7**
European Starling	**3.3**	**Barn Swallow**	**3.3**
Gray Catbird	**2.6**	**Gray Catbird**	**3.0**
American Goldfinch	**2.4**	**House Sparrow**	**2.1**
Brown-headed Cowbird	**2.3**	**Brown Thrasher**	**2.1**
Song Sparrow	**1.6**	**Chipping Sparrow**	**1.5**
Northern Bobwhite	**1.5**	**Tree Swallow**	**1.5**
Yellow-breasted Chat	**1.5**	**Eastern Kingbird**	**1.2**
American Robin	**1.4**	**House Wren**	**1.2**
Meadowlarks	**1.3**	Common Yellowthroat	1.0
Blue Jay	1.1	Field Sparrow	0.9
Barn Swallow	1.0	Eastern Bluebird	0.9
Bell's Vireo	0.8	Northern Bobwhite	0.8
Northern Mockingbird	0.8	Cedar Waxwing	0.7
Vesper Sparrow	0.7	Blue Jay	0.5
Chickadee	0.6	Baltimore Oriole	0.5
Yellow-billed Cuckoo	0.6	Eastern Phoebe	0.5
Willow Flycatcher	0.5	Yellow-breasted Chat	0.4
Eastern Kingbird	0.5	Bell's Vireo	0.4
Orchard Oriole	0.5	Tufted Titmouse	0.4
House Wren	0.4	Red-bellied Woodpecker	0.4
Eastern Bluebird	0.4	Blue Grosbeak	0.3
Northern Flicker	0.4	Orchard Oriole	0.3
Eastern Towhee	0.4	Northern Flicker	0.3
Carolina Wren	0.4	American Crow	0.3
		Downy Woodpecker	0.3
		Lark Sparrow	0.3
		Warbling Vireo	0.3
Number of birds	**1331**		**1206**
Number of species	**61**		**61**

CORN

Corn has been the dominant land cover of Illinois for about 140 years. During our surveys, corn was planted on 11-13 million acres annually, or about 33% of Illinois land area. The Grabers thought the characteristics of corn as bird habitat had changed little from the 1900s to the 1950s, but since the 1950s changes have been dramatic (Fig. 4.24). Corn has become a taller, denser, and less weedy habitat. The median planting date of corn has advanced by 3 weeks since the 1950s to about April 20th, and by May 20th 99% of corn plantings are complete.

"Knee-high by the Fourth of July," the old adage for monitoring a mid-summer corn crop, no longer applies. The Grabers primarily sampled corn that was shorter than 24 inches, whereas we mostly sampled corn that was 24 to 60 inches tall. We had difficulty locating fields less than shoulder-height by late June in the south and early July in the north. Additionally, rows of corn have narrowed from about 40 inches wide to 30 inches wide today with nearly 28,000 plants/acre.

Nowadays, corn fields typically have very few live weeds, and the areas between rows are characterized by variable amounts of bare soil, previous year crop residues, and dead weeds and grasses killed by pre-emergence or post-emergence applications of herbicides. As a result of significant advances in corn genetics, changing cultural practices, and intensive inputs, the average corn yield in the 2000s was 163-179 bushels/acre as compared to 35-39 bushels/acre in 1900s and 64-69 bushels/acre in 1950s. Table 4.16 provides data on survey effort in corn during the three time periods.

The Grabers regarded corn as the poorest bird habitat in the state, and our surveys corroborate this finding. Nine species now constitute 85% of all birds observed in corn, compared to 11 species in the 1950s, and 21 species in the 1900s (Table 4.17), emphasizing the relative reduction in diversity of the bird community since the 1900s. This simplification of the bird community is further supported by the decrease in total number of species seen in corn over the past 100 years. Horned Larks and Killdeer are the only birds that commonly nest in corn, while the other species were only foraging in corn fields or flying over them. Excluding two flocks of European Starlings, we observed little regional variation in bird densities in corn during the 2000s surveys (Fig. 4.23).

Several grassland and shrubland birds, such as Northern Flickers, Brown Thrashers, and meadowlarks, were commonly observed in corn a century ago but are rarely found there now. A century ago, corn fields were relatively small and weedy, most were enclosed by fences and shrubby hedgerows, and most were near pastures and hayfields. These characteristics made corn a more suitable habitat for these bird species in Illinois during previous time periods. Today the reverse is true: corn fields are large and clean of weeds, few are bordered by shrubby hedgerows, few are near pastures or hayfields, and, consequently, grassland and shrubland birds are scarce throughout the state.

Table 4.16. Summary of survey effort in corn during the three surveys.

	Time Period		
	1900s	1950s	2000s
Acres surveyed			
North	3.4	32	18
Central	1.0	50	14
South	85	128	33
Sites surveyed			
North	2	10	8
Central	1	8	6
South	24	17	11

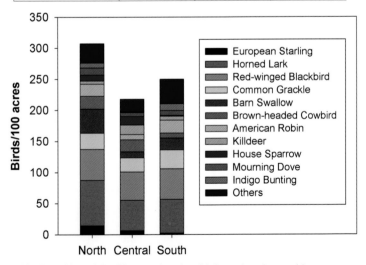

4.23. Densities of the 11 most abundant bird species observed in corn in Illinois by region, 2000s. Two large flocks of starlings recorded in the northern Illinois represented 17% of all birds tallied in corn, and are excluded from this graph.

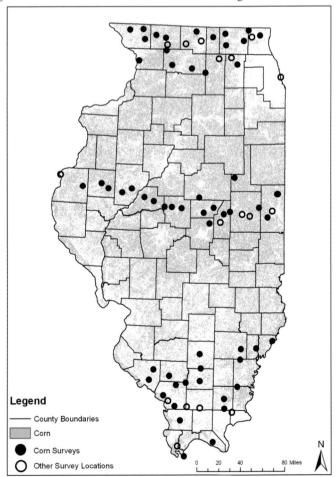

4.22. Distribution of corn (shading) and bird surveys (circles) in Illinois. Filled circles indicate locations where surveys included corn.

4.24. From left to right, photographs taken in corn fields (A) near Wapello, DeWitt County, (B) Champaign County, and (C) near Ina, Jefferson County, illustrate how corn fields have become less weedy and more closely planted over the past century.

Table 4.17. Relative abundance of birds (% of all birds recorded in a specific time period) observed in corn in Illinois, 1900s, 1950s, and 2000s. Species are listed in order of decreasing abundance. Boldfaced text indicates species totaling 85% of birds recorded within each time period; only species totaling 95% of all birds seen are listed.

1900s		1950s		2000s	
Species	%	Species	%	Species	%
Common Grackle	**15.3**	**Horned Lark**	**40.4**	**European Starling**	**19.4**
Horned Lark	**9.8**	**Common Grackle**	**9.8**	**Horned Lark**	**18.8**
House Sparrow	**9.2**	**House Sparrow**	**7.1**	**Red-winged Blackbird**	**15.8**
Mourning Dove	**8.7**	**Red-winged Blackbird**	**6.6**	**Common Grackle**	**8.5**
Killdeer	**3.9**	**European Starling**	**4.0**	**Barn Swallow**	**6.7**
Meadowlarks	**3.8**	**Meadowlarks**	**4.0**	**Brown-headed Cowbird**	**5.5**
Brown-headed Cowbird	**3.4**	**Mourning Dove**	**3.8**	**American Robin**	**4.9**
American Crow	**3.3**	**Barn Swallow**	**2.7**	**Killdeer**	**3.3**
Red-winged Blackbird	**3.2**	**Brown-headed Cowbird**	**2.6**	**House Sparrow**	**3.0**
American Robin	**3.1**	**Killdeer**	**2.5**	Mourning Dove	2.7
Brown Thrasher	**3.1**	**Vesper Sparrow**	**2.1**	Indigo Bunting	1.9
Northern Flicker	**2.9**	American Robin	1.4	Dickcissel	0.9
Eastern Kingbird	**2.2**	Dickcissel	1.0	Eastern Meadowlark	0.7
Red-headed Woodpecker	**2.2**	American Goldfinch	1.0	Song Sparrow	0.7
American Goldfinch	**1.8**	Field Sparrow	0.7	American Goldfinch	0.7
Vesper Sparrow	**1.8**	American Crow	0.7	Chipping Sparrow	0.7
Lark Sparrow	**1.8**	Ring-necked Pheasant	0.7	N. Rough-winged Swallow	0.7
Northern Mockingbird	**1.8**	Chimney Swift	0.6	Field Sparrow	0.6
Loggerhead Shrike	**1.7**	Northern Flicker	0.6		
Eastern Bluebird	**1.5**	Upland Sandpiper	0.6		
Field Sparrow	**1.2**	Indigo Bunting	0.5		
Indigo Bunting	1.1	Brown Thrasher	0.5		
Upland Sandpiper	1.1	Eastern Kingbird	0.5		
Blue Jay	1.1	Bobolink	0.5		
American Kestrel	1.0	Northern Bobwhite	0.3		
Chimney Swift	0.7	Loggerhead Shrike	0.3		
Gray Catbird	0.7				
Dickcissel	0.6				
Northern Bobwhite	0.6				
Common Yellowthroat	0.6				
Purple Martin	0.5				
Northern Cardinal	0.5				
Barn Swallow	0.3				
Number of birds	1255		1024		670
Number of species	60		44		37

SOYBEANS

In the fields that we surveyed, soybeans varied from a few inches tall in late May to 18 inches or taller by early July. While the width of rows in some soybean fields is similar to that of corn (30 inches), most soybeans are now commonly drilled or planted in narrower (about 15-inch) rows. Crop residue (typically corn stubble) and dead weeds (killed by herbicides prior to or following planting) provide some additional structure in "no-till" soybean fields (Fig. 4.27), whereas bare soil is the dominant feature of conventionally tilled soybeans early in the season (Fig. 4.27). More than half of the state's soybeans are grown with no-till methods, and the practice is most prevalent in southern Illinois.

Soybeans were a very minor crop prior to 1920, but by 1954 it had expanded to about 4.0 million acres. The increase in soybean cover was reflected in the greater survey effort allocated to this crop type in the 1950s (Table 4.18). The increasing trend in soybean cultivation has continued to the present, with soybeans typically planted on 9.5 to 10.5 million acres over the past decade. The average soybean yield in Illinois was 44-48 bushels/acre in 2000s compared to 25.5-28.5 bushels/acre in 1950s. The median date for soybean planting in Illinois is about May 15th, with planting virtually complete by June 20th. "Roundup Ready" soybeans, a genetically modified variety resistant to glyphosate

(an herbicide sold under the trade name "Roundup" by Monsanto Corporation), became commercially available in 1996. This technology was quickly adopted, and by 2003, 81% of the Illinois soybean crop was planted to herbicide-resistant varieties.

While soybeans host one of the least diverse bird communities in the state, we recorded more species in soybeans in the 2000s than in the 1950s (41 vs. 31; Table 4.19). Horned larks are the most common species in soybean fields, though their relative abundance in the 2000s is about one-half of what it was in the 1950s. Eleven species now comprise the most important species (again, totaling >85% of birds recorded), versus just 6 birds in the 1950s. In contrast to corn, where we observed almost no nesting birds, nests, or young of Horned Larks, Red-winged Blackbirds, Killdeer, and Dickcissels were observed several times in soybeans, suggesting that soybeans provide nesting habitat for some birds. The increases in species richness and the relative abundances of many species (e.g., Red-winged Blackbird, Killdeer, Brown-headed Cowbird, European Starling, Dickcissel, and American Robin) from the 1950s to the 2000s suggest that birds have adapted to soybean fields as habitat. Furthermore, these changes indicate that the soybean bird community has become more diverse, unlike most other crop types, where bird communities have generally become simpler.

Regional differences in the birds found in soybeans are partly related to species' ranges and cultivation practices (Fig. 4.26). Vesper Sparrows, as expected, were densest in northern Illinois but absent in the south. No-till fields tended to host far greater proportions of Dickcissels, meadowlarks, and Grasshopper Sparrows than more traditionally managed fields (Table 4.20).

Table 4.18. Summary of survey effort in soybeans during the three survey periods.

	Time Period		
	1900s	1950s	2000s
Acres surveyed			
North	0	188	125
Central	4	476	114
South	26	121	98
Sites surveyed			
North	0	10	17
Central	1	21	13
South	9	17	16

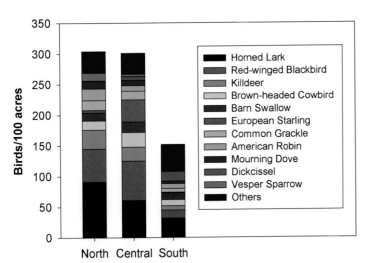

4.26. Densities of the 11 most abundant bird species observed in soybeans in Illinois by region, 2000s.

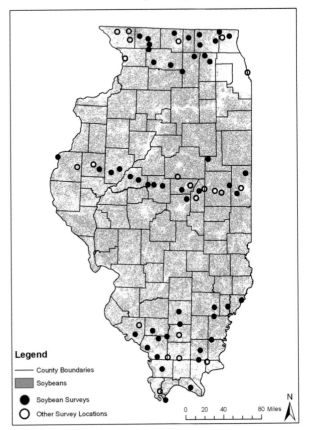

4.25. Distribution of soybeans (shading) and bird surveys (circles) in Illinois. Filled circles indicate locations where surveys included soybeans.

Table 4.19. Relative abundance of birds (% of all birds recorded in a specific time period) observed in soybeans in Illinois, 1950s and 2000s. Species are listed in order of decreasing abundance. Boldfaced text indicates species totaling 85% of birds recorded within each time period; only species totaling 95% of all birds seen are listed. Soybean survey effort was too small to allow a comparison with the 1900s.

1950s		2000s	
Species	%	Species	%
Horned Lark	**55.5**	**Horned Lark**	**24.3**
Common Grackle	**7.4**	**Red-winged Blackbird**	**17.3**
Mourning Dove	**6.8**	**Killdeer**	**8.1**
House Sparrow	**6.6**	**Brown-headed Cowbird**	**6.5**
Red-winged Blackbird	**5.2**	**Barn Swallow**	**5.4**
Meadowlarks	**3.6**	**European Starling**	**5.4**
Barn Swallow	2.2	**Common Grackle**	**4.8**
American Goldfinch	2.2	**American Robin**	**4.8**
Killdeer	1.6	**Mourning Dove**	**3.3**
Vesper Sparrow	0.8	**Dickcissel**	**3.0**
Indigo Bunting	0.8	**Vesper Sparrow**	**2.2**
Chimney Swift	0.8	Meadowlarks [A]	2.1
European Starling	0.6	House Sparrow	1.8
American Robin	0.6	American Goldfinch	1.8
Dickcissel	0.6	Chipping Sparrow	1.5
Lark Sparrow	0.6	Indigo Bunting	0.8
		Grasshopper Sparrow	0.7
		Lark Sparrow	0.5
		Field Sparrow	0.5
		Savannah Sparrow	0.5
		House Finch	0.5
Number of birds	**501**		**757**
Number of species	**31**		**41**

[A] Eastern Meadowlarks outnumbered Western Meadowlarks 15 to 1; Western Meadowlarks were only found in soybeans in northern Illinois.

4.27. Soybeans grown with conventional tillage (A), such as this field near Adair, McDonough County, host a different bird community than soybeans produced with no-till methods (B), such as this field 1 mile south of Sibley, Ford County.

2000s No-Till		2000s Till	
Species	%	Species	%
Red-winged Blackbird	12.7	Horned Lark	34.2
American Robin	10.7	Red-winged Blackbird	16.3
Barn Swallow	10.0	Killdeer	11.1
Horned Lark	10.0	Brown-headed Cowbird	7.0
Common Grackle	7.3	Barn Swallow	4.1
Dickcissel	7.3	Common Grackle	2.9
Killdeer	6.0	American Robin	2.3
Mourning Dove	4.7	Mourning Dove	2.0
American Goldfinch	4.0	Dickcissel	1.8
Brown-headed Cowbird	4.0	Meadowlarks	1.4
Meadowlarks	4.0	American Goldfinch	1.1
Grasshopper Sparrow	3.3	Grasshopper Sparrow	0
Field Sparrow	2.7	Field Sparrow	0
Others	13.3	Others	15.8

Table 4.20. Relative abundances of birds (% of all birds recorded in the 2000s) in no-till and conventional tillage soybeans.

WHEAT

During our surveys, wheat plants were 24-30 inches tall, headed out and beginning to ripen in southern Illinois by late May. Harvest in southern Illinois began in mid-June and rapidly progressed northward. We sampled a few fields of wheat stubble after harvest, but none after double-cropping to soybeans, tillage, or other alterations. Gross noted that about one-tenth of the fields they sampled in 1900s were "cut and shocked" (all in southern Illinois), and the Grabers described most wheat fields they surveyed in the 1950s as green or ripening, and few as stubble. Figure 4.30 shows a typical wheat field in the 1900s and 2000s, and Table 4.21 shows survey efforts in this crop type over the past century.

Acreage of wheat in Illinois has varied greatly over time (see Fig. 3.1), and was probably about 2.0 million acres during the 1900s surveys and 1.5 million acres during the 1950s surveys. From 2004 to 2008, 630,000 to 1.2 million acres have been planted to wheat, with yields of 55-67 bushels/acre compared to 21-37.5 bushels/acre in 1950s. Red clover was commonly planted with wheat in previous decades, although this seldom occurs now. Rather, soybeans are often planted into wheat stubble in late-June or early July after harvest, particularly in years with adequate soil moisture and in southern Illinois, where there is a longer growing season for the soybeans to mature before frost. The timing of the wheat crop appears to have accelerated in recent decades with a far greater proportion of the statewide crop now harvested by early July (90% completed in Illinois by July 4th).

Modern wheat fields support a low-diversity community, with Red-winged Blackbirds comprising more than 60% of all birds seen, nearly double their relative abundance in the bird community 50 years ago (Table 4.22). By contrast, House Sparrows were the most common birds in wheat a century ago, and Northern Bobwhites, an important species observed in the 1900s, were not seen during the 2000s surveys in wheat fields. The number of important species (totaling 85% of birds recorded) in the 2000s was only eight species, compared to 10 species in the 1950s and 11 species in the 1900s. This slight decrease in the number of important species over time combined with the increasing relative abundance of Red-winged Blackbirds in the community suggest that the bird community is becoming more homogenous.

Red-winged Blackbirds were the most commonly encountered bird in wheat in all three zones, although the species was less dense in northern Illinois (Fig. 4.29). House Sparrows were densest in northern Illinois wheat, and the density of Eastern Meadowlarks and Indigo Buntings was greatest in the southern region of the state.

Table 4.21. Summary of survey effort in wheat during the three survey periods.

	Time Period		
	1900s	1950s	2000s
Acres surveyed			
North	6	16	30
Central	168	69	36
South	387	214	83
Sites surveyed			
North	2	6	7
Central	12	14	9
South	26	16	15

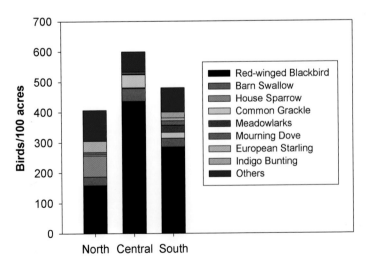

4.29. Densities of the eight most abundant bird species observed in wheat in Illinois by region, 2000s.

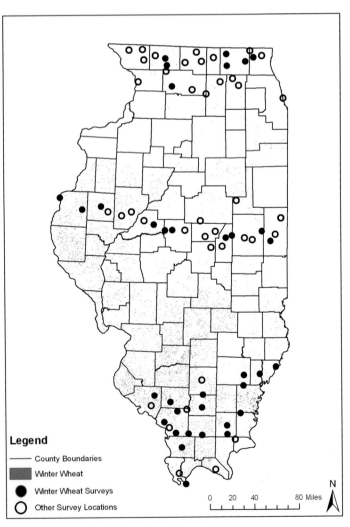

4.28. Distribution of wheat (shading) and bird surveys (circles) in Illinois. Filled circles indicate locations where surveys included wheat.

4.30. A 1900s cut and shocked wheat field (left) in July in Franklin County and a contemporary field (right) 2 miles south of Bondville, Champaign County.

Table 4.22. Relative abundance of bird species (% of all birds recorded in a specific time period) observed in wheat in Illinois, 1900s, 1950s, and 2000s. Species are listed in order of decreasing abundance in each survey period. Boldfaced text indicates species totaling 85% of birds recorded within each time period; only species totaling 95% of all birds seen are listed.

1900s		1950s		2000s	
Species	%	Species	%	Species	%
House Sparrow	**30.5**	**Red-winged Blackbird**	**31.4**	**Red-winged Blackbird**	**60.4**
Mourning Dove	**16.2**	**Meadowlarks**	**10.4**	**Barn Swallow**	**6.3**
Meadowlarks	**8.7**	**Mourning Dove**	**9.7**	**House Sparrow**	**4.8**
Red-winged Blackbird	**6.1**	**Dickcissel**	**9.4**	**Common Grackle**	**4.1**
Dickcissel	**5.8**	**Indigo Bunting**	**7.1**	**Eastern Meadowlark**[A]	**2.9**
Common Grackle	**4.7**	**Common Grackle**	**6.8**	**Mourning Dove**	**2.3**
Horned Lark	**4.3**	**Barn Swallow**	**5.2**	**European Starling**	**2.3**
Northern Bobwhite	**3.2**	**Field Sparrow**	**2.6**	**Indigo Bunting**	**1.9**
Brown-headed Cowbird	**2.8**	**House Sparrow**	**2.3**	Dickcissel	1.6
Field Sparrow	**1.9**	**Brown-headed Cowbird**	**2.3**	Brown-headed Cowbird	1.4
American Crow	**1.5**	**N. Rough-winged Swallow**	**2.3**	N. Rough-winged Swallow	1.2
Red-headed Woodpecker	**1.5**	European Starling	1.9	Horned Lark	1.1
Grasshopper Sparrow	1.3	Chimney Swift	1.6	Cliff Swallow	1.1
Lark Sparrow	1.1	Horned Lark	1.3	American Goldfinch	1.0
Indigo Bunting	0.9	Gray Catbird	1.0	American Robin	1.0
American Goldfinch	0.7			House Finch	1.0
American Robin	0.7			Field Sparrow	0.7
Purple Martin	0.6			Rock Pigeon	0.7
Chimney Swift	0.6				
Common Yellowthroat	0.6				
Northern Flicker	0.6				
Upland Sandpiper	0.6				
Yellow-billed Cuckoo	0.6				
Number of birds	**537**		**309**		**733**
Number of species	**37**		**23**		**36**

[A] Only Eastern Meadowlarks were observed in wheat in 2000s.

ALFALFA

Alfalfa is now a minor crop in Illinois, although it is the most common legume grown for hay in the state. More alfalfa fields occur in the northern and central zones than the southern zone. At maturity, alfalfa forms a dense cover roughly 18 to 24 inches tall, but immediately after harvesting it is reduced to 2-inch stubble. We sampled alfalfa fields at all stages of growth, although nearly all had been harvested at least once prior to our surveys. This section describes fields that were >80% dominated by alfalfa. Mixed hay fields of grasses and alfalfa or other legumes are considered in "Hayed & Mowed Grasslands" (pages 52-53). Too few alfalfa fields were sampled in the 1900s surveys to permit an assessment of their bird communities (Table 4.23).

The acreage of alfalfa in Illinois increased from only 18,000 acres in 1909 to 1.4 million acres in 1957. Since the 1950s, alfalfa acreage has decreased to about 400,000 acres, although per-acre yield has increased to about 4.2 tons/acre in 2006 (compared to 2.3 tons/acre in 1957). Modern cultivars of alfalfa allow early and frequent cuttings. Median date of first cuttings of alfalfa is about May 25th, compared to mid-June as observed by Graber and Graber (1963), and more than two-thirds of alfalfa has been cut twice by the 2nd week of July. Third, and occasionally fourth, cuttings are made into late summer and early fall.

Because of early and frequent cuttings, alfalfa and other legume hay crops are widely regarded as "ecological traps." Some birds, including Ring-necked Pheasants, Dickcissels, and Bobolinks, are attracted to these lush fields early in the season and attempt to nest in them. Haying operations destroy virtually 100% of the eggs and young, as well as many adult birds. The intervals between the initial harvest of alfalfa and subsequent cuttings is generally too short for birds to recolonize the field, build replacement nests, lay and incubate eggs, and raise their young (Warner and Etter 1989, Bollinger et al. 1990, Warner 1994).

Red-winged Blackbirds made up more than one-half of all the birds recorded in alfalfa fields during the latest surveys, and their relative abundance in the bird community was twice as large in the 2000s as in the 1950s. On the other hand, the relative abundance of meadowlarks, Horned Larks, and Bobolinks in alfalfa was far less in the 2000s compared to the 1950s. The overall number of species seen (29-30 species) and the number of most important species (8-9 species) were similar among the two time periods in alfalfa. Nevertheless, the increasing dominance of Red-winged Blackbirds combined with the decreasing relative abundance of these other bird species indicate that the alfalfa bird community is becoming simpler (Table 4.24). Notably, we did not find any Upland Sandpipers in alfalfa in the 2000s (Table 4.24).

The density of the most important bird species varied by region (Fig 4.32). Dickcissels were denser in alfalfa fields in central and southern Illinois than in the north, whereas Savannah Sparrows were densest in the northern region (Fig. 4.32). Although Red-winged Blackbirds were common throughout the state, they reached their highest density in the central region.

Table 4.23. Summary of survey effort in alfalfa during the three surveys.

	Time Period		
	1900s	1950s	2000s
Acres surveyed			
North	6	16	30
Central	168	69	36
South	387	214	83
Sites surveyed			
North	2	6	7
Central	12	14	9
South	26	16	15

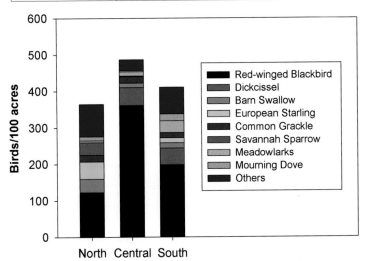

4.32. Densities of the eight most important species observed in alfalfa in Illinois by region, 2000s.

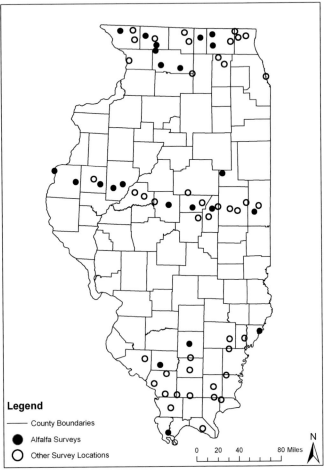

4.31. Distribution of alfalfa is too sparse to show on this map. Filled circles indicate locations where surveys included alfalfa.

4.33. Alfalfa fields, such as this one photographed near West Jersey, Stark County, are harvested 3-4 times each season, giving birds little opportunity to successfully nest within them.

Table 4.24. Relative abundance of bird species (% of all birds recorded in a specific time period) seen in alfalfa in Illinois, 1950s and 2000s. Species are listed in order of decreasing abundance in each survey period. Boldfaced text indicates species totaling 85% of birds recorded within each time period; only species totaling 95% of all birds seen are listed. Too few alfalfa fields were surveyed in the 1900s to permit a summary of the bird community during that time period.

1950s		2000s	
Species	%	Species	%
Red-winged Blackbird	**23.3**	**Red-winged Blackbird**	**56.3**
Meadowlarks	**17.5**	**Dickcissel**	**7.0**
Horned Lark	**11.1**	**Barn Swallow**	**5.2**
Bobolink	**10.4**	**European Starling**	**5.1**
Dickcissel	**6.0**	**Common Grackle**	**4.2**
Barn Swallow	**5.3**	**Savannah Sparrow**	**3.5**
House Sparrow	**5.1**	**Meadowlarks** [A]	**3.0**
European Starling	**4.4**	**Mourning Dove**	**2.1**
Grasshopper Sparrow	**3.7**	American Robin	1.7
Mourning Dove	1.9	Bobolink	1.4
Vesper Sparrow	1.5	House Sparrow	1.4
Common Grackle	1.0	Horned Lark	1.2
Upland Sandpiper	1.0	American Goldfinch	1.2
Savannah Sparrow	0.7	Indigo Bunting	0.9
Indigo Bunting	0.5	Chipping Sparrow	0.9
Brown-headed Cowbird	0.5		
Ring-necked Pheasant	0.5		
Northern Bobwhite	0.3		
Number of birds	**587**		**572**
Number of species	**30**		**29**

[A] Eastern Meadowlarks outnumbered Western Meadowlarks 7.5 to 1; Western Meadowlarks were only found in alfalfa in the northern zone.

OATS

Oats are most common in northern Illinois, but they have become a minor crop in all regions of the state. An estimated 4.3 million acres of oats were planted in 1907; this area declined to 2.8 million acres in 1957 and to 35,000 acres in 2007. As a result, fewer acres of oats were surveyed in each time period (Table 4.25). In late May and early June, plants were about 18 inches tall and headed out, and they were ripe by early July. Scattered weeds were common in oats, and oats were a nurse/cover crop for alfalfa in many of the fields we sampled.

Though we sampled considerably less oats than did the Grabers or Gross and Ray, we recorded more individual birds (Table 4.26). Almost all of these were Red-winged Blackbirds and European Starlings, often in large flocks suggesting post-nesting concentrations. We found a few Bobolinks in these large blackbird flocks, but otherwise there was no indication of Bobolinks nesting in oat fields or that contemporary oat fields were important Bobolink habitat, as were oat fields in the 1950s. House Sparrows, which were the most abundant species in oat fields in the 1900s, were much less abundant in the 1950s and especially the 2000s. Meadowlarks, Dickcissels, Horned Larks, and several other species also declined in abundance from the 1900s to the 2000s. Overall, the total number of species seen in oats decreased from 44 to 21 over the past century. This decrease was mirrored by a decline in the number of most important species from 17 in the 1900s, to 7 in the 1950s, and finally to 2 in the 2000s. The decrease in species richness, decline in relative abundance of many bird species, and the increase in dominance of Red-winged Blackbirds and European Starlings have resulted in a much simpler bird community.

Because of the small number of oat fields available to us, we did not consider regional variation in the birds found in this crop type. Red-winged Blackbirds were the most common bird in every field we sampled.

4.34. In the 1900s oats were regularly encountered by Gross and Ray (left); most oat fields we found were in the northern portion of the state such as this field 1 mile northeast of Harrison in Winnebago County (right).

Table 4.25. Summary of survey effort in oats during the three surveys.

	Time Period		
	1900s	1950s	2000s
Acres surveyed			
North	241	169	33
Central	597	129	23
South	183	10	0
Sites surveyed			
North	8	19	5
Central	16	18	2
South	19	4	0

Table 4.26. Relative abundance of birds (% of all birds recorded in a specific time period) observed in oats in Illinois, 1900s, 1950s, and 2000s. Species are listed in order of decreasing abundance in each survey period. Boldfaced text indicates species totaling 85% of birds recorded within each time period; only species totaling 95% of all birds seen are listed.

1900s		1950s		2000s	
Species	%	Species	%	Species	%
House Sparrow	**16.4**	**Red-winged Blackbird**	**38.0**	**Red-winged Blackbird**	**80.9**
Common Grackle	**11.9**	**Bobolink**	**17.8**	**European Starling**	**4.9**
Meadowlarks	**10.6**	**House Sparrow**	**12.8**	Dickcissel	2.9
Dickcissel	**8.8**	**Meadowlarks**	**5.4**	Barn Swallow	2.8
Red-winged Blackbird	**7.3**	**Dickcissel**	**5.0**	Common Grackle	2.4
Horned Lark	**5.6**	**Common Grackle**	**3.3**	House Sparrow	0.9
Mourning Dove	**5.1**	**Horned Lark**	**3.1**	Cliff Swallow	0.7
American Crow	**2.8**	Ring-necked Pheasant	2.1		
Brown-headed Cowbird	**2.7**	American Goldfinch	2.1		
Northern Bobwhite	**2.5**	Barn Swallow	1.6		
Grasshopper Sparrow	**2.3**	European Starling	1.2		
Northern Flicker	**2.0**	Mourning Dove	0.8		
American Goldfinch	**1.7**	American Robin	0.6		
Eastern Kingbird	**1.7**	Killdeer	0.6		
Bobolink	**1.5**	Northern Flicker	0.6		
Brown Thrasher	**1.5**				
Indigo Bunting	**1.0**				
American Robin	0.8				
Field Sparrow	0.8				
Barn Swallow	0.7				
Chimney Swift	0.7				
Gray Catbird	0.7				
Lark Sparrow	0.7				
Loggerhead Shrike	0.7				
Red-headed Woodpecker	0.7				
Song Sparrow	0.7				
Savannah Sparrow	0.5				
Killdeer	0.5				
Vesper Sparrow	0.5				
Blue Jay	0.5				
Common Yellowthroat	0.5				
Upland Sandpiper	0.3				
Eastern Bluebird	0.3				
Eastern Phoebe	0.3				
Number of birds	**603**		**516**		**680**
Number of species	**44**		**28**		**21**

UNPLANTED CROPLAND

This category includes fields that were cultivated cropland the previous year but not yet cultivated or planted in the year when the bird surveys were done. The fields were either bare soil or crop stubble, with highly variable growth of annual and biennial plants (i.e., agricultural weeds). The vast majority of these fields occurred where weather-related delays had prevented planting and spring cultivation prior to our surveys. Construction was scheduled, but had not yet started, on a few of the unplanted areas that we surveyed near cities. A field of mare's tail and ragweed near Freeport was razed the same day as our survey and converted into a large retail outlet center within a few months. Very little of this habitat in patches large enough for transect surveys survives through the entire growing season uncultivated, unmowed, or unsprayed. Patches of annual weed habitat probably were more common during the late spring and early summer survey periods in the 1900s and 1950s, because corn and soybean planting did not occur as early as it does today. Figure 4.35 shows unplanted croplands in the 1900s and 2000s.

The most analogous habitat to unplanted cropland considered by Graber and Graber (1963) was "plowed field." Unplanted cropland is distinct from "fallow fields" defined by the Grabers as "having been cultivated and then unused for a year or longer" and described as having a dense cover of grasses and weeds and scattered small shrubs. Depending on the age and composition of these old fields, we would have classified them as idle grasslands or shrub areas. Table 4.27 shows how survey effort in unplanted cropland has changed from the 1900s to 2000s.

Unplanted cropland and plowed fields are an imperfect comparison. Graber and Graber (1963) remarked on the "total lack of cover" in plowed fields, with Horned Larks, Killdeer, Brown-headed Cowbirds, and Mourning Doves being among the most common birds reported in these fields in the 1950s (Table 4.28). Annual weeds in some of the unplanted fields we surveyed attracted concentrations of Dickcissels and Grasshopper Sparrows. The vegetation structure and birds found in unplanted fields in the 2000s suggested similarities to both cropland and grassland habitats.

Whereas other crop types were generally characterized by a simplification of the bird community over time, unplanted croplands show relatively little reduction in the number of most important species over the past century, and the total number of species seen in this habitat may have increased. The ranking of species based on their relative abundance appears to have changed substantially over time, suggesting that the compositional nature of the bird community in this habitat has been quite dynamic. Due to possible differences in the definition of unplanted cropland among the time periods, patterns in the bird community need to be interpreted with caution.

4.35. This 1909 fallow corn field in southern Illinois (left) was noted for a large number of meadowlarks. In 2000s we found unplanted cropland in some areas slated for development such as this field in Lake County (right).

	Time Period		
	1900s	1950s	2000s
Acres surveyed			
North	4	20	29
Central	16	28	8
South	131	141	12
Sites surveyed			
North	3	5	5
Central	4	9	2
South	21	16	3

Table 4.27. Summary of survey effort in unplanted cropland during the three survey periods.

Table 4.28. Relative abundance of bird species (% of all birds recorded in a specific time period) seen in unplanted fields in Illinois, 1900s, 1950s, and 2000s. Species are listed in order of decreasing abundance in each survey period. Boldfaced text indicates species totaling 85% of birds recorded within each time period; only species totaling 95% of all birds seen are listed.

1900s		1950s		2000s	
Species	%	Species	%	Species	%
Brown-headed Cowbird	**14.5**	**Horned Lark**	**31.8**	**Red-winged Blackbird**	**24.8**
Mourning Dove	**12.7**	**Red-winged Blackbird**	**19.5**	**European Starling**	**17.9**
Horned Lark	**12.0**	**Killdeer**	**8.2**	**Barn Swallow**	**8.1**
House Sparrow	**9.6**	**Mourning Dove**	**7.2**	**American Goldfinch**	**7.2**
Common Grackle	**7.8**	**Brown-headed Cowbird**	**5.6**	**Brown-headed Cowbird**	**4.6**
American Robin	**6.0**	**Brewer's Blackbird**	**5.1**	**American Robin**	**4.6**
Brown Thrasher	**4.2**	**Meadowlarks**	**3.6**	**Indigo Bunting**	**3.6**
Vesper Sparrow	**3.6**	**Common Grackle**	**2.6**	**Grasshopper Sparrow**	**3.6**
Field Sparrow	**3.0**	**American Crow**	**2.6**	**Dickcissel**	**3.3**
Killdeer	**3.0**	Eastern Kingbird	2.1	**Horned Lark**	**2.9**
Chimney Swift	**2.4**	Lark Sparrow	2.1	**Field Sparrow**	**2.3**
Eastern Kingbird	**2.4**	Indigo Bunting	1.5	**Eastern Meadowlark** [A]	**2.0**
Eastern Bluebird	**2.4**	American Robin	1.0	Mourning Dove	1.6
Red-headed Woodpecker	**2.4**	Dickcissel	1.0	Common Grackle	1.6
Indigo Bunting	1.8	Yellow-headed Blackbird	1.0	Vesper Sparrow	1.6
Lark Sparrow	1.8	American Goldfinch	0.5	Savannah Sparrow	1.6
Bewick's Wren	1.8	Field Sparrow	0.5	Chimney Swift	1.0
Loggerhead Shrike	1.8	Vesper Sparrow	0.5	Killdeer	0.7
Northern Mockingbird	1.8	Northern Flicker	0.5	Northern Flicker	0.7
Meadowlarks	1.2			Chipping Sparrow	0.7
				Mallard	0.7
				Sandhill Crane	0.7
				Song Sparrow	0.7
				Tree Swallow	0.7
Number of birds	**166**		**195**		**307**
Number of species	**26**		**23**		**34**

[A] Only Eastern Meadowlarks were encountered in unplanted fields.

OTHER AGRICULTURE

Orchard Crops. Only about 8,000 acres of orchard crops are estimated to remain in the state compared to about 31,000 acres in 1957 and 300,000 acres in 1909. Most orchards in Illinois are found in the southern region where they produce apples and peaches. We also sampled one section of an orchard growing blueberries. Vineyards are an increasing crop in Illinois, though we did not sample any. Changes in survey effort in orchards over the past 100 years are shown in Table 4.29.

In the 2000s, the trees in orchards were heavily pruned, typically less than 10 feet tall, and were planted in evenly spaced rows. Tall fescue, which was kept mowed, was the normal ground cover (Fig. 4.36). A variety of pesticides were applied to many orchards to improve yield and fruit quality.

American Robins, European Starlings, and Common Grackles were the bird species most often seen in orchards during the 2000s surveys (Table 4.30). We saw no House Sparrows, which were the most common birds found in orchards during the 1900s and 1950s surveys. Otherwise, the birds found in orchards were similar to those observed in residential or low-density developed areas. The relative abundances of several "shrub-nesting" birds, including Mourning Dove, Field Sparrow, Brown Thrasher, Northern Mockingbird, and Orchard Oriole, appear to have decreased across successive time intervals. Overall, the bird communities in orchards have become less diverse, with a lower total number of species and fewer "most important species" (Table 4.30). Changes in the bird community of orchards likely reflect the yard-like, manicured appearance of modern orchards compared to the more natural character of orchards in the past (Fig. 4.36).

Other Legumes. In the past, red clover and sweet clover were important legume crops. Sweet clover is an abundant plant that is considered invasive in grasslands and is no longer grown as a crop. Red clover was commonly found in fields mixed with various grasses, and most of these fields were harvested for hay. See "*Hayed & Mowed Grasslands*" for a description of the birds in this land cover type.

We sampled a single field of red clover in southern Illinois. Of the 54 birds recorded, 38 were Red-winged Blackbirds. Dickcissels, Eastern Meadowlarks, Common Grackles, and Grasshopper Sparrows were also present.

Other Small Grains. We sampled two fields of rye, and while it is impractical to draw conclusions from such a small sample of a scarce land cover type, the birds we found in these fields were not substantially different from the birds seen in oats or wheat (i.e., they were dominated by Red-winged Blackbirds).

Barley and rye are no longer crops of any importance in the state; the National Agricultural Statistics Service has no information on recent acreage of barley in the state, and in 1999 only 7,000 acres of rye was harvested. While only 7,000 acres were harvested, 40,000 acres were planted to rye. The most common uses of rye today are for soil improvement and quickly establishing erosion control.

Other Field Crops. About 75,000 to 80,000 acres of sorghum are grown in southern Illinois for grain and silage. In late spring and early summer, fields of sorghum appear very similar to corn, both in vegetation structure and in bird use.

Potatoes, green beans, green peppers, sunflower, and sod were encountered during our surveys. From our limited samples, birds in these areas were similar to those other croplands, dominated by common, generalist species.

Table 4.29. Summary of survey effort in orchards during the three survey periods.

	Time Period		
	1900s	1950s	2000s
Acres surveyed			
North	0.1	2	22
Central	6	36	8
South	48	78	36
Sites surveyed			
North	1	2	4
Central	8	1	2
South	20	8	6

4.36. Orchards were a common sight in the 1900s such as this orchard near Flora, Clay County (left). In the 2000s, orchards were rarely encountered; this orchard was surveyed 1 mile north of Goreville, Johnson County (right).

Table 4.30. Relative abundance of bird species (% of all birds recorded in a specific time period) observed in orchards in Illinois, 1900s, 1950s, and 2000s. Species are listed in order of decreasing abundance in each survey period. Boldfaced text indicates species totaling 85% of birds recorded within each time period; only species totaling 95% of all birds seen are listed.

1900s		1950s		2000s	
Species	%	Species	%	Species	%
House Sparrow	**19.8**	**House Sparrow**	**14.3**	**American Robin**	**26.3**
Field Sparrow	**8.2**	**Common Grackle**	**10.5**	**European Starling**	**25.6**
Mourning Dove	**7.3**	**American Goldfinch**	**10.5**	**Common Grackle**	**10.5**
Orchard Oriole	**5.8**	**Mourning Dove**	**10.2**	**Red-winged Blackbird**	**8.3**
American Robin	**5.5**	**European Starling**	**6.4**	**Mourning Dove**	**3.8**
Common Grackle	**4.3**	**Red-winged Blackbird**	**6.1**	**American Goldfinch**	**3.0**
Gray Catbird	**3.7**	**Field Sparrow**	**6.1**	**Northern Cardinal**	**3.0**
Brown Thrasher	**3.7**	**Northern Cardinal**	**4.0**	**Indigo Bunting**	**3.0**
Blue Jay	**3.7**	**Indigo Bunting**	**3.8**	**Chipping Sparrow**	**3.0**
House Wren	**3.4**	**Barn Swallow**	**2.8**	Field Sparrow	2.3
Northern Flicker	**2.7**	**Brown Thrasher**	**2.3**	Brown-headed Cowbird	2.3
Meadowlarks	**2.4**	**American Robin**	**2.1**	Barn Swallow	1.5
Northern Mockingbird	**2.4**	**Meadowlarks**	**1.5**	Gray Catbird	1.5
Bewick's Wren	**2.1**	**Chimney Swift**	**1.5**	Cedar Waxwing	1.5
American Crow	**2.1**	**Blue Jay**	**1.2**		
Northern Cardinal	**1.8**	**Northern Bobwhite**	**1.2**		
Indigo Bunting	**1.8**	**Dickcissel**	**1.2**		
Tufted Titmouse	**1.8**	**Yellow-breasted Chat**	**1.2**		
Northern Bobwhite	**1.5**	Gray Catbird	1.0		
Loggerhead Shrike	**1.2**	Song Sparrow	1.0		
American Goldfinch	0.9	Common Nighthawk	1.0		
Common Yellowthroat	0.9	Eastern Phoebe	1.0		
Eastern Kingbird	0.9	Brown-headed Cowbird	0.8		
Eastern Towhee	0.9	Common Yellowthroat	0.8		
Yellow-billed Cuckoo	0.9	Eastern Kingbird	0.8		
Chickadees	0.9	Eastern Towhee	0.8		
Carolina Wren	0.9	Ring-necked Pheasant	0.8		
Red-headed Woodpecker	0.9	Chipping Sparrow	0.5		
Yellow Warbler	0.9	Northern Mockingbird	0.5		
Chipping Sparrow	0.6	Bewick's Wren	0.5		
Baltimore Oriole	0.6	Yellow-billed Cuckoo	0.5		
Great Crested Flycatcher	0.6				
Number of birds	**328**		**387**		**133**
Number of species	**44**		**37**		**20**

DEVELOPED AREAS

The dominant feature of developed areas is human-built structures and infrastructure, such as buildings, roads, and bridges. Developed areas typically have a high proportion of impervious surfaces (concrete or pavement) and landscaping vegetation. Because developed areas are the most rapidly increasing land cover type in Illinois, covering about 2.3 million acres, we sampled three distinct types of development: high-density developed locations that are predominantly covered by structures of pavement, low-density developed areas with up to 50% coverage by structures, and developed open spaces such as parks, cemeteries, and golf courses. In the 1900s and 1950s surveys, habitats comparable to high-density developed and developed open space were not sampled (Table 4.31).

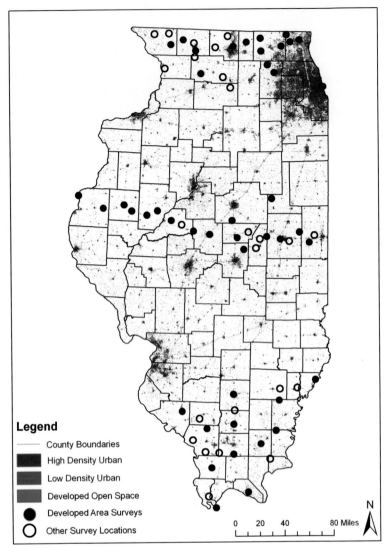

Legend
— County Boundaries
■ High Density Urban
■ Low Density Urban
■ Developed Open Space
● Developed Area Surveys
○ Other Survey Locations

4.37. Distribution of developed areas in Illinois. Filled circles indicate locations where surveys included developed areas.

Table 4.31. Summary of survey effort in developed areas during the three survey periods.

	Time Period				
	1900s Low-density	1950s Low-density	2000s High-density	2000s Low-density	2000s Open Space
Acres surveyed					
North	9	160	40	90	70
Central	6	75	29	71	58
South	20	98	42	81	47
Sites surveyed					
North	3	5	9	12	8
Central	4	2	7	10	9
South	8	3	8	9	8

High-density Developed Areas. High-density developed areas include downtown districts, industrial parks, commercial complexes, and other areas covered almost entirely by buildings, utility lines, and transportation infrastructure; they are unlike low-density urban areas where vegetation eventually becomes a dominant habitat feature. Buildings in high-density developed areas tend to be larger, taller, and except for parking areas, more closely spaced than their counterparts in low-density developed areas.

The amount of high-density urban land cover, estimated at 616,000 acres in the 1999-2000 Land Cover of Illinois, continues to increase, although at a slower rate than low-density developments. In many cities, high-density downtown areas have seen a net loss of residents to suburban areas and a shift of commercial and retail activity to new complexes in suburban-type areas.

While the abundance of birds in high-density developed areas was high during the 2000s surveys, species diversity was lower than in low-density and open-space developed areas. Just five species (European Starling, Chimney Swift, House Sparrow, Common Grackle, and Rock Pigeon) totaled 85% of all birds seen (Table 4.32), with very little difference in composition among northern, central, and southern Illinois (Fig. 4.39). Perhaps the most surprising bird was an adult Bald Eagle that flew over us in downtown Freeport in 2006. European Starlings and Common Grackles reached their lowest densities in northern Illinois, and House Sparrows were least dense in the south; otherwise, regional differences in the bird community of high-density developed areas were minor. Overall, the bird communities in high-density developed areas were the least variable across regions when compared to low-density and open-space developed areas.

4.38. Although these are not the typical locations at which ornithologists survey birds, we sampled bustling, high-density developed areas (left, Benton, Franklin County), and established high-density developed areas (right, Carthage, Hancock County).

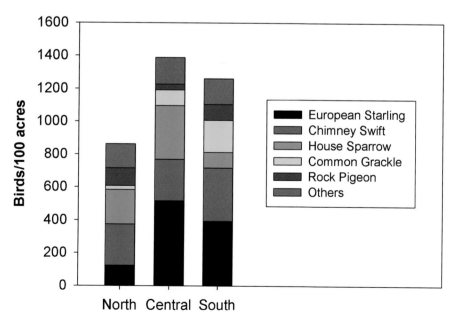

4.39. Densities of the five most abundant species observed in high-density developed areas in Illinois by region, 2000s.

Low-density Developed Areas. Low-density developed areas were characterized by up to 50% scattered buildings, roads, parking lots, and other impervious surfaces; the remaining 50% is usually composed of highly manicured lawns, trees, shrubs, and other landscaping. These areas are mostly residential, as were the developed areas surveyed by the Grabers. Mature neighborhoods had an open canopy of tall trees, whereas new developments were dominated by buildings and lawns with few or small trees (Fig. 4.40).

The Grabers estimated 350,000 acres of urban residential area in 1907 and 820,000 acres in 1957. At present, low-density developed areas cover more than 1.0 million acres and are expanding rapidly. Between 1940 and 2002, the U.S. Census Bureau documented a reduction in average household size from 3.7 to 2.6 people, while average home size more than doubled from 1,100 to 2,340 square feet. New residential areas typically have much larger lots as well. Thus, the amount of low-density developed area is increasing at a greater rate than population growth. Suburban development is most extensive and most rapid in the collar counties of Chicago in northeastern Illinois, but is also apparent on the edges of cities throughout Illinois.

Just seven species totaled 85% of all birds seen in low-density developed areas (Table 4.32). The relative abundance of House Sparrows was much lower in the recent surveys compared with the 1900s and 1950s surveys. Unless it is an observer effect, the increase in the relative abundance of Chimney Swifts seems curious, given fewer buildings have chimneys than 50 or 100 years ago. House Finches, which initially colonized Illinois in the 1980s, are now one of the most common birds in low-density developed areas. The common birds of low-density developed areas do not vary much among the regions of the state (Fig. 4.41).

4.40. Established low-density developed areas (left, Mulkeytown, Franklin County) had a more diverse bird community than newly constructed low-density developed areas (right, near Lake Villa, Lake County) that typically lacked mature trees.

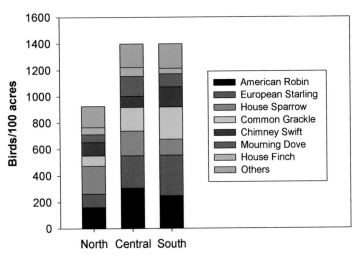

4.41. Densities of the seven most abundant species observed in low-density developed areas in Illinois by region, 2000s.

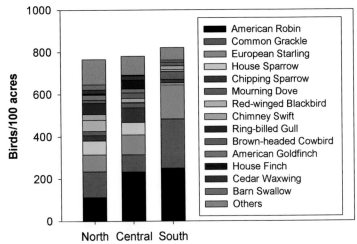

4.42. Densities of the 14 most abundant species observed in developed open space in Illinois by region, 2000s.

Developed Open Space. Developed open space – parks, cemeteries, and golf courses – were mostly located within and on the edges of towns and cities. Developed open space is most similar to low-density developed areas, with deliberate plantings of trees, shrubs, and flowers, mowed lawns, some roads or paths, but few buildings. Many locations had a savanna-like character (Fig. 4.42).

While specific data are not available, urban open space probably is increasing at a rate similar to low-density development, as green space is incorporated into suburban areas, and residents seek outdoor recreation opportunities. As of 2008, there were at least 770 golf courses in Illinois. Some of these were designed and managed for compatibility with birds and other wildlife, including the use of native vegetation along fairways. Pesticides and herbicide use, however, can be fairly intense in some areas.

The birds seen in developed open areas were similar to those in low-density and high-density developed areas, with American Robins, Common Grackles, and European Starlings making up more than half the individual birds recorded (Table 4.32). American Robins were less dense in the northern zone,

4.43. Developed open space included parks, golf courses, and cemetaries (1.5 miles southwest of Easton, Mason County) often had a savanna-like character.

and House Sparrows were less dense in the south (Fig. 4.42). Both Common Grackles and European Starlings reached peak densities in the southern zone.

Table 4.32. Relative abundance of birds (% of all birds recorded in a specific time period) observed in developed areas in Illinois, 1900s, 1950s, and 2000s. Open space and high-density development were not surveyed in the 1900s or 1950s. Species are listed in order of decreasing abundance in each survey period. Boldfaced text indicates species totaling 85% of birds recorded within each time period; only species totaling 95% of all birds seen are listed.

1900s – Low-density		1950s – Low-density		2000s – High-density		2000s – Low-density		2000s – Open Space	
Species	%	Species	%	Species	%	Species	%	Species	%
House Sparrow	**58.9**	**House Sparrow**	**39.3**	**European Starling**	**28.5**	**American Robin**	**18.8**	**American Robin**	**24.1**
American Robin	**7.0**	**European Starling**	**14.5**	**Chimney Swift**	**24.2**	**European Starling**	**17.4**	**Common Grackle**	**17.6**
Brown Thrasher	**4.2**	**Common Grackle**	**12.5**	**House Sparrow**	**17.0**	**House Sparrow**	**14.3**	**European Starling**	**13.6**
Orchard Oriole	**3.3**	**American Robin**	**12.4**	**Common Grackle**	**9.5**	**Common Grackle**	**13.3**	**House Sparrow**	**6.2**
Common Grackle	**2.8**	**Rock Pigeon**	**5.7**	**Rock Pigeon**	**7.3**	**Chimney Swift**	**9.9**	**Chipping Sparrow**	**4.7**
Purple Martin	**2.8**	**Mourning Dove**	**3.0**	American Robin	3.4	**Mourning Dove**	**8.0**	**Mourning Dove**	**3.3**
Chipping Sparrow	**2.3**	Purple Martin	2.6	Mourning Dove	2.5	**House Finch**	**4.3**	**Red-wing Blackbird**	**3.1**
Eastern Kingbird	**1.9**	Blue Jay	1.9	House Finch	2.3	Chipping Sparrow	2.7	**Chimney Swift**	**2.8**
N. Mockingbird	**1.9**	Chimney Swift	1.7	Ring-billed Gull	1.2	Northern Cardinal	1.6	**Ring-billed Gull**	**2.7**
Gray Catbird	**1.9**	House Wren	1.7			Cedar Waxwing	1.3	**Br-headed Cowbird**	**2.4**
Northern Flicker	**1.9**					Purple Martin	1.2	**American Goldfinch**	**2.0**
Blue Jay	1.4					American Goldfinch	1.0	**House Finch**	**2.0**
Chimney Swift	0.9					Br-headed Cowbird	0.9	**Cedar Waxwing**	**1.8**
House Wren	0.9					Barn Swallow	0.9	**Barn Swallow**	**1.8**
Bewick's Wren	0.9							Rock Pigeon	1.4
Yellow-bill Cuckoo	0.9							Caspian Tern	0.9
								American Crow	0.7
								Purple Martin	0.7
								Canada Goose	0.7
								Northern Cardinal	0.7
								Eastern Bluebird	0.6
								Eastern Wood-Pewee	0.6
								Tree Swallow	0.6
Number of birds	214		3165		1279		2773		1375
Number of species	28		27		29		43		48

MARSH & OPEN WATER

Marsh. Marshes are characterized by hydric soils, emergent or moist soil plants, and intermittent to semi-permanent surface water, generally less than 3 feet deep. Because they are now so scarce, we included wet meadows, true marshes, and artificial wetlands managed for marsh-like, shallow water conditions. Wet meadows were near-monocultures of reed canary grass with some sedges in most areas. Emergent vegetation in natural and artificial marshes included cattails, rushes, and bulrushes, but also invasive reed canary grass and phragmites. Open water varied from near-zero in wet meadows to roughly 60% in some newly-created artificial marshes. If water depth, soil conditions, and vegetation allowed, we surveyed transects through wetlands. Many patches were small enough that we could enclose the entire wetland within a transect. At larger wetlands that were impractical to walk across due to vegetation density, water depth, or flocculent soil, we surveyed them from the perimeter.

The 1999-2000 Land Cover of Illinois project estimated about 134,000 acres of shallow marsh/wet meadow and deep marsh in the state; the amount of this habitat has probably seen a net increase since the 1950s, when the Grabers estimated just 60,000 acres of marsh in Illinois. The Grabers estimated 558,000 acres of marsh existed in Illinois in 1906. It should be noted that what constituted a marsh for the 1999-2000 Land Cover project in Illinois likely differed from what the Grabers called a marsh. Regardless of how a marsh is defined, there has been a large decline in marsh acreage since the 1900s. The survey effort in marshes over the past 100 years is shown in Table 4.33. Over the past 20 years, wetland mitigation, restoration, and creation on public lands, and restoration on private lands through programs including the Wetlands Reserve Program and Conservation Reserve Enhancement Program, may have resulted in a net increase of wetlands in Illinois. It is not clear what proportion of these created or enhanced wetlands are marsh-like, compared to forested wetlands and open water. Invasive plants, among them reed canary grass, phragmites, and purple loosestrife, have significantly degraded the condition of marsh habitat in the state. Isolation, siltation, and altered hydrology are also important degrading factors (Ward et al. 2010a).

More than half of the birds seen in marshes were Red-winged Blackbirds (Table 4.34). The high relative abundances of three state-endangered species – Black Tern, Little Blue Heron,

4.44. Marshes such as this one at Spunky Bottoms Preserve, Brown County, are rare across the landscape.

and Yellow-crowned Night-heron – were caused by encounters of several birds of each species at single locations. Mallards and Great Blue Herons were among the common wetland-dependent birds we recorded. Regional differences in bird communities and species densities also reflect the clumped distribution of some birds (Fig. 4.46), such as a large concentration of Tree Swallows encountered along the Mississippi River near Nauvoo in central Illinois.

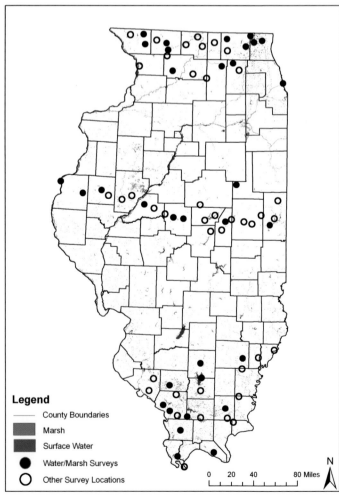

Legend

— County Boundaries
▨ Marsh
▨ Surface Water
● Water/Marsh Surveys
○ Other Survey Locations

0   20   40   80 Miles

N

4.45. Distribution of wetlands and open water (shading) and bird surveys (circles) in Illinois. Filled circles indicate locations where surveys included wetlands or open water.

Table 4.33. Summary of survey effort in marshes during the three survey periods.

	Time Period		
	1900s	1950s	2000s
Acres surveyed			
North	6	6	8
Central	3	1	5
South	8	6	5
Sites surveyed			
North	19	89	33
Central	3	1	16
South	28	9	19

Open Water. While this is a category for the open water of rivers, streams, ponds, reservoirs, lakes, and waste water treatment lagoons, the birds detected are better described as shoreline observations. In our surveys, the two observers either walked opposite sides of narrow ponds or streams, or they both walked along a single bank of wider water bodies and counted birds out to 50 yards over the water. Open water was not a habitat type we actively sought out, but rather one that we surveyed whenever convenient relative to sampling other land-cover types. As a result, much of the water we sampled was associated with developed areas where the shoreline was accessible and easily traversed.

The amount of surface water in the state has increased from the 1900s, to the 1950s and to the 2000s sampling periods, as impoundments of all sizes have been created for water supply, recreation, and flood control. In general, there are relatively few natural lakes in the state of Illinois. Open water/shorelines were not sampled for birds in the 1900s or 1950s.

Canada Geese and Red-winged Blackbirds made up the bulk of birds seen along shorelines, on, or over water, but Mallards, Wood Ducks, Great Blue Herons, Ring-billed Gulls, Spotted Sandpipers, and other aquatic birds were well-represented in our sample (Table 4.34). Several species of swallows were often seen foraging over water. The density of bird species seen on the water in the three regions differed because of encounters with flocks of birds (Fig. 4.48). As examples, 24 Mallards were found at one urban site in northern

4.47. Open water was surveyed from the shorelines of streams, rivers, reservoirs, lakes, and ponds like this one photographed in Grant Woods Forest Preserve, Lake County.

Illinois, flocks of 25 and 69 Canada Geese were found at two sites in central Illinois, and 29 Great Blue Herons were seen at a fish hatchery in southern Illinois. Other results may reflect true regional differences: the density of Common Grackles and Cliff Swallows was greatest in southern Illinois, and Song Sparrows, Tree Swallows, and Northern Rough-winged Swallows were densest in the northern and central zones.

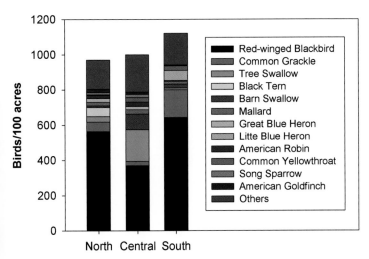

4.46. Densities of the 12 most abundant species observed in marshes in Illinois by region, 2000s.

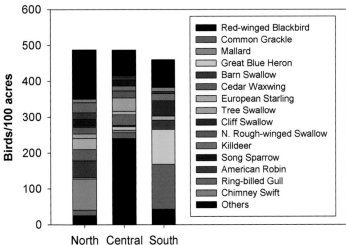

4.48. Densities of the 15 most abundant bird species observed in open water in Illinois by region, 2000s.

Table 4.34. Relative abundance of bird species (% of all birds recorded in a specific time period) seen in marshes, 1900s, 1950s, and 2000s, and over open water, 2000s, in Illinois. Species are listed in order of decreasing abundance in each survey period. Boldfaced text indicates species totaling 85% of birds recorded within each time period; only species totaling 95% of all birds seen are listed.

1900s - Marsh		1950s - Marsh		2000s - Marsh		2000s - Open Water	
Species	%	Species	%	Species	%	Species	%
Red-winged Blackbird	**71.6**	**Red-winged Blackbird**	**36.8**	**Red-winged Blackbird**	**54.3**	**Canada Goose**	**21.9**
Common Grackle	**12.6**	**Common Grackle**	**15.3**	**Common Grackle**	**7.7**	**Red-winged Blackbird**	**15.6**
Bobolink	**7.7**	**Black Tern**	**5.8**	**Tree Swallow**	**6.1**	**Common Grackle**	**9.3**
Green Heron	1.4	**Yellow-headed Blackbird**	**5.2**	**Black Tern**	**4.0**	**Mallard**	**7.1**
Common Yellowthroat	0.9	**Mourning Dove**	**4.7**	**Barn Swallow**	**3.1**	**Great Blue Heron**	**6.3**
Dickcissel	0.9	**Swamp Sparrow**	**4.0**	**Mallard**	**2.1**	**Barn Swallow**	**4.2**
Eastern Meadowlark	0.9	**Sedge Wren**	**2.3**	**Great Blue Heron**	**1.6**	**Cedar Waxwing**	**3.2**
Yellow-breasted Chat	0.9	**Killdeer**	**1.9**	**Little Blue Heron**	**1.6**	**European Starling**	**2.8**
		American Robin	**1.5**	**American Robin**	**1.5**	**Tree Swallow**	**3.0**
		Blue-winged Teal	**1.5**	**Common Yellowthroat**	**1.5**	**Cliff Swallow**	**2.5**
		Common Yellowthroat	**1.4**	**Song Sparrow**	**1.2**	**N. Rough-winged Swallow**	**2.0**
		Song Sparrow	**1.4**	**American Goldfinch**	**1.2**	**Killdeer**	**2.0**
		Eastern Meadowlark	**1.2**	Wood Duck	0.9	**Song Sparrow**	**1.8**
		Brown-headed Cowbird	**1.2**	Yellow-crowned Night-Heron	0.9	**American Robin**	**1.7**
		Spotted Sandpiper	**1.1**	Killdeer	0.7	**Ring-billed Gull**	**1.3**
		European Starling	1.0	Green Heron	0.7	**Chimney Swift**	**1.3**
		Least Bittern	1.0	Great Egret	0.7	American Goldfinch	1.1
		American Goldfinch	0.8	Indigo Bunting	0.7	Eastern Kingbird	1.0
		Barn Swallow	0.7	Blue-winged Teal	0.6	Wood Duck	0.8
		Brewer's Blackbird	0.7	Mute Swan	0.6	Mourning Dove	0.8
		Prothonotary Warbler	0.7	Turkey Vulture	0.6	Gray Catbird	0.8
		American Coot	0.5	Mourning Dove	0.4	Baltimore Oriole	0.8
		Marsh Wren	0.5	Swamp Sparrow	0.4	House Sparrow	0.7
		Mallard	0.4	Dickcissel	0.4	Bank Swallow	0.7
		Dickcissel	0.4	Cliff Swallow	0.4	Spotted Sandpiper	0.5
		Brown Thrasher	0.4	Yellow Warbler	0.4	Rock Pigeon	0.5
		American Bittern	0.4	Sedge Wren	0.3	Indigo Bunting	0.5
		Ring-necked Pheasant	0.4	European Starling	0.3	House Wren	0.5
		Great Blue Heron	0.3	Brown Thrasher	0.3	Great Egret	0.5
		Green Heron	0.3	N. Rough-wing Swallow	0.3	Brown-headed Cowbird	0.5
		American Crow	0.3	Eastern Kingbird	0.3		
		Louisiana Waterthrush	0.3	Chimney Swift	0.3		
		Northern Cardinal	0.3	Common Moorhen	0.3		
		Savannah Sparrow	0.3	Ruby-throated Hummingbird	0.3		
		Carolina Wren	0.3	Sandhill Crane	0.3		
		Pied-billed Grebe	0.3				
		Northern Bobwhite	0.3				
		Upland Sandpiper	0.3				
		White-breasted Nuthatch	0.3				
Number of birds	**222**		**726**		**675**		**599**
Number of species	**16**		**57**		**53**		**48**

SUMMARY

Within habitat types, our estimates of bird densities are greater now than the estimates of 50 or 100 years ago (Fig. 4.49). This can be explained partially by the hours during which Gross and Ray and the Grabers conducted their surveys. During both the 1900s and 1950s some surveys were conducted in the afternoon hours, when bird activity is less than in the morning hours and when they recorded fewer birds. However, even when only comparing data from morning surveys, density estimates were higher for the 2000s than either the 1900s or 1950s, suggesting that other factors contributed to this pattern.

Increased abundance of a few birds, including American Robins, Common Grackles, and European Starlings, was an important factor in our higher density estimates. For instance, the average number of American Robins recorded on a Breeding Bird Survey route in Illinois increased from about 40 birds in the late 1960s to over 100 birds in the early 2000s. Some of the differences in densities may have been attributed to errors and observer differences among the three time periods. Thus, we urge caution in comparing unadjusted densities among the time periods.

The overall trends of bird density are similar across time periods, however, with more birds per area in developed areas, marshes, and shrublands, intermediate densities in grasslands, and lowest densities in corn and soybeans (Fig. 4.49). Bird diversity, as indexed by the number of most important species (totaling 85% of all birds recorded), is lowest at the extremes of bird density (Fig. 4.50). In developed areas, high bird densities are recorded, but the majority of birds belong to just a few species; in other words, bird communities are quite simple (Table 4.32). Corn and soybeans, on the other hand, have low bird densities and there are few individuals of any species (Tables 4.17 and 4.19).

Just as the amount of forest and average forest maturity increased across the 20th century, so did the number

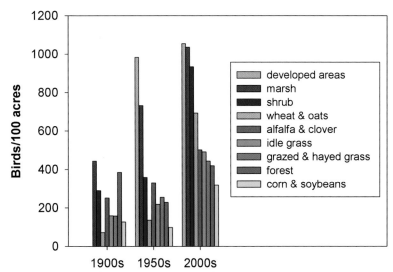

4.49. Total density of birds in various habitat types sampled by transect surveys in Illinois, 1900s, 1950s, and 2000s.

of bird species in forests. Unique among habitat types, the most important species, their rank, and their relative abundance in the forests of Illinois were similar in the 1950s and 2000s (Table 4.10). In most other habitats, diversity (number of most important species) was highest during the 1900s survey period (Fig. 4.50). Grassland diversity was similar between the 1950s and the 2000s, although the rank of true grassland birds (meadowlarks, Dickcissels, Bobolinks, Grasshopper Sparrows, and others) fell between the two periods (Tables 4.2, 4.4, and 4.6). Several generalist birds – European Starlings, Barn Swallows, Common Grackles, and American Robins – were among those increasing in relative abundance in grassland areas. Due to a reduction in crop diversity, increased field sizes, fewer edge habitats for shelter and nesting sites, and changes in agricultural practices, bird diversity in cropland has decreased over all three intervals.

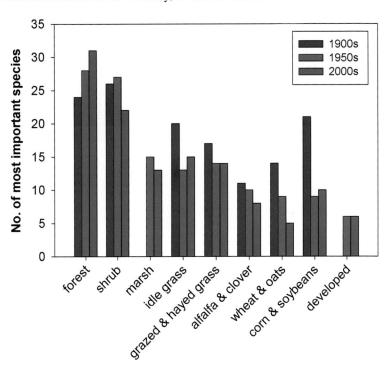

4.50. Number of Most Important Species, totaling 85% of all birds seen, in various habitat types in Illinois, 1900s, 1950s, 2000s.

4.51. Gross and Ray's field assistant in southern Illinois.

Section V
SPECIES ACCOUNTS

Changes across the landscape and within habitats have fundamentally affected the abundance and distribution of many bird species in Illinois. Some species, such as Canada Geese, were not observed during the 1900s or 1950s surveys but are now among the more common birds in Illinois. Others, such as Bewick's Wrens, were once common but have become rare throughout Illinois. Differences among species in how they "reacted" to changes in Illinois prompt many questions. For example, why have Mourning Doves been consistently abundant over the past 100 years? Have the populations of forest birds increased as the extent of forest habitat in the state expanded? Are the northward shifts in some species' ranges the consequence of a warming climate? Why were the 1950s such an apparently poor time for many species?

In this section, we discuss patterns of change in 44 species (presented in standard taxonomic order). We believe this suite of species tells us much about how the overall avifauna of the state has changed over the past century. Each species account is formatted similarly, providing basic natural history for the species in Illinois; data on changes in the species' distribution, abundance, and habitat preferences; and finally an overview of how the species has fared over the past century, how these statewide changes relate to changes across the species' entire range, and the outlook for the species' fate in the future. We use occupancy data (see Section II) to investigate how bird populations have changed over time (1900s to 1950s to 2000s) and across regions (northern, central, and southern Illinois). We use transect data to illustrate current habitat preferences for each species. In addition to the data collected via this survey, the Breeding Bird Survey, provides an excellent annual trend index for most species (Sauer et al. 2008). The Breeding Bird Survey graphs in this chapter show the average number of birds counted on survey routes in Illinois for each year from 1966, when the Breeding Bird Survey began, to 2007. For some species, due to a lack of data, fewer graphs and data are provided.

Alfred Gross and colleagues on an "expedition" to St. Joseph, Champaign County.

Canada Goose. The "giant" subspecies of the Canada Goose (Fig. 5.1), which commonly nests around suburban ponds in northern and central Illinois today, was thought to be extinct by the 1950s. In 1962, however, Harold Hanson, the Grabers' colleague at the Illinois Natural History Survey, discovered a small flock of this subspecies in Minnesota (Hanson 1997). Through careful protection and reintroductions, the Giant Canada Goose recovered —perhaps too well for many Illinois residents who now view this species as a nuisance.

Canada Geese prefer landscapes with open water near manicured areas (Fig. 5.2). The lush grasses (not to mention frequent hand-outs of bread, crackers, and popcorn) at lawns, parks, and golf courses make these preferred foraging areas. Goose droppings, which are quite numerous at such areas, can be an aesthetic and public health problem. Additionally, geese vigorously defend their nests and goslings, and particularly

aggressive individuals occasionally attack people. Flocks of geese near airports are an obvious concern for air traffic. Giant Canada Geese are sometimes referred to as "resident" Canada Geese because they migrate a short distance or not at all (Fig. 5.3). Warm-water discharge and aerators maintain open water in urban areas where Canada Geese are less vulnerable to hunting, and only deep snow that covers their food supplies for many days forces them to move southward (Havera 1999).

The Breeding Bird Survey data for Illinois also illustrate a rapid increase in the Canada Goose population (Fig. 5.4). Canada Geese have experienced a rapid increase across much of their range. Although Canada Geese were not recorded during the breeding season surveys of the 1900s and 1950s, since that time they have adapted well to open water and urban environments, and it is likely their populations will continue to increase across the state.

5.1. "Giant" Canada Geese are a common sight throughout Illinois; however, this species was not detected in Illinois in the 1900s or the 1950s.

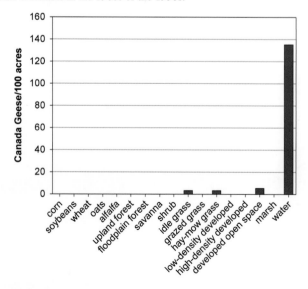

5.2. Average density (birds per 100 acres) of Canada Geese in various habitats from the 2000s transect surveys.

5.3. "Resident" Canada Geese, and some Mallards, are hardy birds that only migrate when ice and deep snow force them to fly south.

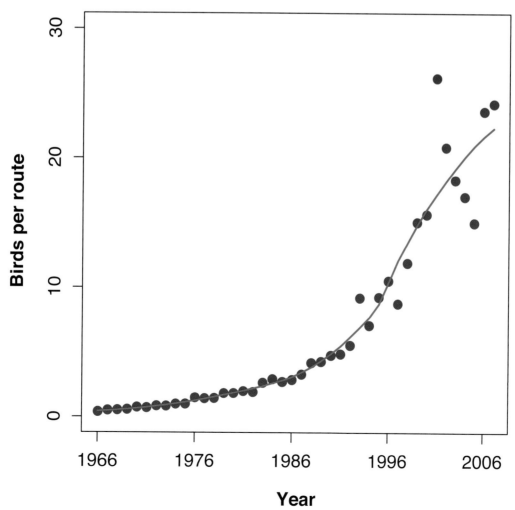

5.4. Abundance of Canada Geese on Breeding Bird Survey routes in Illinois, 1966–2007.

Wood Duck. We regularly observed Wood Ducks in floodplain forests where they were nesting in natural tree cavities and in marshes where nest boxes were erected (Figs. 5.5, 5.6, 5.7). Gross and Ray and the Grabers saw no Wood Ducks, however, during their surveys. By 1913, many naturalists, including George Grinnell, predicted the extinction of Wood Ducks was imminent. Market hunting for their plumage and meat, combined with the drainage of swamps and cutting of forests, left Wood Duck populations in a free-fall.

With the passage of the Migratory Bird Treaty Act in 1918, Wood Ducks were given complete protection. In 1939, Frank Bellrose of the Illinois Natural History Survey put up the first Wood Duck nest boxes, and more than half of them had nests in the first year. With improved designs, other states followed suit with massive nest box programs (Bellrose 1976, 1980). Thanks to legal protection, nest boxes, and improved habitat conditions, Wood Ducks are now one of the more common ducks in eastern North America. Wood Ducks became a legal game bird again in 1941 and are among the three or four most frequently harvested ducks along the Mississippi Flyway (Raftovich et al. 2009).

Wood Ducks are experiencing a steady increase in Illinois (Fig. 5.8) and across much of their range. In spite of dire predictions of their fate a century ago, Wood Ducks are one of the most prominent wildlife management success stories of the twentieth century. Given the on-going restoration and management of habitats along the major rivers in Illinois, we expect the Wood Duck population to remain steady or increase.

5.5. Wood Ducks are the most common nesting duck in Illinois; however, in both the 1900s and 1950s the species was not seen on transects.

5.6. Renowned waterfowl researcher Frank Bellrose of the Illinois Natural History Survey checks a Wood Duck nest box.

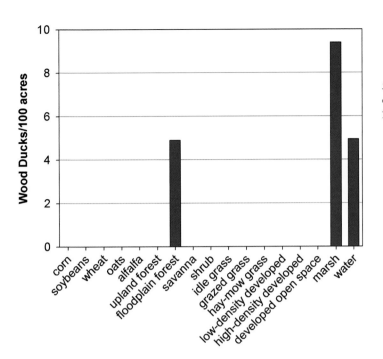

5.7. Average density (birds per 100 acres) of Wood Ducks in various habitats from 2000s transect surveys.

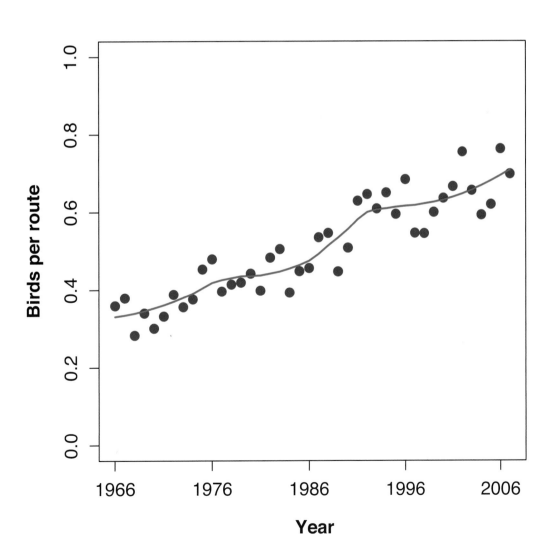

5.8. Abundance of Wood Ducks on Breeding Bird Survey routes in Illinois, 1966–2007.

Northern Bobwhite. In our conversations with landowners across Illinois, one of the most common concerns was the scarcity of bobwhites (Fig. 5.9). In all three survey periods, the bobwhite has been most common in the south and least common in the north (Fig. 5.10). Bobwhites were once fairly common in northern areas, however, and were abundant enough in southern Wisconsin in the late 1920s and early 1930s to be the subject of some of Paul Errington's pioneering research in population ecology (Errington 1934). This popular game bird and its familiar namesake whistle have become less common across the state between each survey period (Fig. 5.10). The species has become so rare that we detected it on too few transects to assess its habitat preferences.

Wildlife biologists have effective techniques for managing habitats at a small-scale for bobwhites. Thus far they have been unable to stop long-term, large-scale declines within Illinois (Fig. 5.11) and throughout the species range. Bobwhite declines in Illinois and elsewhere are almost certainly a classic case of habitat loss owing to changes in agricultural practices, including reductions in grassland nesting habitat, the application of herbicides and insecticides that decrease the availability of insect-rich weedy areas preferred by young broods, and the elimination of shrubby habitat and connecting features like hedgerows that are crucial for winter survival (Roseberry and Cole 2006). While the Grabers suggested populations of Northern Bobwhite had not changed much between the 1900s and 1950s, they did predict that changes in the amount of pasture and grassland may negatively affect populations. The loss of habitat is made even more challenging for bobwhites, because populations of predators such as raccoons, opossums, Red-tailed Hawks, and Great Horned Owls have also increased.

The conservation of farmland birds, including bobwhites, will require cooperation among private landowners, conservation organizations, and public agencies for developing effective strategies that fit into the working lands of Illinois. A recent Conservation Reserve Program practice to establish field borders of native grasses has been widely adopted in some parts of the state. Initial results are encouraging for bobwhites and other birds (Evans et al. 2008); whether the practice will be adopted widely enough to stabilize regional or statewide populations remains to be seen. While we are encouraged by the interest and programs that are being developed to improve bobwhite populations, their steady decline suggests this may become an extremely rare species in the state.

5.9. Northern Bobwhites were once one of the most common birds of rural Illinois; however, their populations are experiencing widespread declines (left, male Northern Bobwhite; right, female Northern Bobwhite on nest in 1907).

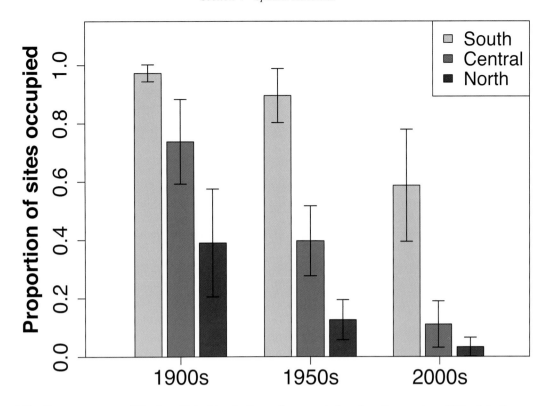

5.10. Occupancy rates of Northern Bobwhites in the northern, central, and southern region of Illinois in the 1900s, 1950s, and 2000s.

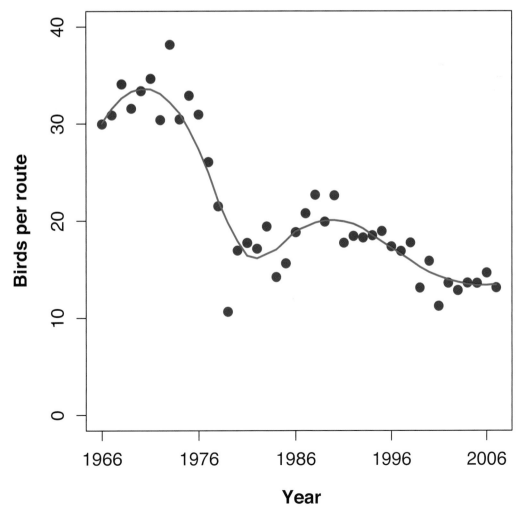

5.11. Abundance of Northern Bobwhites on Breeding Bird Survey routes in Illinois, 1966–2007.

American Kestrel. The kestrel, or "sparrow hawk," is frequently seen perched on utility lines or hovering over grassy rights-of-way along roads, hunting for large insects and small vertebrates (Fig. 5.12). The Grabers noted that "farmers have become less tolerant of trees at the margins of their cultivated fields" and the cavities in those "trees are ideal nesting sites for the sparrow hawk." Although not enough were found to produce a habitat preference graph, a surprising number of kestrels were detected in developed habitats, including the downtown areas of several cities as well as suburban and park settings.

Our results suggest kestrels are more widespread today than in the 1950s, but less abundant than a century ago (Fig. 5.14). The Breeding Bird Survey shows a steady growth in the number of kestrels in the state since the mid-1960s (Fig. 5.15). Studies of American Kestrels were important in showing the effects of organochlorine pesticides such as DDT on birds (Wiemeyer and Lincer 1987). Eggshell thinning caused by organochlorine pesticides nearly caused the extinction of the kestrel's larger relative, the Peregrine Falcon, and probably depressed kestrel abundance and occupancy rates in the mid-twentieth century.

While American Kestrels are rebounding in Illinois and a few Midwestern states, kestrel populations are declining over much of North America (Fig. 5.13). The consistent long-term increases and adaptability to developed areas bode well for kestrels in Illinois. More research is needed to understand why kestrel populations in Illinois are increasing while populations as nearby as Indiana are faring poorly.

5.12. The American Kestrel is the smallest, most common falcon in Illinois. Their population in Illinois appears to have experienced large declines in the early portion of the century and has steadily recovered in recent decades.

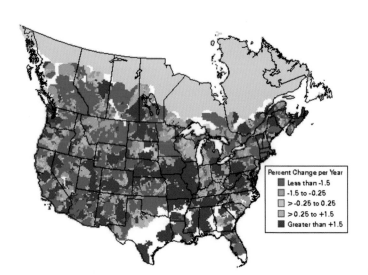

5.13. Geographic pattern of American Kestrel population trends from Breeding Bird Survey routes across North America, 1966 to 2003 (Sauer et al. 2008).

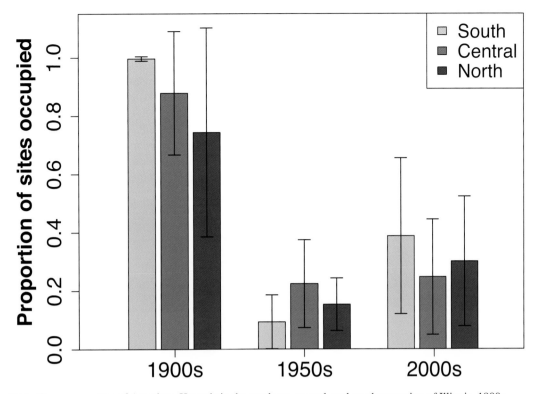

5.14. Occupancy rates of American Kestrels in the northern, central, and southern region of Illinois, 1900s, 1950s, and 2000s.

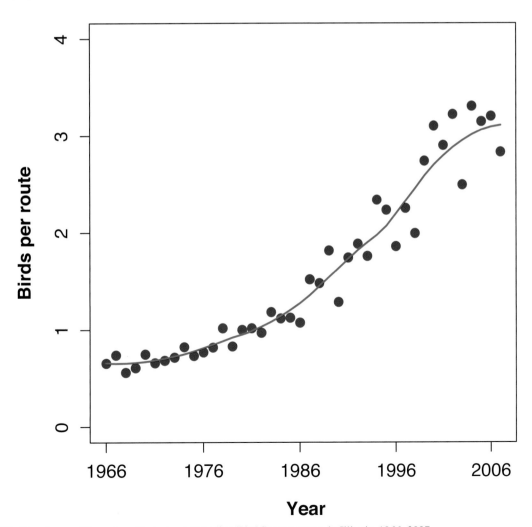

5.15. Abundance of American Kestrels on Breeding Bird Survey routes in Illinois, 1966–2007.

Great Blue Heron. A couple of years before Gross and Ray were conducting their fieldwork, President Theodore Roosevelt established the first federal bird sanctuary at Pelican Island, Florida, in response to the slaughter of herons and egrets for their plumage.   By the 1950s, pollution had seriously impaired water quality. The passage of the Clean Water Act led to tremendous improvements in water quality, and populations of fish and Great Blue Herons flourished (Figs. 5.16, 5.19).   Today, Great Blue Heron rookeries can be found in nearly every county in Illinois. Though the transect method is not an effective way to survey

herons and egrets, we encountered Great Blue Herons in marshes and along shorelines of water bodies (Fig. 5.17).

Great Blue Herons along with many other fish-eating birds (e.g., Great Egrets, Bald Eagles, Double-crested Cormorants) are scarcely mentioned by the Grabers and were rare species in both the 1900s and 1950s. The relatively recent increase of Great Blue Herons (Fig. 5.18) and other fish-eating birds is likely the result of regulations improving the water quality of many rivers and streams in Illinois. Great Blue Herons are currently rather common across Illinois and are likely to remain so as long as aquatic habitats are protected.

5.16. Great Blue Herons have consistently been the most common wading bird in Illinois; however, they have become much more common over the past several decades.

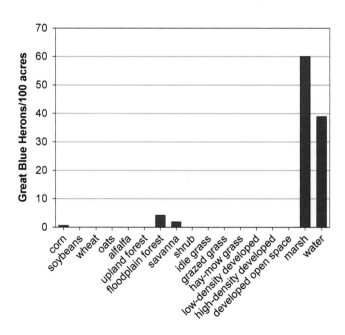

5.17. Average density (birds per 100 acres) of Great Blue Herons in various habitats from 2000s transect surveys.

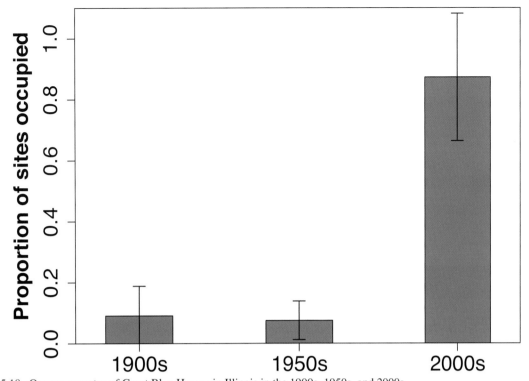

5.18. Occupancy rates of Great Blue Herons in Illinois in the 1900s, 1950s, and 2000s.

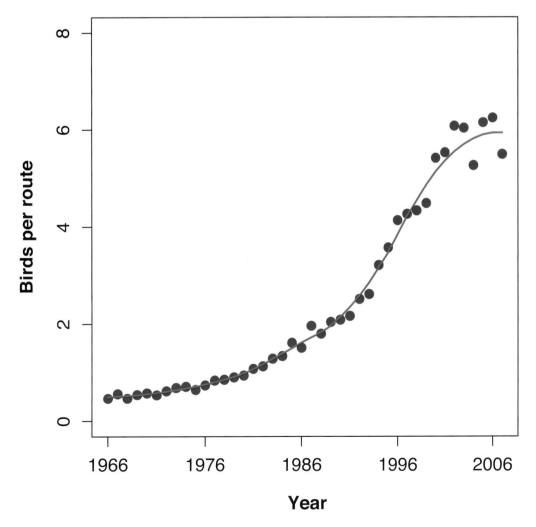

5.19. Abundance of Great Blue Heron on Breeding Bird Survey routes in Illinois, 1996–2007.

Killdeer. Killdeer are, by far, the most common shorebird nesting in Illinois (Fig. 5.20). Though widely distributed in all three survey periods (Fig. 5.23), their regional occupancy rates have shifted over time. Most of the state's Killdeer were in the southern region in the 1900s (83% by the Grabers' estimate), and they decreased in occurrence northward. By the 1950s, Killdeer occurrence was about the same in northern and southern Illinois, but lowest in the central region. In the 2000s, we found Killdeer to be about twice as common in the central region than in northern or southern Illinois.

Killdeer nest on bare soil in crop fields and along gravel roadsides early in the spring. Their eggs have often hatched by the time farmers begin spring field work; the downy young leave the nest within hours of hatching and are soon able to run and escape the path of machinery. Since the average planting date has advanced by a few weeks, corn may have become less suitable for nesting Killdeer since the 1950s. Soybeans are planted later than corn and appear to be a good habitat for Killdeer, with twice the density of birds as corn (Fig. 5.22). The increase in acres planted to soybeans since the 1950s, largely at the expense of oats and alfalfa, has probably benefited Killdeer. In the recent surveys, grazed grasslands and shorelines also hosted high densities of Killdeer. Breeding Bird Survey data show a 5.5% annual rate of increase from 1966 to 2007 (Fig. 5.24).

Although the Illinois population of Killdeer is robust (Figs. 5.23, 5.24), the North American population is declining, a pattern similar to that of the American Kestrel (Fig. 5.21). While all indications are that Killdeer will remain common nesting birds in Illinois as long as corn and soybeans are common crops, the large declines of this species over much of North America are not easily explained.

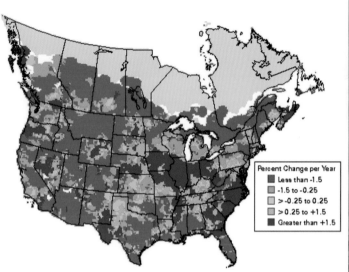

5.21. Geographic pattern of Killdeer population trends from Breeding Bird Survey routes across North America, 1966 to 2003 (Sauer et al. 2008).

5.20. Killdeer are a common species of open country throughout Illinois.

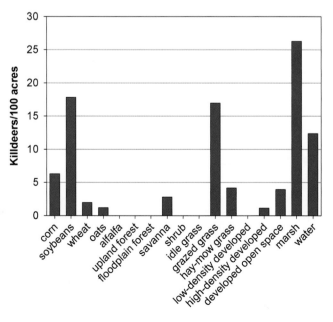

5.22. Average density (birds per 100 acres) of Killdeer in various habitats from 2000s transect surveys.

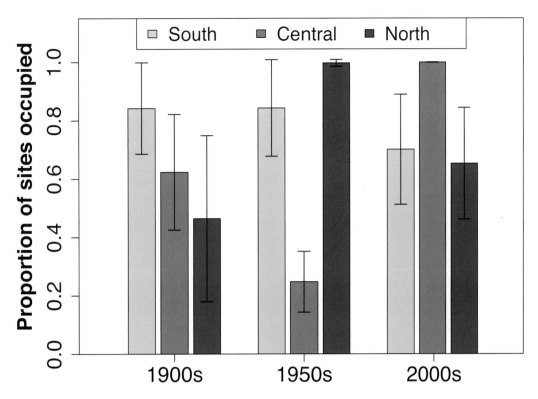

5.23. Occupancy rates of Killdeer in the northern, central, and southern regions of Illinois in the 1900s, 1950s, and 2000s.

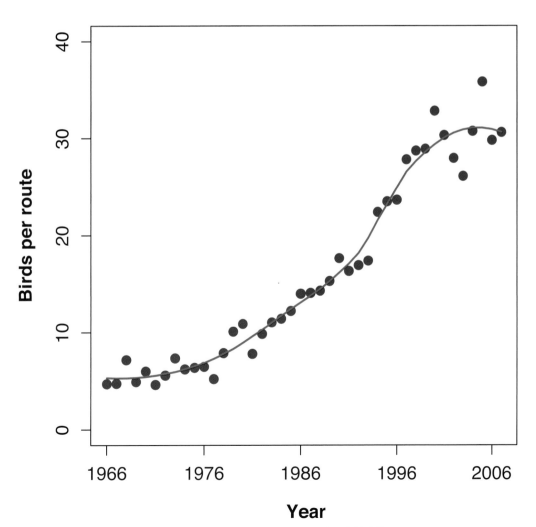

5.24. Abundance of Killdeer on Breeding Bird Survey routes in Illinois, 1966–2007.

Mourning Dove. The highly adaptable Mourning Dove (Fig. 5.25) has maintained a consistently high occupancy rate throughout the state and across the three survey periods (Fig. 5.27). We saw Mourning Doves in all habitats we sampled in the recent survey (Fig. 5.26). Dick and Jean Graber described Mourning Doves as having the largest "ecological distribution" of any bird in Illinois. They also suggested that doves were expanding their distribution northward. Only two native species, Red-winged Blackbird and Common Grackle, were recorded more often on transects over the 100-year period. Though they are the most harvested game bird on the continent (estimated at about 20 million birds per year, nearly 1 million harvested in Illinois; Raftovich et al. 2009), hunting appears to have no significant adverse effect on the overall population.

Mourning Doves begin nesting in March and keep breeding through late summer and early fall. Over this time period, they often produce several broods, and frequently nest on the ground in grasslands and crop fields. The vast majority of the birds we encountered in these habitats appeared to be feeding. Shrublands and savannas hosted more doves than closed-canopy forests (Fig. 5.26). The highest densities of Mourning Doves were recorded in low-density developed areas. The combination of evergreens and dense shrubbery for nesting and winter roosting, short vegetation at ground level, and availability of grain at bird feeders and near grain elevators make low-density developed areas well suited to Mourning Doves.

Eurasian Collared-Doves have colonized most of the state since the mid-1990s and also appear to favor developed areas (Walk and Esker 2001). Despite their similar ecologies, there is no conclusive evidence of competition between Collared-Doves and Mourning Doves. Mourning Doves have been successful over the past century; the Breeding Bird Survey shows increases in the species (Fig. 5.28), and it seems likely that doves will be common for years to come.

5.25. Mourning Doves are found at relatively high densities in many habitats throughout Illinois.

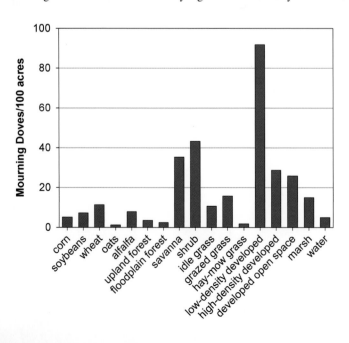

5.26. Average density (birds per 100 acres) of Mourning Doves in various habitats from 2000s transect surveys.

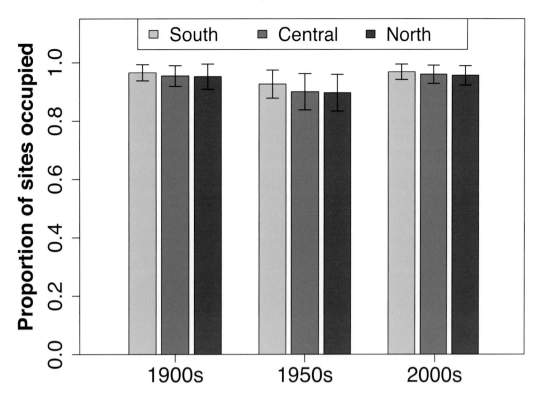

5.27. Occupancy rates of Mourning Doves in the northern, central, and southern regions of Illinois in the 1900s, 1950s, and 2000s.

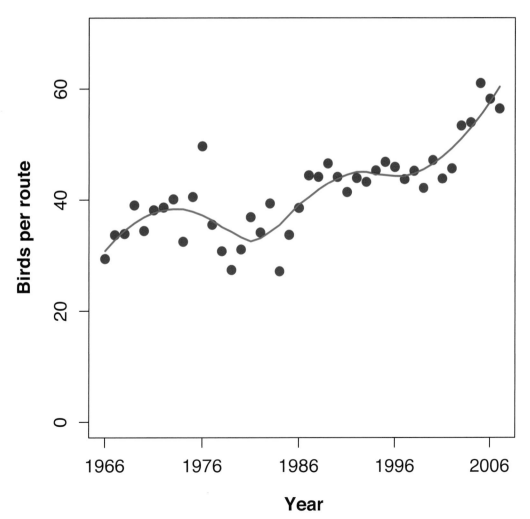

5.28 Abundance of Mourning Doves on Breeding Bird Survey routes in Illinois, 1966–2007.

Yellow-billed Cuckoo. Yellow-billed Cuckoos are an interesting species in that they are known to be facultative brood parasites – from time to time they will lay their eggs in other birds' nests while continuing to have their own nest – and are erratic in their distribution and abundance throughout the state (Fig. 5.29). Some researchers suggest cuckoo populations are highly variable because they track the emergence of periodic cicadas and caterpillars (Jackson et al. 1996). The three "snapshots" in time may, therefore, not accurately represent the species' population trend. While Yellow-billed Cuckoos occur statewide, they are about twice as common in southern Illinois as in other regions (Fig. 5.31). We found cuckoos most often in shrublands followed by savannas and upland forests (Fig. 5.30).

While birds that prefer forest edges, such as Indigo Buntings and Summer Tanagers, are generally increasing, Yellow-billed Cuckoos are declining across the state in a pattern similar to shrubland birds such as Northern Bobwhites and Brown Thrashers (Figs. 5.31, 5.32). Because cuckoos use a variety of habitats, including secondary forests, factors besides habitat availability are likely contributing to population declines. Changes in the size, timing, and frequency of mass-emergences of caterpillars, cicadas, and other insect prey could alter the productivity of cuckoos nests. The closely related Black-billed Cuckoo was just added to the state's threatened species list, and it appears that Yellow-billed Cuckoo may be heading in the same direction.

5.29. Yellow-billed Cuckoos are erratic species that are present throughout the state but most common in areas with caterpillar outbreaks.

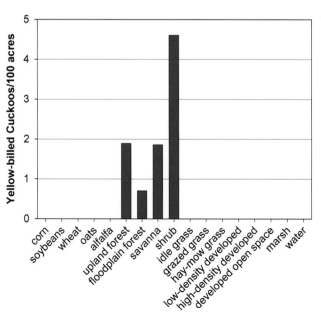

5.30. Average density (birds per 100 acres) of Yellow-billed Cuckoos in various habitats from 2000s transect surveys.

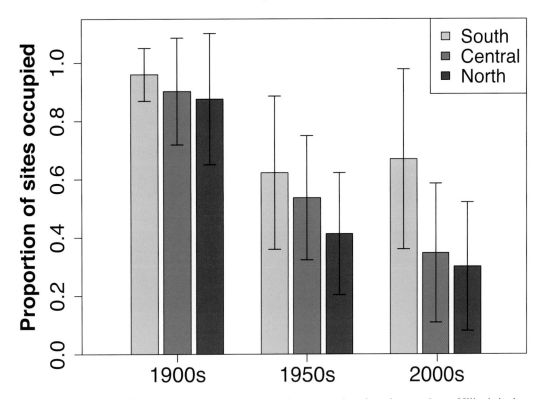

5.31. Occupancy rates of Yellow-billed Cuckoos in the northern, central, and southern regions of Illinois in the 1900s, 1950s, and 2000s.

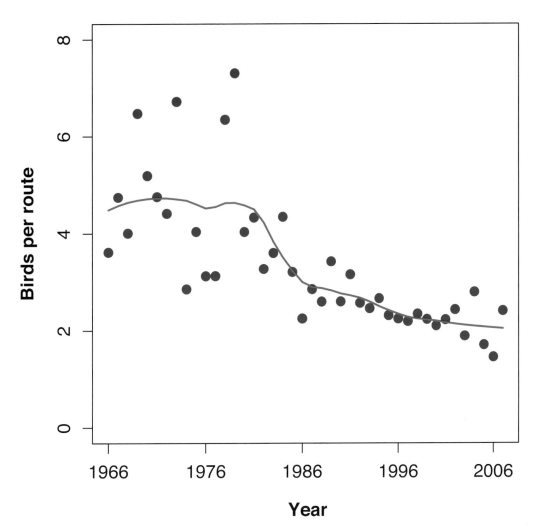

5.32. Abundance of Yellow-billed Cuckoos on Breeding Bird Survey routes in Illinois, 1966–2007.

Chimney Swift. As their name suggests, Chimney Swifts are largely dependent on human structures, especially chimneys, for nesting sites (Fig. 5.33). Chimney Swifts show an interesting pattern of occupancy (Fig. 5.35) and, not surprisingly, are most common in high-density developed areas (Fig. 5.34). While comparable high-density developed areas were not surveyed in the 1900s or 1950s, we recorded a greater proportion of swifts in low-density developed areas (9.9% of all birds) than the Grabers did (1.7% of all birds). In contrast to our data, the Breeding Bird Survey shows a declining trend for chimney swifts (Fig. 5.36). Perhaps the gradual loss of old buildings with open masonry chimneys has reduced nesting sites for swifts, but Breeding Bird Survey routes are regularly moved out of developed areas, where swifts are most common, because of noise and safety concerns associated with roadside surveys. Furthermore, the extent of developed areas preferred by swifts is rapidly expanding. While their population trend is unclear, Chimney Swifts are currently common throughout the state (Fig. 5.35). The most likely threats to this species are modern building codes that require chimney caps that may reduce the availability of breeding sites. If chimneys become unsuitable for swifts they will find far fewer suitable sites for nesting in forests. In some areas people have constructed chimneys for the sole purpose of providing habitat for swifts (Cink and Collins 2002), and this practice may need to be expanded in the future.

5.33. Chimney Swifts are a common species in urban areas. Before the advent of chimneys, they used hollow, broken-off trees and a large population of Chimney Swifts still nests in hollow bald cypresses in the swamps of southern Illinois.

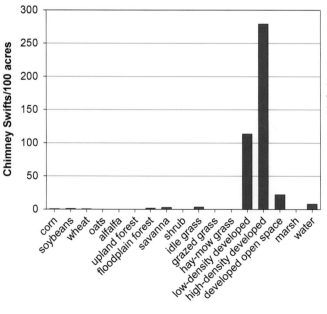

5.34. Average density (birds per 100 acres) of Chimney Swifts in various habitats from 2000s transect surveys.

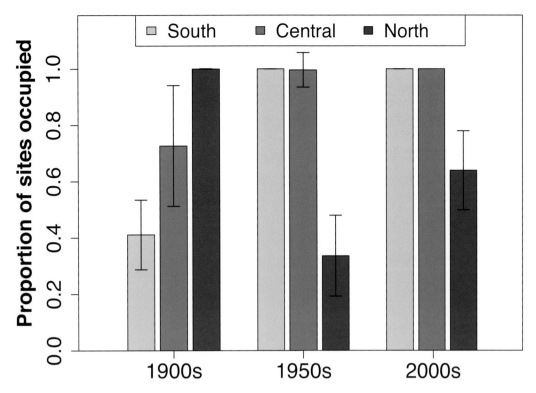

5.35. Occupancy rates of Chimney Swifts in the north, central, and southern regions of Illinois in the 1900s, 1950s, and 2000s.

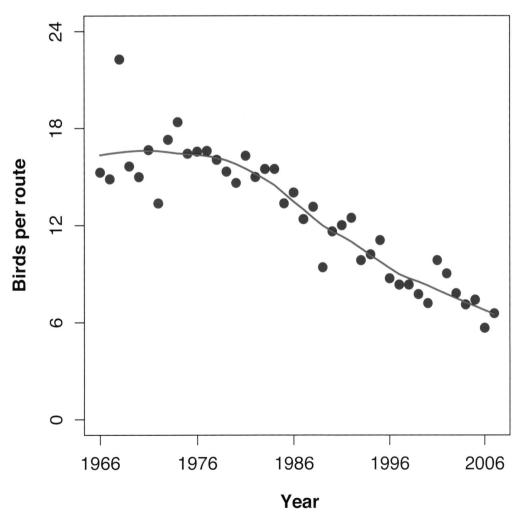

5.36. Abundance of Chimney Swifts on Breeding Bird Survey routes in Illinois, 1966–2007.

Woodpeckers. The six species of woodpeckers that commonly nest in Illinois can be easily classified as "winners" (Downy, Hairy, Red-bellied, and Pileated) and "losers" (Red-headed and Flicker) based on their population trends (Fig. 5.37). The four "winners" are nonmigratory and have benefited from the increasing quantity and quality of forest over the past century. All four species have expanded their ranges northward over the past 100 years, probably because of the increasing availability of mature forest that has occurred mostly in central and northern Illinois.

The two "losers" are both migratory and prefer open woodlands and savanna-like habitats, and the transition of open- to closed-canopy forests has likely contributed to the declines in these populations. The Grabers suggested competition with European Starlings for nest cavities was one reason for the decline of Red-headed Woodpeckers and Northern Flickers. Regardless of the factors driving declines, Red-headed Woodpeckers and Northern Flickers have experienced some of the most dramatic declines of any species in Illinois over the past century.

Red-bellied Woodpecker. A century ago, the Red-bellied Woodpecker (Fig. 5.38) was rarely found in central or northern Illinois. In the 1950s surveys, it was still scarce in northern Illinois but about equally widespread in the central and southern zones (Fig. 5.40). Today, Red-bellied Woodpeckers are found well northward throughout most of Wisconsin, and it may be the most common woodpecker in Illinois. Their expansion from southern Illinois in the 1900s to other regions of the state by the 2000s represents about a 300-mile expansion of their range. The increase in forest cover, due primarily to the transition of shrublands, savannas, and open woodlands into closed-canopy forests, has helped the Red-bellied Woodpecker. Currently, Red-bellied Woodpeckers use a variety of habitats, including low-density developed areas (Fig. 5.39), which may be a new

phenomenon as the Grabers reported the species was not associated with humans. Our results and the Breeding Bird Survey (Fig. 5.41) have shown consistent population increases for this species. Because the amount of forest in Illinois is likely to remain constant or increase slightly, and because Red-bellied Woodpeckers (like Downy Woodpeckers) regularly visit bird feeders and readily utilize wooded habitats in developed areas, we expect their population to remain steady or increase.

5.38. Red-bellied Woodpeckers have expanded their geographic range over the past century.

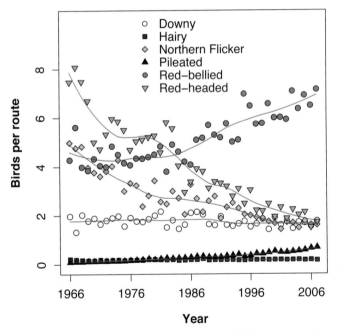

5.37. Abundance of woodpeckers on Breeding Bird Survey routes in Illinois, 1966–2007.

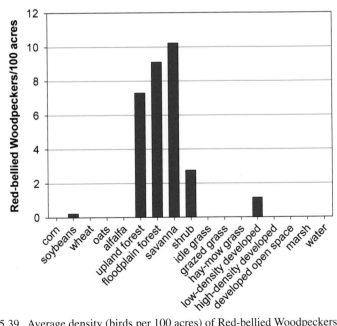

5.39. Average density (birds per 100 acres) of Red-bellied Woodpeckers in various habitats from 2000s transect surveys.

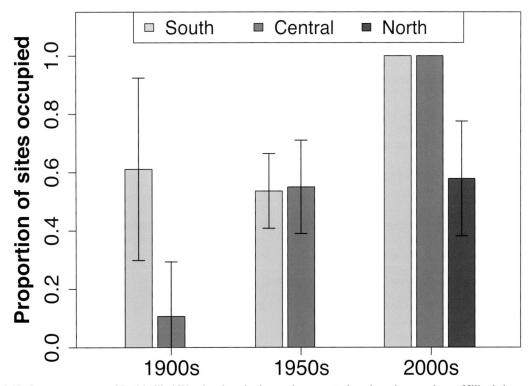

5.40. Occupancy rates of Red-bellied Woodpeckers in the northern, central, and southern regions of Illinois in the 1900s, 1950s, and 2000s.

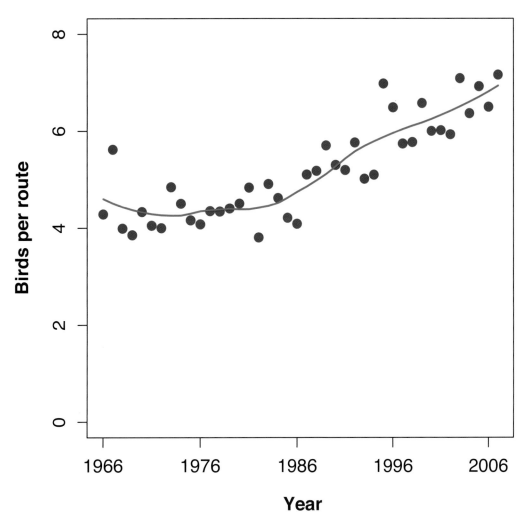

5.41. Abundance of Red-bellied Woodpeckers on Breeding Bird Survey routes in Illinois, 1966–2007.

Red-headed Woodpecker. The Red-headed Woodpecker is the signature bird of Midwestern oak savannas, but it is also found in floodplain forests and savanna-like cemeteries, parks, and golf courses (Figs. 5.42, 5.43). Red-headed Woodpeckers are short-distance migrants, but their winter abundance at any given location varies considerably from one year to the next, as they tend to congregate in floodplain forests with an abundant crop of acorns (Smith et al. 2000).

Red-headed Woodpeckers have declined since the 1900s as their preferred savanna-type nesting habitats have become increasingly scarce due to outright habitat destruction and succession into closed forests through fire suppression and reductions in grazing. Ridgway (1889) reported that Red-headed Woodpeckers were the most numerous woodpecker in wooded areas of the state. Gross and Ray saw more Red-headed Woodpeckers in corn fields than we did in all habitats combined; overall, they recorded about 10 times as many Red-headed Woodpeckers as we did.

Occupancy models show that the occurrence of Red-headed Woodpeckers crashed between the 1900s and 1950s surveys, during the interval when European Starlings colonized and increased in abundance in Illinois (Fig. 5.44). Red-headed Woodpeckers aggressively defend their nest cavities, however, and are much more frequently the aggressors towards European Starlings than vice versa (Ingold 1989). Kendeigh (1982)

observed that Red-headed Woodpeckers and Northern Flickers increased in east-central Illinois in the late 1950s when Dutch elm disease killed elm trees, creating canopy gaps and abundant snags for nesting and foraging. Red-headed Woodpeckers appear to have been more widely distributed in the northern than the southern region in the 1950s, but that pattern was reversed by the 2000s (Fig. 5.44). Overall, the Breeding Bird Survey data reveal a negative population trend for the species in the state of Illinois over the past four decades (Fig. 5.45).

The fortunes of Red-bellied and Red-headed Woodpeckers in Illinois are complete opposites. In the 1900s, the Red-headed Woodpecker was the most common species occurring throughout the state while the Red-bellied was limited to southern Illinois. Over the next century Red-bellied Woodpeckers expanded throughout the state and are now much more common than Red-headed Woodpeckers, which occur sporadically across the state. It is unlikely that competition between the two species resulted in these changes; rather, subtle changes in wooded habitats have allowed Red-bellied Woodpeckers to take advantage of close-canopy forests and wooded urban areas, while the decline of savanna has affected Red-headed Woodpeckers. Though still widely distributed in Illinois (Kleen et al. 2004), Red-headed Woodpecker populations are sparse across most of the state, and it may be this species warrants listing as threatened in the near future.

5.42. The Red-headed Woodpecker is a species that uses a variety of habitats but is most common in savannas.

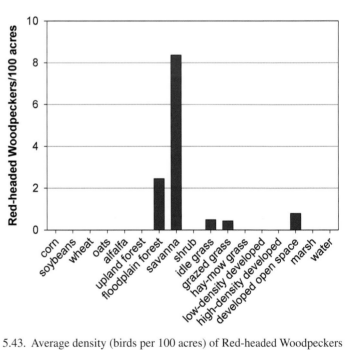

5.43. Average density (birds per 100 acres) of Red-headed Woodpeckers in various habitats from 2000s transect surveys.

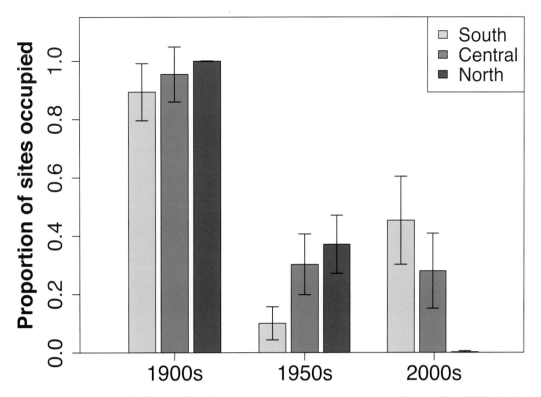

5.44. Occupancy rates of Red-headed Woodpeckers in the northern, central, and southern regions of Illinois in the 1900s, 1950s, and 2000s.

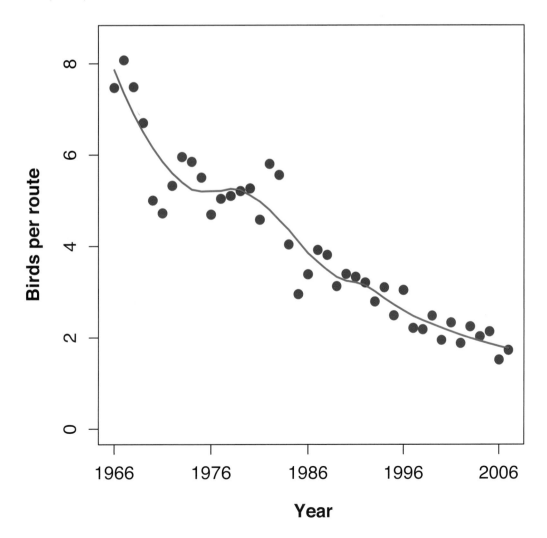

5.45. Abundance of Red-headed Woodpeckers on Breeding Bird Survey routes in Illinois, 1966–2007.

Northern Flicker. The Northern (yellow-shafted) Flicker is similar to the Red-headed Woodpecker as it is most common in savanna-like habitats. Flickers nests in all forest types and are regularly seen feeding on the ground in grasslands, along roadsides, and in crop fields (Figs. 5.46, 5.47). Like Red-headed Woodpeckers, Northern Flickers have experienced significant population reductions between the 1900s and 2000s (Fig. 5.48).

Flickers are occasionally found in low-density developed and developed open space areas. In the 1950s, the Graber's stated that flickers were more closely associated with man than any other woodpecker. They suggested that competition with starlings drove the large declines they noticed between the 1900s and 1950s, and there is some evidence to back this idea (Wiebe and Moore 2008). In the 1900s, flickers were common statewide but are now scarce in the southern region (Fig. 5.48). One possible contributing factor in southern Illinois is the recovery of forests from extensive timber harvesting in the late 1800s; as a result of this recovery, preferred open-forest habitat gave way to closed-canopy forests between the 1900s and 1950s. This reasoning is supported by increases in other species that prefer closed-canopy forests in southern Illinois. As with Red-headed Woodpeckers, Kendeigh (1982) noticed a temporary increase of Northern Flickers after Dutch elm disease created a burst of new habitat, but populations dropped to pre-elm disease levels by the 1970s. The Breeding Bird Survey demonstrates the population has continued to decline ever since (Fig. 5.49).

There are several unanswered questions about Northern Flickers; in particular, why are they associated with different habitats in different regions of the state? In northern and central Illinois, flickers were found primarily in shrublands, savannas, and forests. In southern Illinois, we found few flickers outside of developed areas; flickers were about four times more common in developed areas in southern Illinois than in developed areas of central and northern Illinois. Unlike the other woodpeckers, flickers spend a large percentage of their time on the ground feeding on ants. The widespread use of insecticides is one hypothesis of why flickers have declined in recent decades, (Wiebe and Moore 2008). Additional research may help resolve the puzzling habitat distributions and population trend of this species. Given expected land use trends in Illinois, we expect the decline of flickers to continue.

5.46. Northern Flickers spend much of their time searching for insects on the ground. Widespread use of insecticides may be contributing to the species' decline.

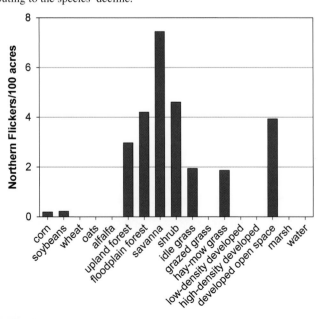

5.47. Average density (birds per 100 acres) of Northern Flickers in various habitats from 2000s transect surveys.

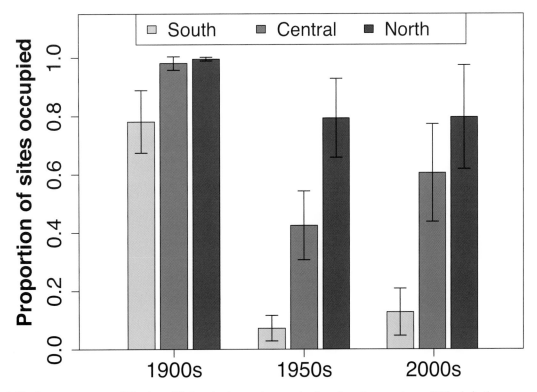

5.48. Occupancy rates of Northern Flickers in the northern, central, and southern regions of Illinois in the 1900s, 1950s, and 2000s.

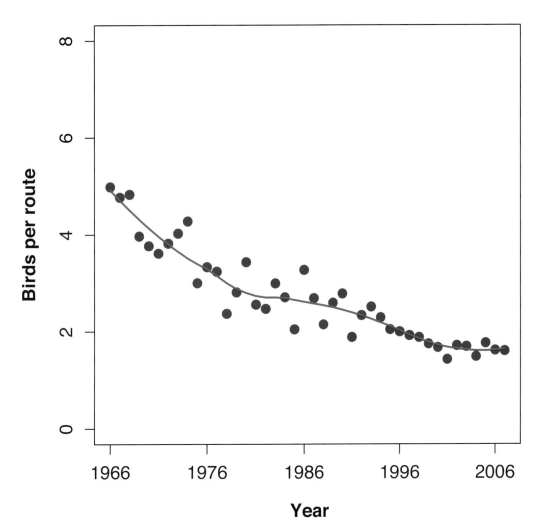

5.49. Abundance of Northern Flickers on Breeding Bird Survey routes in Illinois, 1966–2007.

Eastern Wood-Pewee. Pewees are one of the most common flycatchers in Illinois, often observed sitting patiently in forests waiting for insects to fly by (Fig. 5.50). Pewees are also one of 10 species whose occupancy pattern has not changed among the three survey periods or regions of the state (Fig. 5.53). Eastern Wood-Pewees are most common in upland and floodplain forests, savannas/open woodlands, and developed open spaces with mature trees (Fig. 5.52). Similar to the occupancy data, the Breeding Bird Survey shows this Neotropical migrant with stable abundance in Illinois (Fig. 5.54).

The consistency of the pewee's population in Illinois over the past century is remarkable. The structure and composition of Illinois forests have changed substantially since the widespread logging in the 1800s and early 1900s. Also, the advent of synthetic pesticides likely reduced the food available for pewees, not to mention the reduction of habitat on the pewee's wintering grounds of northern South America. Despite these challenges, pewee populations have been resilient in Illinois, though the species is declining over most of the rest of its breeding range (Fig. 5.51).

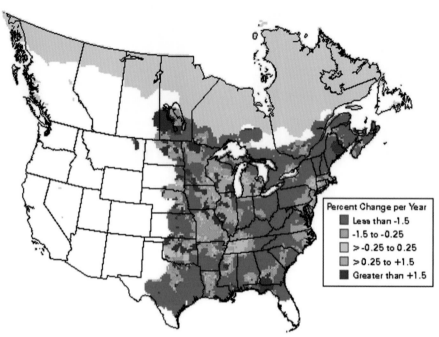

5.51. Geographic pattern of Eastern Wood-Pewee population trends from Breeding Bird Survey routes, 1966 to 2003 (Sauer et al. 2008).

5.50. Eastern Wood-Pewees have maintained a consistent population in forests of Illinois over the past 100 years.

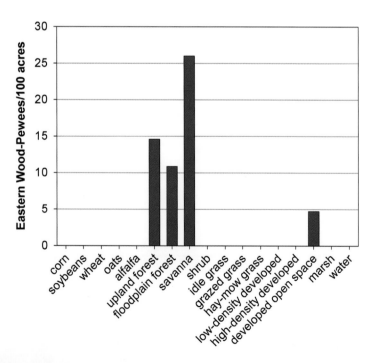

5.52. Average density (birds per 100 acres) of Eastern Wood-Pewees in various habitats from 2000s transect surveys.

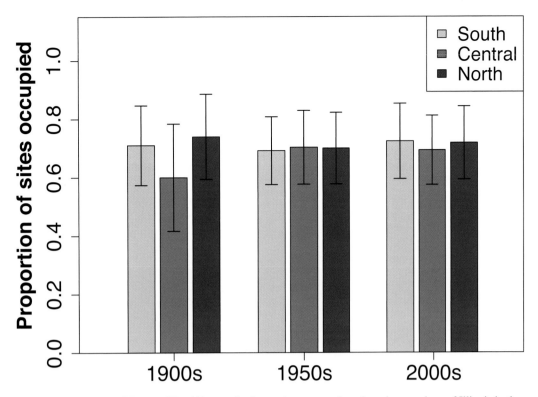

5.53. Occupancy rates of Eastern Wood-Pewees in the northern, central, and southern regions of Illinois in the 1900s, 1950s, and 2000s.

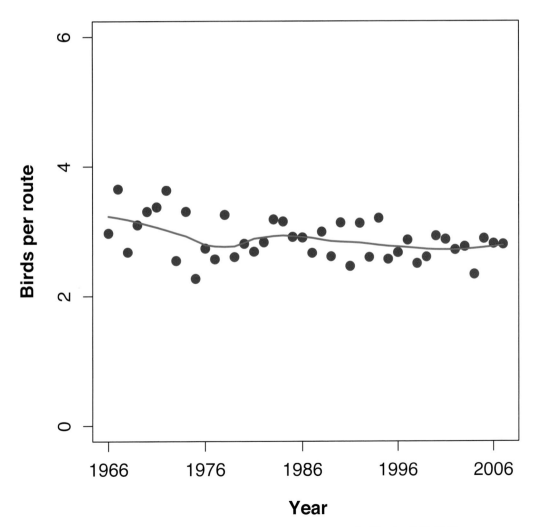

5.54. Abundance of Eastern Wood-Pewees on Breeding Bird Survey routes in Illinois, 1966–2007.

Acadian Flycatcher. In all periods, Acadian Flycatchers had far greater occupancy rates in the southern than central or northern regions of Illinois (Figs. 5.55, 5.57). Floodplain forests and steep ravines extending into upland forests are the Acadian Flycatcher's preferred habitats (Fig. 5.56). Because Acadian Flycatchers are common and their nests are relatively easy to find, they have been one of the most frequently studied Neotropical migratory birds. Research in southern Illinois has found that Acadian Flycatcher nests within 600 yards of forest edges experience higher rates of predation and brood parasitism by Brown-headed Cowbirds (Hoover et al. 2006, Chapa-Vargas and Robinson 2007). At the Hutchin's Creek study area in Union County, where The Nature Conservancy and the U.S. Forest Service have worked to reforest a narrow opening, Hoover et al. (2006) estimated that every acre reforested will add up to six acres of "interior" forest conditions to the landscape where Acadian Flycatchers will be much safer from predators and cowbirds.

Similar to Eastern Wood-Pewees, Acadian Flycatcher populations have been among the most stable in the state (Figs. 5.57, 5.58). Unlike Northern Cardinals, Indigo Buntings, Tufted Titmice, and other forest birds with similar regional distributions in the 1900s, Acadian Flycatchers have not expanded their distribution northward. The Grabers thought there was some indication that their range was starting to move north, and we recorded Acadian Flycatchers on point counts at a few sites in northern Illinois. We cannot explain why Acadian Flycatchers have not expanded north as available habitat has increased in the central and northern regions of the state. While the species has not expanded its range, the population appears to be stable.

R. Graber

5.55. Acadian Flycatchers' tendency to nest only a couple yards above the ground in wooded ravines makes them convenient for studying reproductive success.

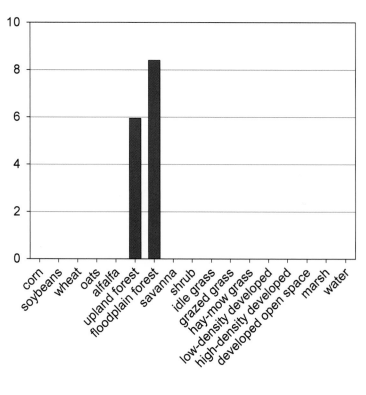

5.56. Average density (birds per 100 acres) of Acadian Flycatchers in various habitats from 2000s transect surveys.

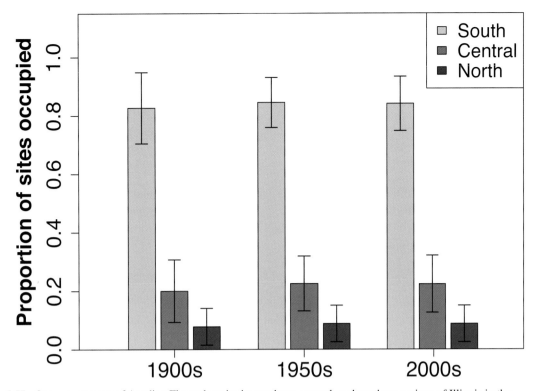

5.57. Occupancy rates of Acadian Flycatchers in the northern, central, and southern regions of Illinois in the 1900s, 1950s, and 2000s.

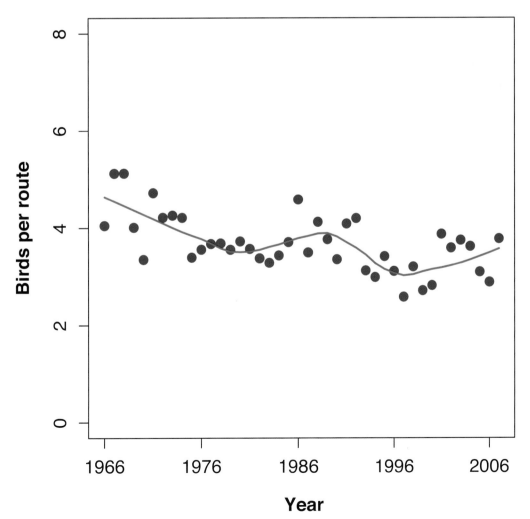

5.58. Abundance of Acadian Flycatchers on Breeding Bird Survey routes in Illinois, 1966–2007.

Eastern Kingbird. Kingbirds are a familiar sight in the open spaces of Illinois, where they are often seen perched on fences, utility lines, and exposed tree branches, sallying out to catch insect prey on the wing (Figs 5.59). Kingbirds currently breed throughout the state (Fig. 5.61, Kleen et al. 2004), often in areas with grassy openings and scattered trees such as savannas or riparian areas (Fig. 5.60). Kingbirds seem to be particularly fond of placing their nests in tree branches that over-hang water, and we found high densities of kingbirds in marshy areas and along shorelines.

In spite of sharp declines in their preferred savanna, pasture, and linear wooded habitats, the Breeding Bird Survey shows only slight declines in Eastern Kingbirds in the state since the mid-1960s (Fig. 5.62). Interestingly, the decline is less severe in Illinois compared to most parts of its range. The Grabers noted that Eastern Kingbirds had declined substantially between the 1900s and 1950s surveys, especially in southern Illinois. They speculated that the change could be related to either a reduction in orchards or other preferred habitats, or to a change in their insect prey. Specifically, they thought spraying herbicides and insecticides in orchards and along roadsides had played an important role in the decline of kingbirds. Our occupancy analyses show a similar pattern of mid-century declines for many birds, including American Robins, Common Grackles, and Brown-headed Cowbirds, that feed primarily on invertebrates and are most often found in habitats likely to be sprayed with insecticides. In the final section we address how the advent of synthetic insecticides may have impacted bird populations in the 1950s. The Eastern Kingbird population in Illinois appears to have rebounded from its 1950s low and is holding its own.

5.59. Eastern Kingbirds, like many other species in Illinois, live two lives. In Illinois the species is highly territorial, often seen foraging by themselves on insects along open roads. When Eastern Kingbirds leave Illinois in the late summer, they become gregarious, feeding on fruit as they overwinter in Amazonia.

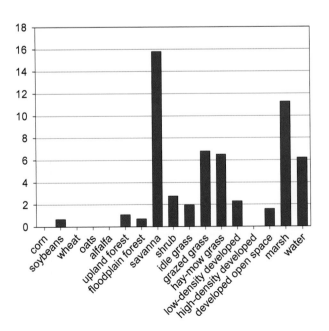

5.60. Average density (birds per 100 acres) of Eastern Kingbirds in various habitats from 2000s transect surveys.

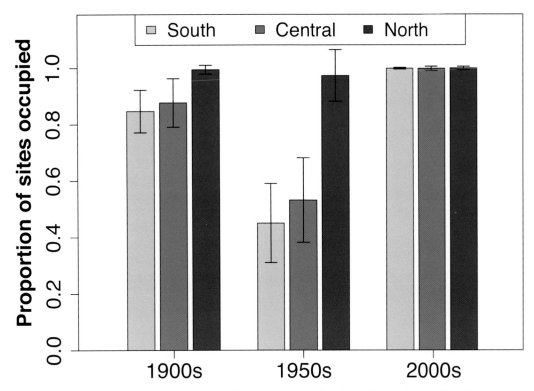

5.61. Occupancy rates of Eastern Kingbirds in the northern, central, and southern regions of Illinois in the 1900s, 1950s, and 2000s.

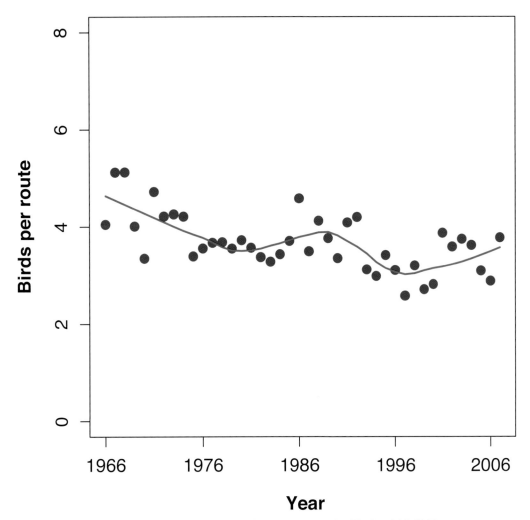

5.62. Abundance of Eastern Kingbirds on Breeding Bird Survey routes in Illinois, 1966–2007.

Bewick's Wren. To Gross and Ray, the Bewick's Wren (Fig. 5.63), and not the House Wren, was the most common wren found in residential areas of Illinois. Early accounts of the Bewick's Wren in Illinois agreed that this species was the most common wren in the state (Ridgway 1889, Musselman 1921). By the 1950s, however, Bewick's Wren populations had crashed in Illinois (Fig. 5.64), and the species is now scarce throughout eastern North America. The Grabers recorded just two Bewick's Wrens at one location in the 1950s, and we did not find any. The Illinois Breeding Bird Atlas project (Kleen et al. 2004), reports from birders (e.g., Bohlen 1989), and the Breeding Bird Survey (Fig. 5.65) confirm this scarcity. Bewick's Wrens are listed as endangered in Illinois (Illinois Endangered Species Protection Board 2009).

      The reasons for the decline in Bewick's Wrens are a mystery, but competition with House Wrens, which are increasing in abundance, is strongly suspected (Ridgway 1915, 1920; Kennedy and White 1997). They may also compete with Carolina Wrens, European Starlings, and House Sparrows. Bewick's Wrens have a strange affinity for human junk. The "classic" Bewick's Wren nest is constructed in a dilapidated building, shell of an automobile, or pile of abandoned farm equipment being swallowed by brushy growth at the edge of a forest (Fig. 5.66). A lack of potential nesting sites would not seem to explain the extreme rarity of Bewick's Wrens during the past half century. The decline of a common bird, associated with human structures and degraded habitats with no obvious threats, highlights the difficulty in predicting which species will experience large population declines and why monitoring programs are important. Bewick's Wren would have to be near the top of the list of species likely to be extirpated from the state in the next 10 to 20 years.

5.63. Bewick's Wrens are currently endangered in Illinois with the only known nesting sites in western Illinois.

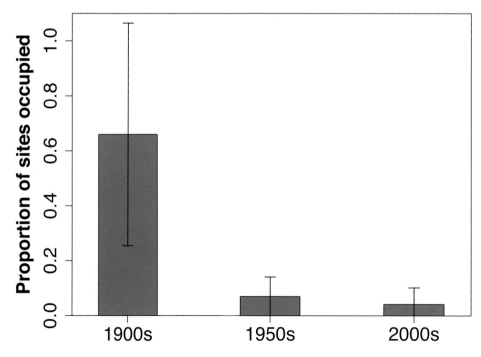

5.64. Occupancy rates of Bewick's Wrens in the 1900s, 1950s, and 2000s in Illinois.

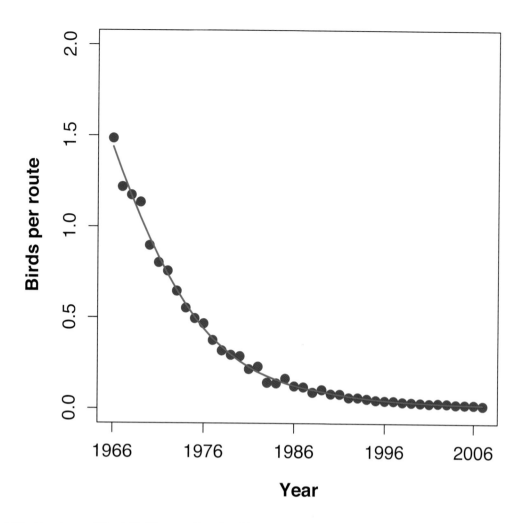

5.65. Abundance of Bewick's Wrens on Breeding Bird Survey routes in eastern North America, 1966–2007.

5.66. Bewick's Wrens are likely not declining due to habitat. As this photograph illustrates an ideal habitat for wrens, old sheds and dilapidated machinery. The wren in the upper right corner was nesting in an old barbeque grill in Morgan County.

Carolina Wren. Carolina Wrens are a species of southern Illinois forest and wooded urban areas but may be poised to rapidly expand their range north (Fig. 5.67). While the Breeding Bird Survey and Christmas Bird Count data show Carolina Wrens are increasing and expanding their range northward (National Audubon Society 2002, Sauer et al. 2008), we encountered them at too few of our random locations in northern Illinois to suggest much change in occupancy across the state over the past century (Fig. 5.69). All our sampling confirms that Carolina Wrens are most common in southern Illinois. While not as common as House Wrens in residential areas, Carolina Wrens were regularly found in neighborhoods with a canopy of mature trees (Fig. 5.68).

Overall, we found a tendency for nonmigratory birds of forested and developed habitats, such as the Carolina Wren, to have northward expanding ranges. But, winter weather probably limits the distribution of Carolina Wrens in Illinois. Northerly populations are markedly smaller following winters with colder temperatures and longer periods of snow cover, and rebound over the course of a few years (Bohlen 1989, Haggerty and Morton 1995). The dip in abundance shown by Breeding Bird Survey data in the mid-1970s is associated with several particularly severe winters (Fig. 5.70). Global climate change models that suggest Illinois winters will become milder support the prediction that the Carolina Wren's range will expand northward (Matthews et al. 2004; see the next section for more on climate change and birds).

One behavior that Carolina Wrens employ to survive winter weather is to use developed habitats. In winter, they are known to forage in barns, out buildings, and garages looking for spiders, insect pupae, and other invertebrate prey. If Carolina Wrens do expand their ranges farther north, look for the species to utilize many of the developed residential areas in northern Illinois.

5.67. The Carolina Wren is the only nonmigratory wren in Illinois and may be expanding its range north in response to milder winters.

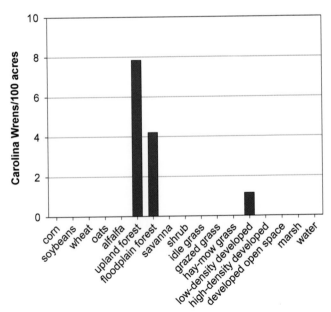

5.68. Average density (birds per 100 acres) of Carolina Wrens in various habitats from 2000s transect surveys.

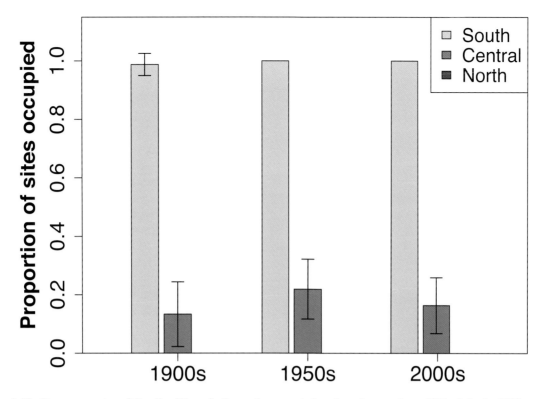

5.69. Occupancy rates of Carolina Wrens in the northern, central, and southern regions of Illinois in the 1900s, 1950s, and 2000s.

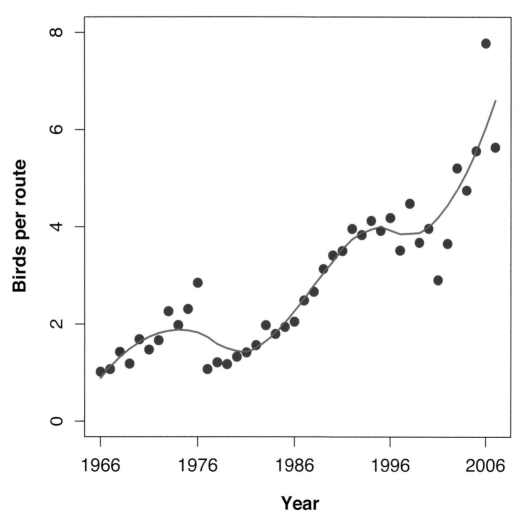

5.70. Abundance of Carolina Wrens on Breeding Bird Survey routes in Illinois, 1966–2007.

House Wren. While most species of wrens have a reputation as feisty birds, House Wrens might be the most aggressive of the bunch (Fig. 5.71). House Wrens regularly take over nest boxes occupied by much larger Eastern Bluebirds and other species, destroying their eggs and killing nestlings (Johnson 1998). While House Wrens are a common sight in developed areas throughout Illinois, there is an obvious gradient from north to south. Our occupancy analyses suggest that in all three periods they were much less common in the southern region of the state (Fig. 5.74).

Ridgway (1915) reported House Wrens as absent in Richland and Wabash counties in southeastern Illinois until the 1870s. The species did not nest in Kentucky and Arkansas until the 1910s or 1920s (Mengel 1965, James and Neal 1986). What historically limited their distribution to the northern states is unknown, but their use of residential areas is a common theme of the House Wren's southern range expansion (James and Neal 1986, Robbins and Easterla 1992).

5.71. House Wrens are one of the most common backyard birds in Illinois, readily using nest boxes and foraging in yards and gardens.

It is unlikely that habitat limited their distribution as they are most abundant in floodplain forests, but also occur in upland forests and savanna-open woodlands. These habitats are available throughout the state (Fig. 5.73). One potential factor that may be limiting their distribution is competition for nesting cavities in the south. For example, in the 1900s there were at least 13 species of cavity nesting birds in southern Illinois, compared to only six in northern Illinois. However, most of the cavity nesting species are only found in forested areas; therefore, developed areas may enable House Wrens to expand their ranges southward due to reduced competition for cavities in developed areas. Densities from our point count data suggest a fundamental difference in the habitat association of House Wrens in southern Illinois from those in the central and northern regions today (Fig. 5.72). In southern Illinois, House Wrens were found almost exclusively in developed areas and rarely in more natural habitats. Similarly, the Grabers found House Wrens were about equally abundant in residential areas statewide, but absent from forests in southern Illinois. While House Wrens may be at lower densities in southern Illinois, there is no reason for concern about this species as both our data and the Breeding Bird Survey suggest a stable or increasing House Wren population in the state (Fig. 5.75).

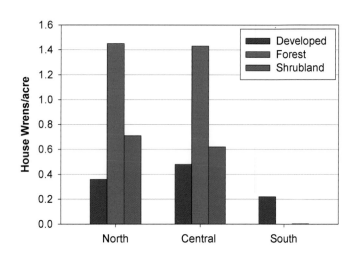

5.72. Density of House Wrens in 2000s as determined by point counts in developed, forest, and shrubland habitats in northern, central, and southern Illinois.

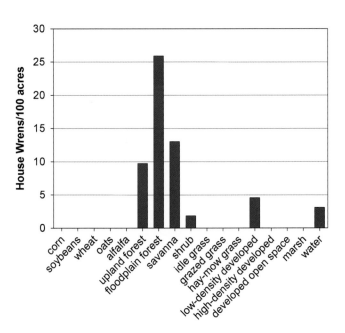

5.73. Average density (birds per 100 acres) of House Wrens in various habitats from 2000s transect surveys.

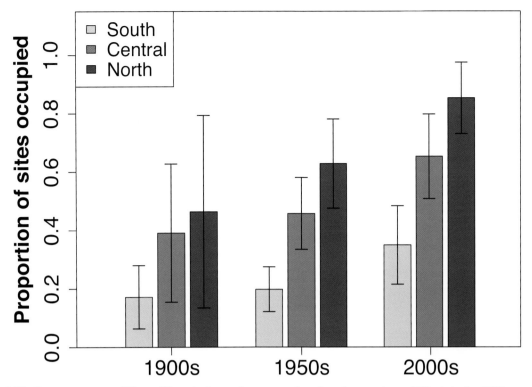

5.74. Occupancy rates of House Wrens in the northern, central, and southern regions of Illinois in the 1900s, 1950s, and 2000s.

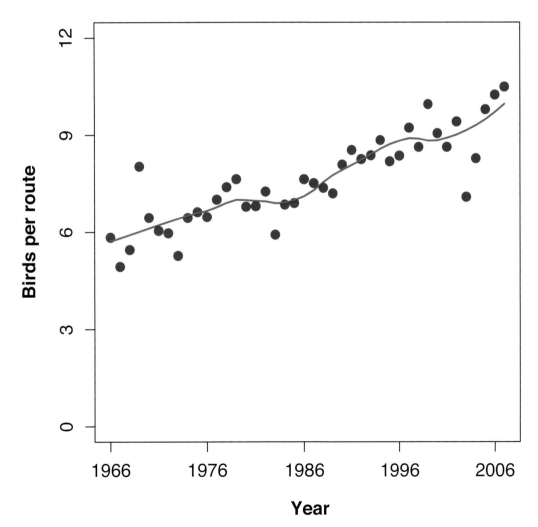

5.75. Abundance of House Wrens on Breeding Bird Survey routes in Illinois, 1966–2007.

Loggerhead Shrike. If shrikes (Fig. 5.76) were much larger, they would pose a hazard to pets and small children. Also known as the "butcher bird," shrikes are the only songbirds that regularly kill other vertebrates. Shrikes impale prey such as large insects, frogs, snakes, mice, and small birds on thorns and barbed wire. This behavior seems to be a combination of a mating display (males showing females they are good providers), prey storage, and anchoring their prey so they can tear it apart (Yosef 1996). Historically, hedge rows of Osage orange trees and pastures with scattered shrubs and trees were prime shrike habitat, and both are much reduced compared with 50 or 100 years ago (Fig. 5.77). Over time, the shrike's range in Illinois has contracted southward and the state population as a whole has declined (Figs. 5.78, 5.79). A few outpost populations and scattered pairs persist in northern and central Illinois (Kleen et al. 2004), and numbers in southern Illinois are shrinking, similar to shrike populations throughout most of the Midwest and southeastern United States

(Sauer et al. 2008). Recent studies in southern Illinois found the lowest nest success rates ever reported for Loggerhead Shrikes (Collins 1996, Walk et al. 2006). In 2009, the status of the Loggerhead Shrike in Illinois was changed from threatened to endangered (Illinois Endangered Species Protection Board 2009). Given the occupancy rate of 90% in the 1900s, the current status of Loggerhead Shrikes is sobering. The mix of grasslands and agriculture found at the shrike's few remaining strongholds (e.g., Prairie Ridge State Natural Area, Lost Mound National Wildlife Refuge, Midewin National Tallgrass Prairie) perhaps better mimic the patchwork of habitats on the Illinois landscape in the early 1900s when Loggerhead Shrikes thrived. With sharp population declines continuing across its range and grazed grasslands and shrublands unlikely to return as a dominant part of the Illinois landscape, perhaps the best Illinoisans can hope for is that a small number of Loggerhead Shrikes will manage to persist in a few localized areas.

5.76. Loggerhead Shrikes were once a common bird of Illinois; however, their current breeding populations are confined to only a handful of areas in Illinois.

5.77. This rural road near Easton, Mason County, was the only location in which a Loggerhead Shrike was encountered during the 2000 surveys. The road is not particularlry unique other than it is not excessively manicured. Woody vegetation that was allowed to grow along the road possibly provided the nesting habitat for the shrike.

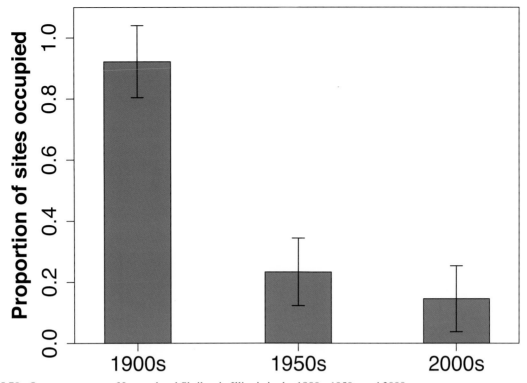

5.78. Occupancy rates of Loggerhead Shrikes in Illinois in the 1900s, 1950s, and 2000s.

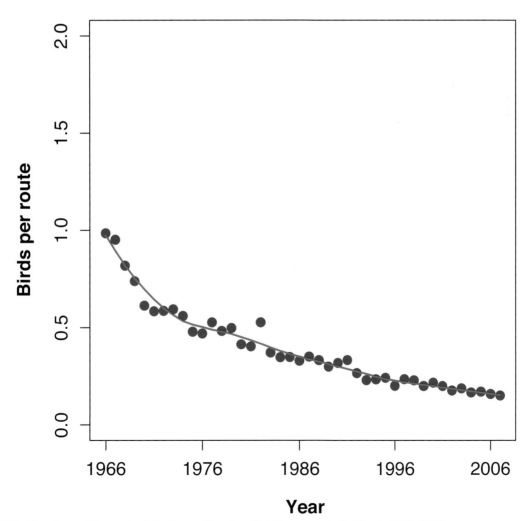

5.79. Abundance of Loggerhead Shrikes on Breeding Bird Survey routes in Illinois, 1966–2007.

Red-eyed Vireo. The song of Red-eyed Vireos (Fig. 5.80) is commonly heard in Illinois forests, but owing to this species often skulking high in the canopy, the sight of a vireo is a much rarer occurrence. Red-eyed Vireos are far more common in upland forest than other wooded habitats (Fig. 5.81). We have documented that there is now more forest habitat and with greater average maturity than at any time over the past century, and that species such as Acadian Flycatchers and Eastern Wood-Pewees have shown steady populations. In contrast, occupancy models show a consistent state-wide decline of Red-eyed Vireos (Fig. 5.82). This decline is also surprising given that the Breeding Bird Survey trend for Red-eyed Vireos in Illinois has been stable (Fig. 5.83). This difference between occupancy and Breeding Bird Survey data could result if the number of Red-eyed Vireos in the state has remained fairly constant, but birds have become clustered into fewer areas. Since forested areas have increased over time, particularly in the northern region where we found highest densities of Red-eyed Vireos, this does not seem like a plausible explanation. Like many forest-nesting birds, Red-eyed Vireos are a common victim of nest parasitism by Brown-headed Cowbirds (Cimprich et al. 2000). Previous research in Illinois suggests that Illinois forests may be ecological "sinks," areas where reproductive success is too low to offset annual mortality (Robinson et al. 1995). Additionally, changes in their wintering ground (northern South America) may be affecting the Illinois nesting population. While our occupancy data show some reductions, Red-eyed Vireos are generally increasing range wide and are likely to remain a common species in Illinois forests for decades to come.

5.80. Red-eyed Vireos are one of the most common forest canopy species in Illinois and their broods are often parasitized by Brown-headed Cowbirds.

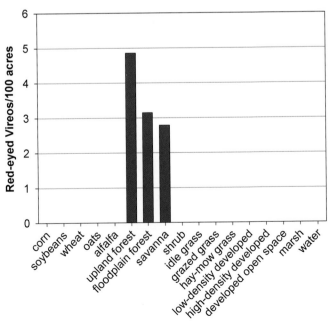

5.81. Average density (birds per 100 acres) of Red-eyed Vireos in various habitats from 2000s transect surveys.

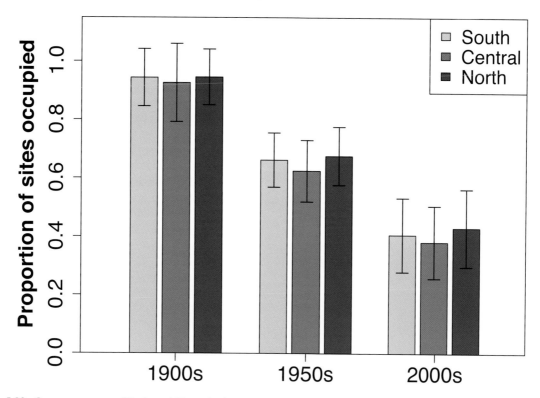

5.82. Occupancy rates of Red-eyed Vireos in the northern, central, and southern regions of Illinois in the 1900s, 1950s, and 2000s.

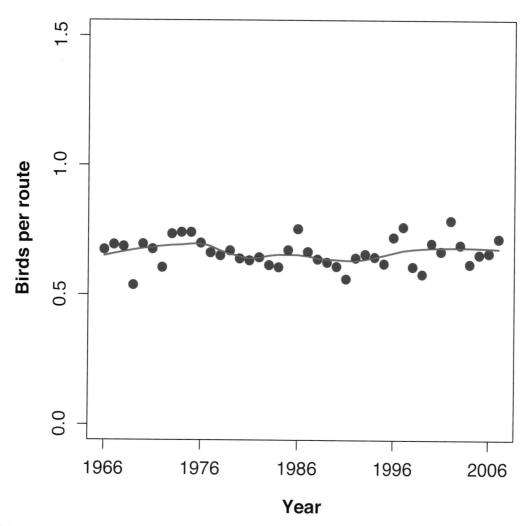

5.83. Abundance of Red-eyed Vireos on Breeding Bird Survey routes in Illinois, 1966–2007.

Cedar Waxwing. Cedar Waxwings (Fig. 5.84) are beautiful birds with a nomadic lifestyle that is well suited to finding patches of fruits – especially small berries. Large flocks will quickly strip a tree or shrub of fruit and move on. Waxwings are one of the few Illinois species that feed almost exclusively on fruit. Waxwings were not recorded in the 1900s or 1950s surveys, but we regularly encountered them in shrublands, savanna-open woodlands, and developed areas (Figs. 5.85, 5.86). The Breeding Bird Survey also shows dramatic growth of the waxwing population in Illinois (Fig. 5.87). This rapid population increase is to some degree the result of an expansion of their breeding range southward in recent decades, from Canada and the northern states throughout the Midwest and across Appalachia (Witmer et al. 1997).

There are several potential reasons for their expansion south, but the most likely is the large increase in food availability.

Fruiting trees, shrubs, and evergreens, which are preferred nesting and foraging substrates for Cedar Waxwings, are common landscaping plants in developed areas. Waxwings could be "stopped short" on their northward spring migration and prompted to nest where they encounter an abundant supply of food and good nesting sites. The southward expansion of their range may also have negative consequences if waxwings are contributing to the spread of invasive fruiting shrubs by dispersing the seeds of bush honeysuckle, buckthorn, autumn olive, and other plants (McCusker et al. 2010). This may be a positive feedback loop where waxwings are spreading the seeds of invasive shrubs, thereby creating more food sources and nesting structures for a larger population of waxwings, which are dispersing greater amounts of invasive shrub berries. Given the rapid expansion of waxwings and the ubiquity of invasive fruiting shrubs in Illinois, it is likely the population will remain large and possibly increase into the future.

5.84. Cedar Waxwings have recently become a relatively common nesting species throughout much of Illinois.

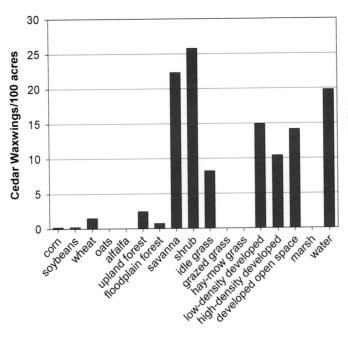

5.85. Average density (birds per 100 acres) of Cedar Waxwings in various habitats from 2000s transect surveys.

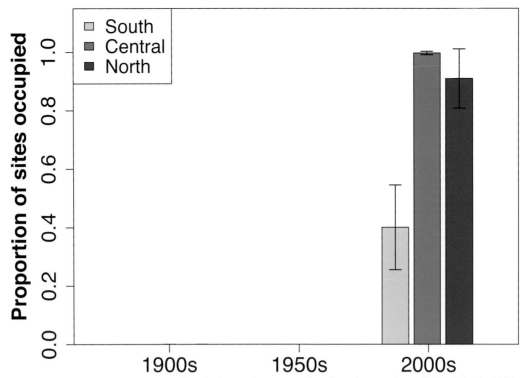

5.86. Occupancy rates of Cedar Waxwings in the northern, central, and southern regions of Illinois in the 1900s, 1950s, and 2000s.

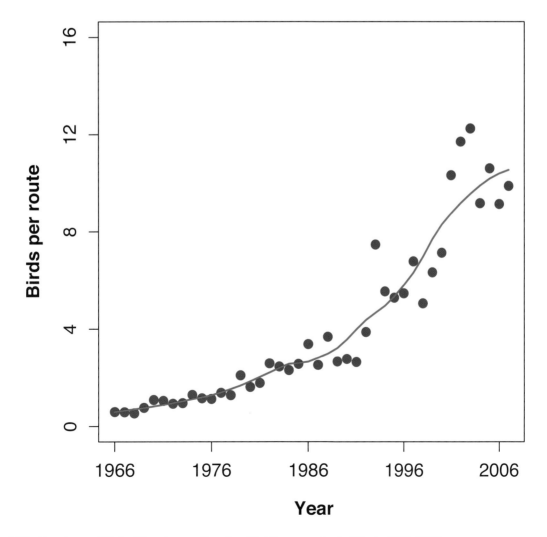

5.87. Abundance of Cedar Waxwings on Breeding Bird Survey routes in Illinois, 1966–2007.

European Starling. European Starlings (Fig. 5.88) were intentionally released in 1890 in New York as an ill-advised attempt to introduce all the birds mentioned in the works of Shakespeare (Bent 1950). Those roughly 100 released starlings have grown to a population now estimated around 200 million in North America (Cabe 1993). The first starlings in Illinois were reported from the University of Illinois campus in Urbana-Champaign in 1922 (Ford 1956). By the 1950s, starlings occurred throughout the state, although occupancy rates were lower in the southern than in the central and northern portions of the state (Fig. 5.90). By the 2000s, occupancy rates were similar in all three regions with their highest densities in developed areas (Fig. 5.89). Like the House Sparrow, which arrived in Illinois 40 years earlier, starlings nest in natural cavities, buildings, and nest boxes at the expense of native species like Eastern Bluebirds, Purple Martins, and Red-headed Woodpeckers. At the time of the

Grabers' surveys in the 1950s, the starling population was still increasing.

Today, the state is effectively saturated with starlings; Breeding Bird Survey data show the abundance of starlings has leveled off in recent decades (Fig. 5.91). Starlings are serious agricultural pests causing more than $1.6 billion in damages to crops and disease transmission among livestock annually (Linz et al. 2007). Though it seems bizarre for a bird that is so abundant here, starlings are now of conservation concern in many parts of their native Europe (BirdLife International 2004). If the North American population of starlings were to decline, it may alleviate some competition with native species. However, starlings prefer developed areas (which undoubtedly will expand in the future) and have proven to be highly adaptable and are likely to remain highly abundant in the coming decades.

5.88. European Starlings are a common bird of developed habitats throughout Illinois.

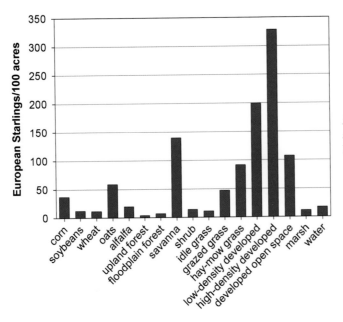

5.89. Average density (birds per 100 acres) of European Starlings in various habitats from 2000s transect surveys.

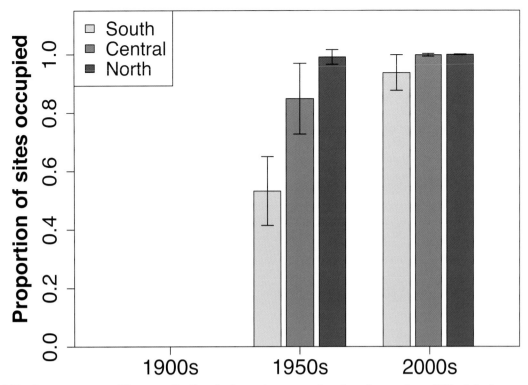

5.90. Occupancy rates of European Starlings in the northern, central, and southern regions of Illinois in the 1900s, 1950s, and 2000s.

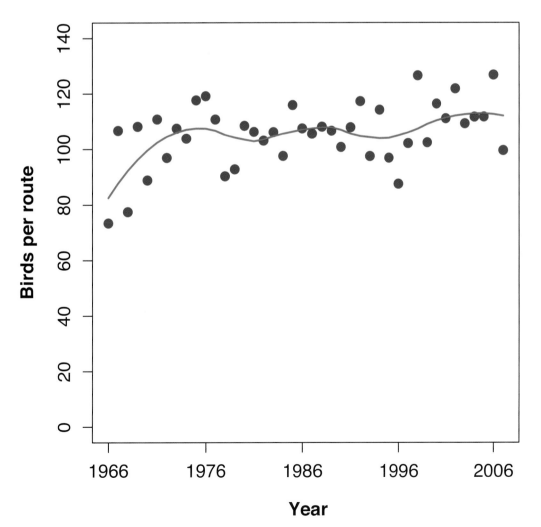

5.91. Abundance of European Starlings on Breeding Bird Survey routes in Illinois, 1966–2007.

Horned Lark. "No Illinois species increased more dramatically between 1909 and 1957 than the Horned Lark," wrote the Grabers. Much of the population growth during the first half of the twentieth century can be attributed to a shift in preferred habitat. Found mostly in grazed and hayed grasslands in the 1900s, Horned Larks (Fig. 5.92) had become abundant in fields of corn, soybeans, and alfalfa by the 1950s surveys, and in the 2000s they were essentially ubiquitous in row crop fields across Illinois (Fig. 5.95). The increase in occupancy of southern Illinois by Horned Larks since the 1950s probably reflects the roughly 2.1 million acre increase of corn and soybeans in that region.

Horned Larks survive in landscapes dominated by corn and soybeans by nesting early in the season in the sparse cover of the previous year's stubble (Fig. 5.94). However, changes in agricultural practices, such as earlier planting, may be contributing to the long-term decline in abundance of Horned Larks shown by the Breeding Bird Survey (Fig. 5.96). While Horned Larks can still be found in nearly every corn and soybean field in Illinois (i.e., ~100% occupancy rate), the number of Horned Larks in those fields has declined. Horned Larks are still very common in Illinois but are experiencing widespread declines (Fig. 5.93). While Horned Larks likely will thrive in Illinois so long as row crops remain the dominant land use, subtle changes in agricultural practices may significantly alter Horned Lark reproduction and abundance.

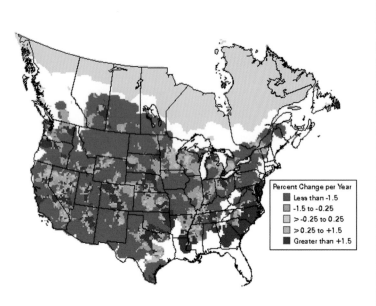

5.93. Map of the geographic pattern of Horned Lark population trends as represented by Breeding Bird Survey routes, 1966 to 2003 (Sauer et al. 2008).

Percent Change per Year
- Less than -1.5
- -1.5 to -0.25
- >-0.25 to 0.25
- >0.25 to +1.5
- Greater than +1.5

5.92. Horned Larks are the quintessential row crop birds, spending much of their lives in corn and soybean fields.

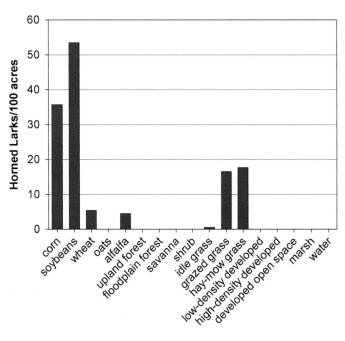

5.94. Average density (birds per 100 acres) of Horned Larks in various habitats from 2000s transect surveys.

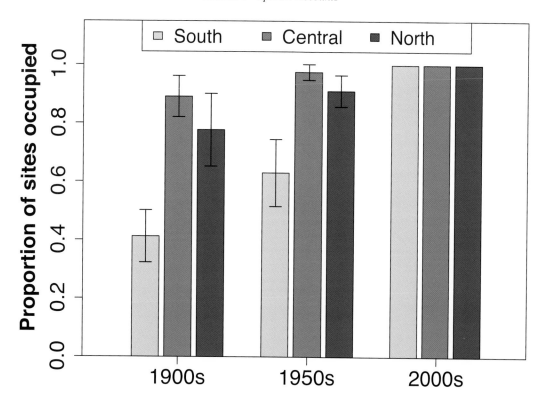

5.95. Occupancy rates of Horned Larks in the northern, central, and southern regions of Illinois in the 1900s, 1950s, and 2000s.

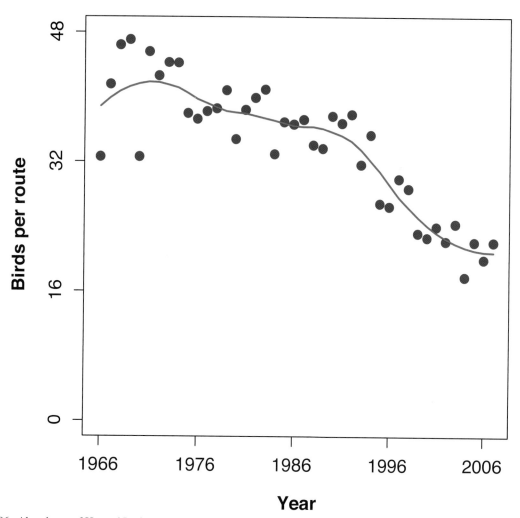

5.96. Abundance of Horned Larks on Breeding Bird Survey routes in Illinois, 1966–2007.

Swallows. In the 1900s surveys, Gross and Ray encountered Barn Swallows (Fig. 5.97) only once in southern Illinois. At that time, Barn Swallows did not nest in Arkansas, Tennessee, or other southern states (James and Neal 1986, Nicholson 1997). By the 1950s, the Grabers reported that Barn Swallows had "increased greatly," particularly in southern Illinois. Over the past 50 years, both Barn and Tree Swallows have expanded southward (Brown and Bomberger Brown 1999, Robertson et al. 1992; Fig. 5.99). With the exception of Purple Martins, which have had a stable or slightly declining abundance over the past few decades, the five other species of swallows in Illinois (Barn, Bank, Northern Rough-winged, Cliff, and Tree) have increased (Fig. 5.100).

The success of swallows surprised us, particularly the range expansion of the Barn Swallow. Historically (200+ years ago), the extensive forest cover of southern Illinois may have restricted Barn Swallows to the more open landscapes (e.g.,

prairies) of the northern and central regions. By the 1900s, much of the forest had been removed from southern Illinois and barns for nesting were abundant, so the delay in the Barn Swallows' southward range expansion remains unexplained. Tree Swallows have also increased in overall abundance and moved southward, a trend that has been noted in other parts of their range (Robertson et al. 1992).

The continued increase in Barn Swallow abundance in Illinois is somewhat surprising given there are fewer open barns for nesting and their preferred foraging habitat (grazed grasslands, Fig. 5.98) is less common. It appears that Barn Swallows, and more recently Cliff Swallows, have begun nesting under bridges and in large culverts. These nesting sites are abundant and typically safe from nest predators. Except for Purple Martins, we expect that populations of swallows will continue to increase.

5.97. Barn Swallows are a common species throughout Illinois, but were absent from southern Illinois in the 1900s.

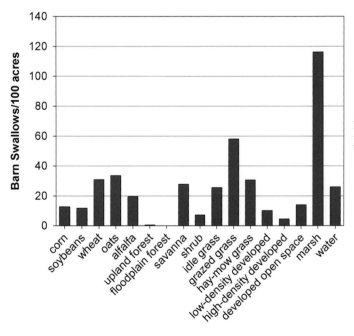

5.98. Average density (birds per 100 acres) of Barn Swallows in various habitats from 2000s transect surveys.

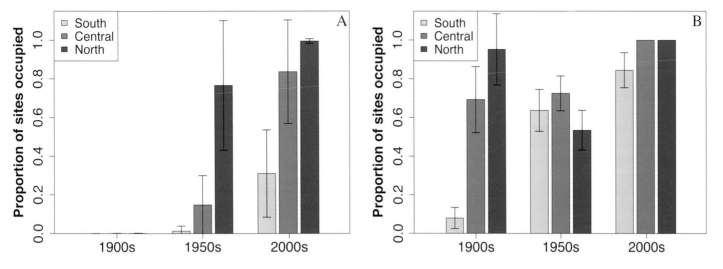

5.99. Occupancy rates of Barn (A) and Tree Swallows (B) in the northern, central, and southern regions of Illinois in the 1900s, 1950s, and 2000s.

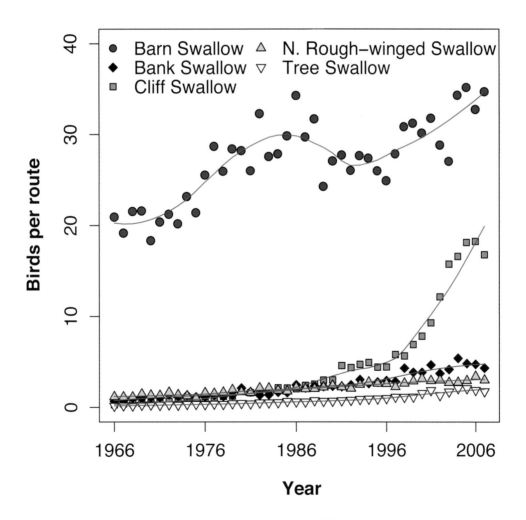

5.100. Abundance of swallows on Breeding Bird Survey routes in Illinois, 1966–2007.

Chickadees. Illinois is home to both the Black-capped Chickadee (Fig. 5.101) in the north and the Carolina Chickadee in the south. A contact zone between the two species occurs across central Illinois, roughly from East St. Louis to Danville (Kleen et al. 2004; Fig. 5.102). Within this contact zone, birders might encounter birds that sing hybrid songs of Black-capped and Carolina Chickadees or "bilingual" birds that sing both songs. The location of this contact zone appears to have been stable since the 1960s (Enstrom and Bollinger 2009).

The occupancy data show that Black-capped Chickadees have overall higher occupancy rates than Carolina Chickadees (Fig. 5.104); this trend is also supported by density estimates from point count data. This difference may be due to competition

with Tufted Titmice, which are common in southern Illinois and decrease in abundance farther north. North American Breeding Bird Survey trends also differ, with Black-capped Chickadees increasing and Carolina Chickadees stable (Fig. 5.105). Both Black-capped and Carolina Chickadees are forest species (Fig. 5.103), and the recent increases in northern Illinois forests, as opposed to the only slight increases in the south, may explain the differences in Breeding Bird Survey trends. Given the improvements in forest quantity, and to some degree quality, we expect chickadee populations to remain stable. There are some indications that like crows and jays, chickadee populations were impacted by West Nile virus (LaDeau et al. 2007). This highlights that novel diseases can have rapid and severe effects on bird populations, regardless of their size.

5.101. The Black-capped Chickadee is the chickadee species that occurs in the northern and central portions of the state.

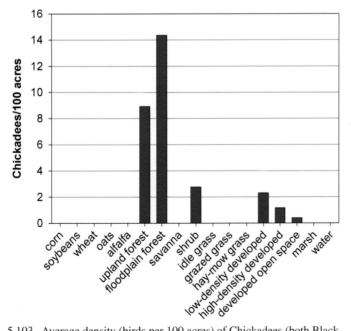

5.103. Average density (birds per 100 acres) of Chickadees (both Black-capped and Carolina) in various habitats from 2000s transect surveys.

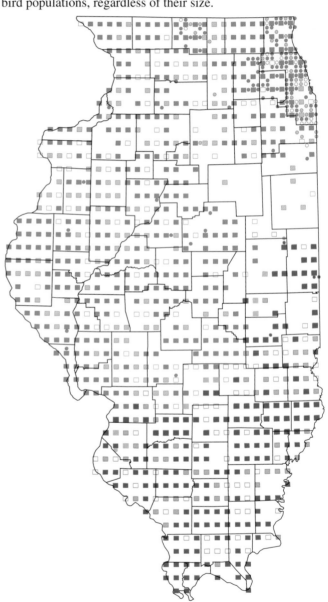

5.102. Distribution of Black-capped (blue) and Carolina Chickadees (red) from the Illinois Breeding Bird Atlas (Kleen et al. 2004). The dark red or blue means that the species was confirmed breeding in the block, the lighter shade means the species was a probable breeder, and the white boxes bordered in either red or blue mean the species was a possible breeder in the block. The squares are the priority blocks and circles represent non-priority areas. There were eight blocks with both species, which are represented by gray.

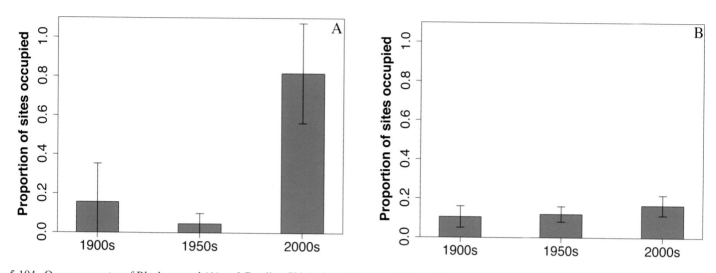

5.104. Occupancy rates of Black-capped (A) and Carolina Chickadees (B) in the 1900s, 1950s, and 2000s in Illinois.

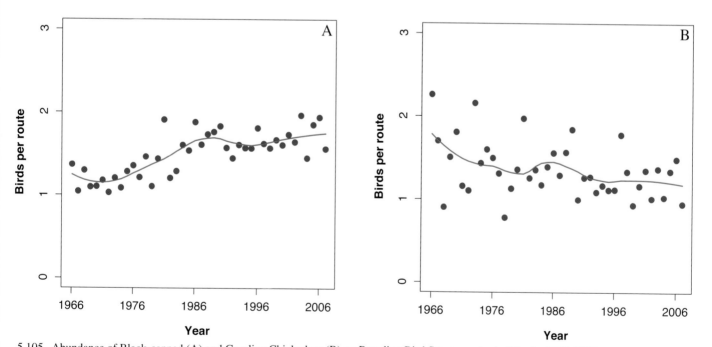

5.105. Abundance of Black-capped (A) and Carolina Chickadees (B) on Breeding Bird Survey routes in Illinois, 1966–2007.

Tufted Titmouse. Like Carolina Wrens, Tufted Titmice (Fig. 5.106) are ubiquitous in southern Illinois, and scarcer and locally distributed in the central and northern regions (Kleen et al. 2004; Fig. 5.108). Titmice nest in tree cavities, inhabit a variety of forest types, and are regular visitors to sunflower feeders in low-density developed areas (Fig. 5.107). While titmice were regularly found in various habitats in central and southern Illinois, we found titmice only in developed areas in the northern region. The Breeding Bird Survey shows the abundance of titmice has remained fairly stable since the 1960s (Fig. 5.109), but these routes often do not sample developed areas. While the occupancy data suggest a slight increase in occupancy in northern Illinois, titmice, like Carolina Wrens, are poised to expand in northern Illinois. Other species such as Northern Cardinals and Red-bellied Woodpeckers, both of which in the 1900s had similar occupancy patterns as titmice, have now become well-established in northern Illinois. Although competition with Black-capped Chickadees might be a factor limiting the distribution of the Tufted Titmice in the north, it seems likely that titmice will increase in abundance in the developed areas and forests of northern Illinois, particularly if predictions about climate change hold true.

5.106. The Tufted Titmouse is primarily a bird of southern Illinois forests. This species may be poised to increase its distribution and density in the northern portions of the state.

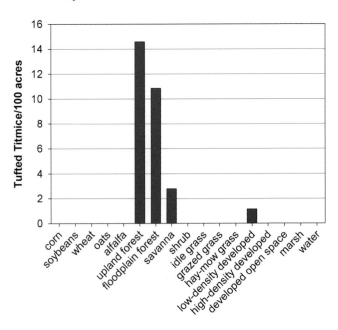

5.107. Average density (birds per 100 acres) of Tufted Titmice in various habitats from 2000s transect surveys.

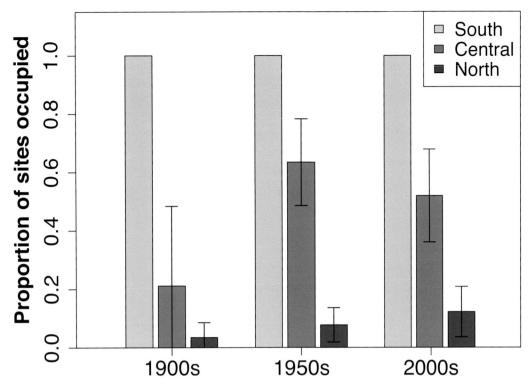

5.108. Occupancy rates of Tufted Titmice in the northern, central, and southern regions of Illinois in the 1900s, 1950s, and 2000s.

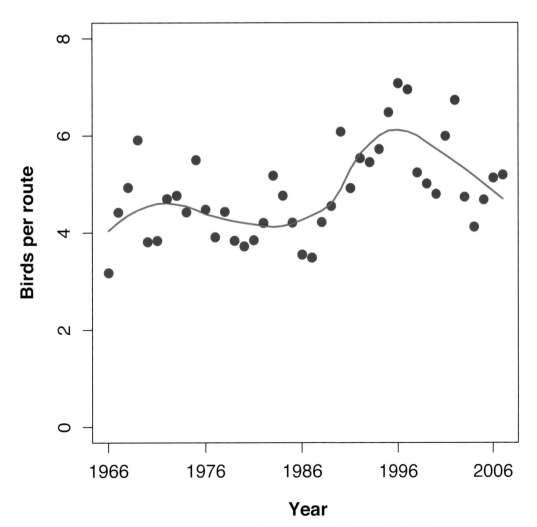

5.109. Abundance of Tufted Titmice on Breeding Bird Survey routes in Illinois, 1966–2007.

Brown Thrasher. Forest clearing in the eastern United States and establishment of windbreaks and hedgerows in the Great Plains has enabled the Brown Thrasher's range to expand in all directions from the center of the continent (Cavitt and Haas 2000). Both of these habitat changes occurred in Illinois in the late 1800s, and as a result Brown Thrashers (Fig. 5.110) were among the most common species in cropland, grassland, and shrubland habitats during Gross and Ray's 1900s surveys. Since then, removal of woody field borders and increasing field size have left far less habitat for thrashers in the state. The decline of Brown Thrashers was first evident between 1900s and 1950s in southern Illinois (Fig. 5.113). This decline has continued in the south, but has recently spread to the northern and central regions. In 2000s, we encountered thrashers regularly only

in linear wooded habitats, shrublands, and the understory of savanna-open woodlands (Fig. 5.112). The alarming population trends of Brown Thrashers in Illinois (Fig. 5.114) and throughout their range (Fig. 5.111) highlights the need for management. Brown Thrashers, like Eastern Towhees, Field Sparrows, Yellow-breasted Chats, and many shrubland birds, do not require large tracts of habitat but can utilize small "messy" areas. We think that thrashers and other shrubland birds are at a critical point, and specific conservation and management of shrublands will be necessary to arrest population declines. Otherwise, Brown Thrashers may be endangered in 50 years. Management of shrubland habitats will have the greatest effect while there is still a robust population of thrashers throughout the state.

5.110. Brown Thrashers have broad habitat requirements that include shrubland, hedgerow, and other successional habitat, but have been experiencing declines over the past century.

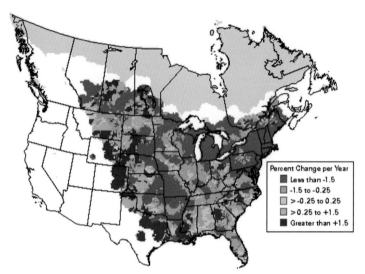

5.111. Geographic pattern of Brown Thrasher population trends as represented by Breeding Bird Survey routes, 1966 to 2003 (Sauer et al. 2008).

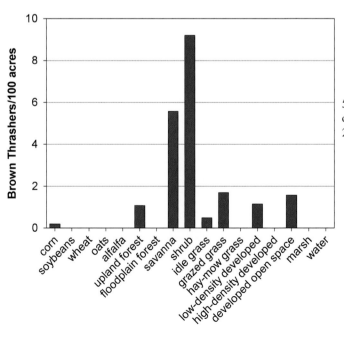

5.112. Average density (birds per 100 acres) of Brown Thrashers in various habitats from 2000s transect surveys.

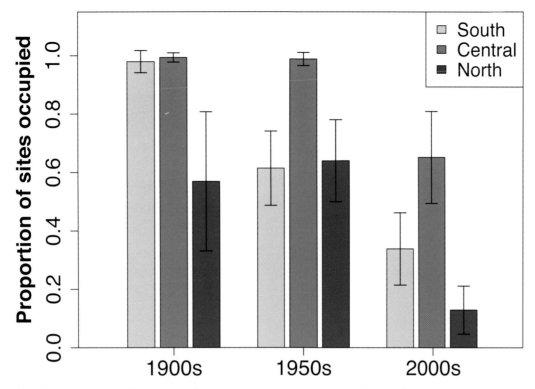

5.113. Occupancy rates of Brown Thrasher in the northern, central, and southern regions of Illinois in the 1900s, 1950s, and 2000s.

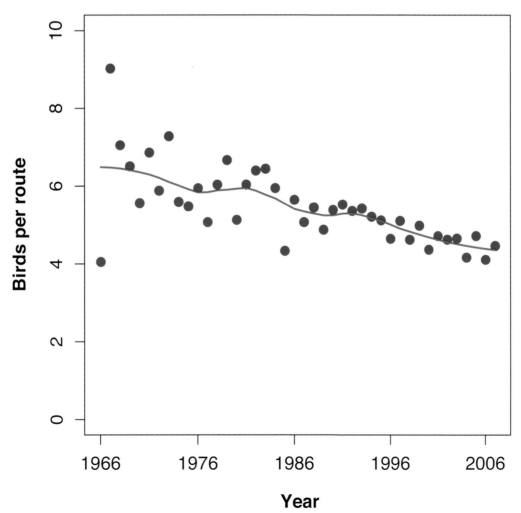

5.114. Abundance of Brown Thrashers on Breeding Bird Survey routes in Illinois, 1966–2007.

American Robin. The American Robin (Fig. 5.115) has greatly benefited from the suburbanization of North America. Soft-bodied invertebrates, especially earthworms, are an important part of the robin's diet during the nesting season. However, most earthworms are not native to North America. Robins followed the spread of residential areas and earthworms - to the southeastern United States, to the Great Plains, and recently to the desert southwest and California where irrigation supports green lawns and keeps worms and other invertebrates near the surface. Today, nesting robins can be seen pulling up earthworms in backyards across the continent (Sallabanks and James 1999).

In the 1900s, Gross and Ray found only about 6% of the state's robins in developed areas, increasing to about 28% during the Grabers' 1950s surveys. We found 61% of all robins in developed areas, with the species having its highest density in developed areas (Fig. 5.116). The overall regional occupancy of robins has also changed over time: greatest in the southern region in the 1900s, but greatest in northern Illinois in the 1950s and 2000s (Fig. 5.117).

The most significant change in the bird community of forests from the 1950s to 2000s was the robin's rise from about 20th place to first in the ranking of most commonly encountered birds (Section IV). Most of this change happened in northern Illinois, where robins are three times more abundant in forests compared to southern Illinois forests. Since robins, like waxwings, are proficient at spreading the seeds of fruits they eat, the abundance of robins is probably an important factor in the rapid spread of invasive fruiting shrubs like bush honeysuckle (McCusker et al. 2010).

The Breeding Bird Survey trend for American Robins shows impressive population increases in recent years (Fig. 5.118). Occupancy rates dropped in the 1950s in southern and central Illinois (Fig. 5.117), perhaps related to organochlorine chemicals that were being used at the time and were highly toxic to robins (also discussed in the last section). Robins are wintering hundreds of miles farther north today than they did 40 years ago (Niven et al. 2009), which could be related to climate change and milder winters and/or to increased food availability and secure habitat in developed areas. Robins are found in almost all habitats in Illinois (Fig. 5.116) and are abundant in many of them. Robins will likely continue to be one of the most common birds in Illinois well into the future.

5.115. American Robins have become one of the most common birds in Illinois, inhabiting and thriving in a variety of habitats.

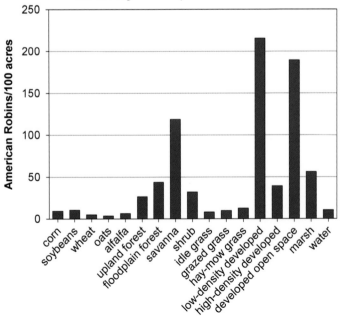

5.116. Average density (birds per 100 acres) of American Robins in various habitats from 2000s transect surveys.

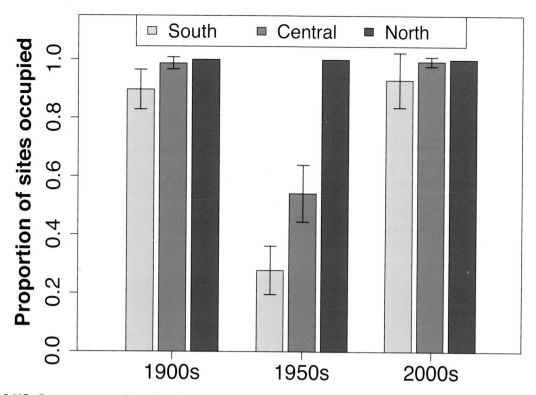

5.117. Occupancy rates of American Robins in the northern, central, and southern regions of Illinois in the 1900s, 1950s, and 2000s.

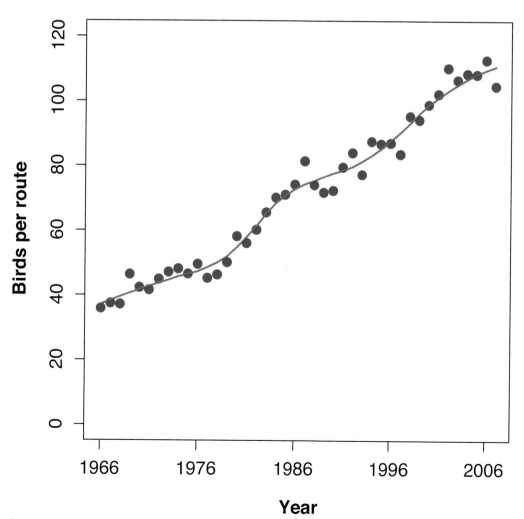

5.118. Abundance of American Robins on Breeding Bird Survey routes in Illinois, 1966–2007.

Red-winged Blackbird. During the late-spring and early-summer months, Red-winged Blackbirds (Fig. 5.119) are exceptionally abundant throughout Illinois. The Red-winged Blackbird has probably been the most common bird in Illinois throughout the past century, and it is among the 10 most common birds in North America (Yasukawa and Searcy 1995). Red-winged Blackbirds are generalists because they are abundant, and not abundant because they are generalists: their densities are highest in their original preferred habitat (marshes) and in fields planted to small grains like wheat, where they can probably nest successfully before the grain is harvested (Fig. 5.120). However, because of frequent mowing of alfalfa and hayed grasslands (Bollinger et al. 1990, Frawley and Best 1991), and high predation rates in linear grassland habitats (Bryan and Best 1994, Camp and Best 1994, Kammin 2003, Henningsen and Best

2005), the Red-winged Blackbirds in these areas are probably not contributing much recruitment to the overall population.

Although Red-winged Blackbirds have always been abundant in Illinois, their occupancy rates were lowest in the 1950s, possibly related to some pesticides in use at that time (Fig. 5.121, see final section). While the species' abundance is stable in Illinois (Fig. 5.122), Red-winged Blackbirds are slightly declining range-wide. Looking ahead, the state's Red-winged Blackbird population is likely to drop. The two most rapidly expanding land cover types, development and forest, are the two habitats with the lowest densities of Red-winged Blackbirds. While it's unlikely that Red-winged Blackbirds will be uncommon in 50 years, it is possible that their status as the most abundant bird in the state will be overtaken by species common to urban and suburban environments such as Common Grackles, European Starlings, or American Robins.

5.119. The Red-winged Blackbird is currently the most common bird in Illinois.

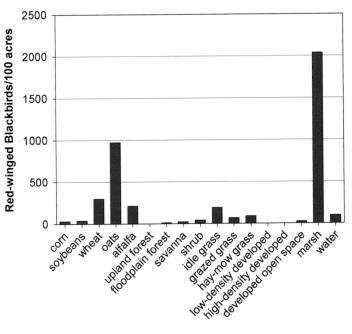

5.120. Average density (birds per 100 acres) of Red-winged Blackbirds in various habitats from 2000s transect surveys.

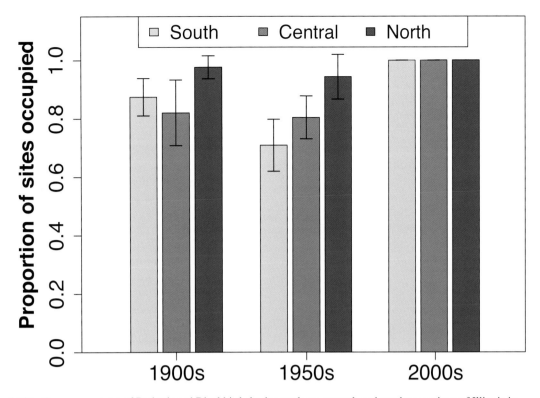

5.121. Occupancy rates of Red-winged Blackbirds in the northern, central, and southern regions of Illinois in the 1900s, 1950s, and 2000s.

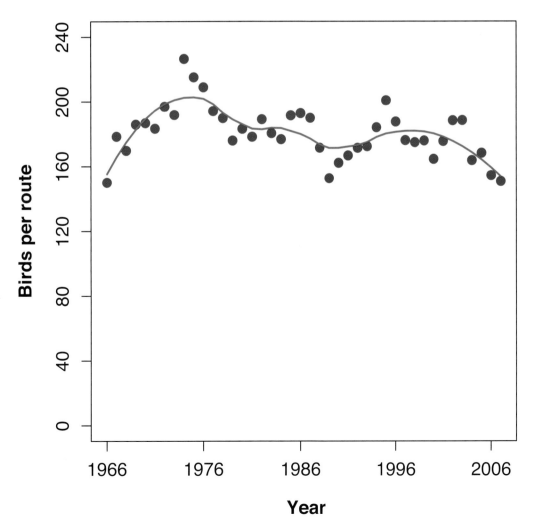

5.122. Abundance of Red-winged Blackbirds on Breeding Bird Survey routes in Illinois, 1966–2007.

Brown-headed Cowbird. Brown-headed Cowbirds are obligate brood parasites; they lay their eggs in the nests of other birds (Fig. 5.123), and they never build their own nests, incubate their own eggs, or feed their own nestlings. This behavior probably evolved when cowbirds followed nomadic herds of bison across the Great Plains and could not remain in one place long enough to raise their own young (Lowther 1993). Cowbird parasitism can be problematic for the host birds, because fast-growing cowbird hatchlings are aggressive and crowd out or kill their nest mates. Cowbirds also engage in mafia-like behavior; female cowbirds re-visit nests they have parasitized, and if the cowbird eggs have been removed from the nest, the cowbird will destroy the host's eggs (Hoover and Robinson 2007). Research in Illinois and adjacent states has shown that exceptionally high rates of cowbird parasitism can significantly reduce breeding success by thrushes, vireos, and warblers in the most fragmented forests of the Midwest (Robinson et al. 1995).

However, brood parasitism is not a new threat to songbirds in Illinois. Ridgway (1889) described the cowbird as common throughout the state, adding the female cowbird:

…hunts stealthily through the woods, usually in the undergrowth, and when a nest is discovered, patiently awaits from a convenient hiding place for the temporary absence of the parent, when the nest is stealthy and hastily inspected, and if found suitable she takes possession and deposits her egg, when she departs as quietly as she came.

Cowbirds are currently ubiquitous across the state, but in the 1950s it appears as if their population was reduced (Fig. 5.125). While we found cowbirds in all habitats, their highest density was in shrublands (Fig. 5.124). Not surprisingly, common shrub-nesting birds like Field Sparrows, Indigo Buntings, and Northern Cardinals are frequent victims of cowbird parasitism. In southern Illinois, cowbirds are found more often in forests than in grasslands, whereas they are about equally common in forests and grasslands in central and northern Illinois. The 2000s surveys found higher overall occupancy rates of Brown-headed Cowbirds compared to the 1950s, and the Breeding Bird Survey shows an increasing trend since the mid-1960s (Fig. 5.126). Given their current distribution and the large number of available hosts, cowbirds will likely remain common into the future.

5.123. This Eastern Meadowlark nest, found in western Illinois in 1907, contains two meadowlark eggs and three cowbird eggs.

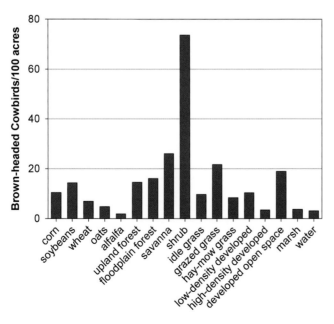

5.124. Average density (birds per 100 acres) of Brown-headed Cowbirds in various habitats from 2000s transect surveys.

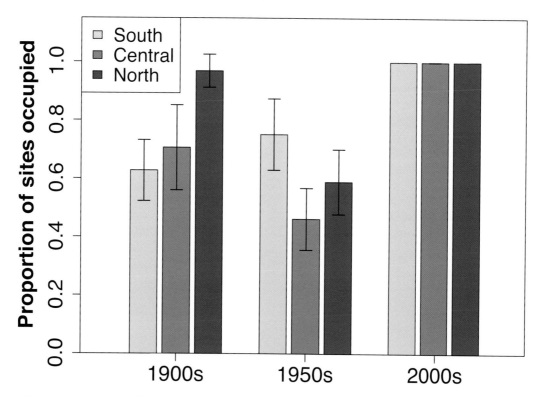

5.125. Occupancy rates of Brown-headed Cowbirds in the northern, central, and southern regins of Illinois in the 1900s, 1950s, and 2000s.

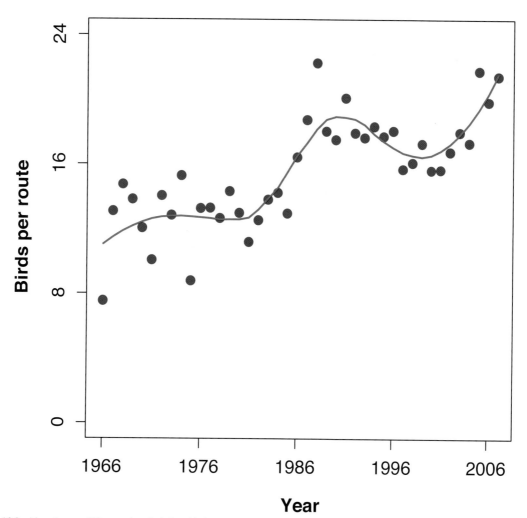

5.126. Abundance of Brown-headed Cowbirds on Breeding Bird Survey routes in Illinois, 1966–2007.

Bobolink. From their South American wintering grounds, Bobolinks return to the meadows and prairies across the northern United States and southern Canada each year to nest. While the females' plumage is rather nondescript and sparrow-like, male Bobolinks (Fig. 5.127) "look like they are wearing a tuxedo backward" (Martin and Gavin 1995). The Grabers reported that Bobolinks had increased in abundance between the 1900s and 1950s in central Illinois, and though our occupancy models suggest a slight southward range expansion over the past 50 years (Fig. 5.129). We suspect the few birds encountered in the southern region were late migrants en route to more northerly nesting areas. We detected Bobolinks most often in grasslands and occasionally in oat and alfalfa fields (Fig. 5.128). Bobolink density was three times greater in northern Illinois grasslands than in central Illinois habitats. In central Illinois, we regularly found Bobolinks in grasslands at sites west of the Illinois River but rarely to the east. Even though Bobolinks remain relatively widespread over the northern half of the state, their abundance and occupancy rates have dropped considerably. The Breeding Bird Survey estimates a decline of 8.5% per year over the past 40 years —a cumulative decline of well over 90% (Fig. 5.130). Many of the locations where we detected large numbers of Bobolinks were grasslands managed by county forest preserve districts in northeastern Illinois. While Bobolinks historically nested in hayfields, the scarcity of hayfields coupled with the frequency that these fields are mowed is likely to result in a few large conservation areas in northern Illinois being the last strongholds for Bobolinks in the state.

R. Graber

5.127. Bobolinks, such as this one photographed by Dick Graber in the 1960s, have experienced large declines in Illinois.

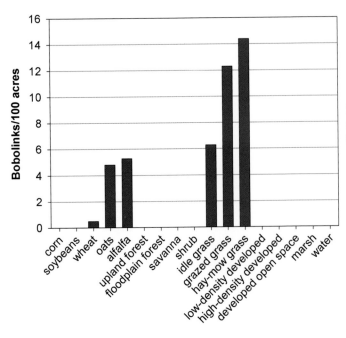

5.128. Average density (birds per 100 acres) of Bobolinks in various habitats from 2000s transect surveys.

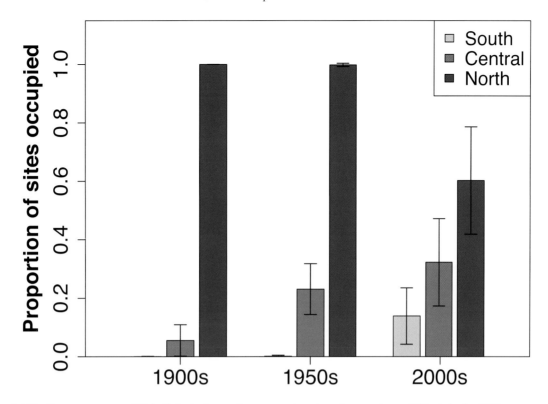

5.129. Occupancy rates of Bobolinks in the northern, central, and southern regions of Illinois in the 1900s, 1950s, and 2000s.

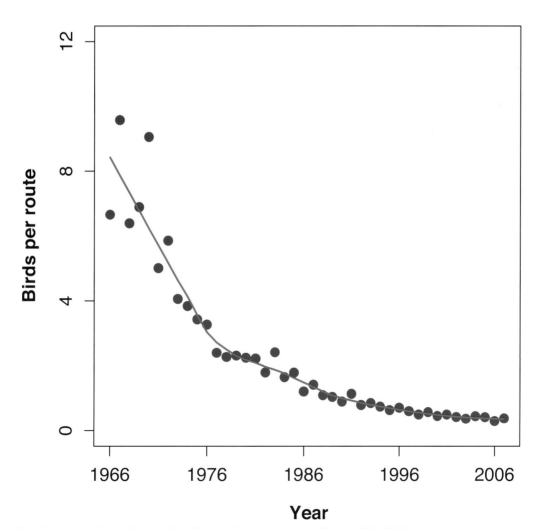

5.130. Abundance of Bobolinks on Breeding Bird Survey routes in Illinois, 1966–2007.

Meadowlarks. Meadowlarks may have been the most familiar birds to Illinois residents during the surveys of Gross and Ray in the early 1900s. Throughout most of the state, only the Eastern Meadowlark is present (Fig. 5.131). Western Meadowlarks are common in the northwestern counties, but are found locally in northeastern and central Illinois (Kleen et al. 2004). Although they have become less common in Illinois over time, meadowlarks remain widespread and can still be found in most grasslands, including rural roadsides (Figs. 5.132, 5.133). Eastern Meadowlark densities in grasslands are greater in southern Illinois than in the northern or central regions. The Breeding Bird Survey offers hope that the Eastern Meadowlark population "bottomed out" around 1980 and has been stable or only slightly declining since (Fig. 5.134).

Our occupancy models show that meadowlarks were present statewide in the 1900s and 1950s, but were less widespread in northern Illinois in the 2000s (Fig. 5.133). Considering information on density raises deeper concerns for meadowlarks. We divided all counts of meadowlarks over the three survey periods into "high-density" and "low-density" categories. Nearly all of the 1900s and 1950s surveys found high-densities of meadowlarks, but about half of the places where we found meadowlarks in the 2000s in central and northern Illinois were low-density counts (Fig. 5.133). Recently, meadowlarks were still at high-densities in the southern region, where grasslands remain more common. If loss of grassland habitat continues, meadowlarks are likely to be absent from many areas of central and northern Illinois in the near future. The meadowlark's pattern of remaining widespread at a low-density rather than becoming localized has probably kept many people from realizing how severely their abundance has declined.

I. Petrov

5.131. While Eastern Meadowlarks remain a common sight in Illinois, occupancy data suggest the species may be on the cusp of vanishing from many areas.

5.132. Average density (birds per 100 acres) of Eastern Meadowlarks in various habitats from 2000s transect surveys.

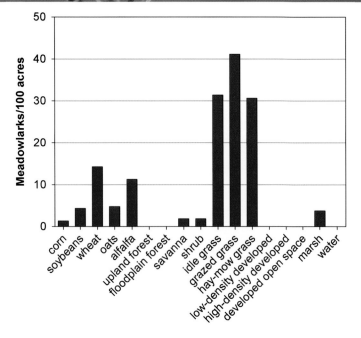

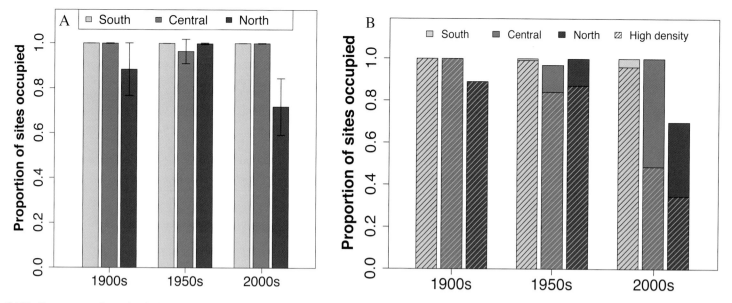

5.133. Occupancy of meadowlarks has remained high throughout Illinois (A), but they now occur at lower densities in central and northern Illinois (B).

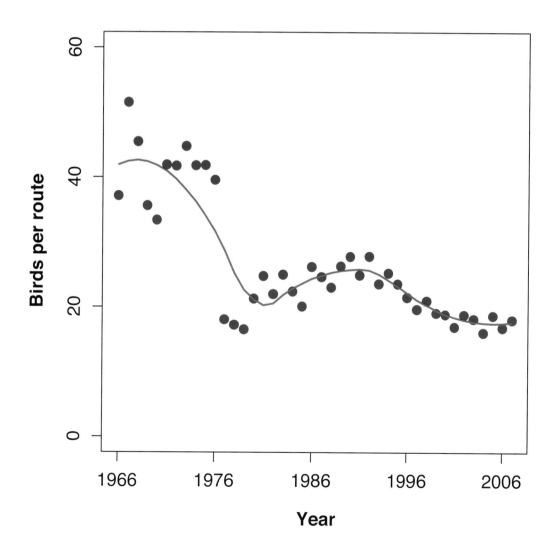

5.134. Abundance of Eastern Meadowlarks on Breeding Bird Survey routes in Illinois, 1966–2007.

Chipping Sparrow. Chipping Sparrows have adapted well to suburban living — nearly every yard in the state with a blue spruce also hosts a pair of Chipping Sparrows (Fig. 5.135). Like American Robins and Brown Thrashers, Chipping Sparrows have been able to expand their range as a result of the forest clearing and residential development that accompanied European settlement (Middleton 1998). However, the abundance and habitat preference of Chipping Sparrows have shifted considerably over the past century in Illinois. In the 1900s surveys, only 29 Chipping Sparrows were recorded, 19 in grasslands or small grain fields. Only eight birds (five in residential areas) were recorded in the 1950s surveys. By our 2000s surveys, Chipping Sparrows had recovered throughout the state and occupancy rates were much higher, especially in central Illinois (Fig. 5.137). Nearly two-thirds of the 227 Chipping Sparrows observed in the 2000s surveys were in developed areas (Fig. 5.136). In addition to low-density developed areas and developed open space, Chipping Sparrows were common in savanna-type habitats.

It is unclear why Chipping Sparrows were so rare during the 1950s surveys. Perhaps their low numbers were due to pesticide use (addressed in the final section) or the same factors that also caused the mid-century "dips," or decreases in occupancy rates, of American Robins, Brown-headed Cowbirds, and Common Grackles. Others besides the Grabers noticed the absence of Chipping Sparrows during the mid-part of the twentieth century. Ford et al. (1934) stated that the Chipping Sparrow was a "fairly common summer resident….. However, it has become rare in the immediate vicinity of Chicago where formerly it was exceedingly common." The Breeding Bird Survey confirms they have increased significantly since the mid-1960s (Fig. 5.138). Although the Chipping Sparrow is doing well, the decline between the 1900s and the 1950s is a sobering reminder that even robust populations can decline quickly. Given their strong rebound and preference for developed habitats, they will likely remain common in the state for many years to come.

M.K. Rubey

5.135. Over the past century, Chipping Sparrows populations may have experienced the most dramatic change of any species. As the data from this survey suggest, they went from nearly absent in central Illinois to being one of the most common species.

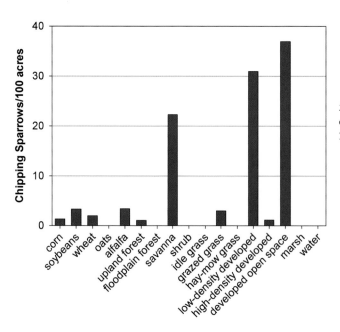

5.136. Average density (birds per 100 acres) of Chipping Sparrows in various habitats from 2000s transect surveys.

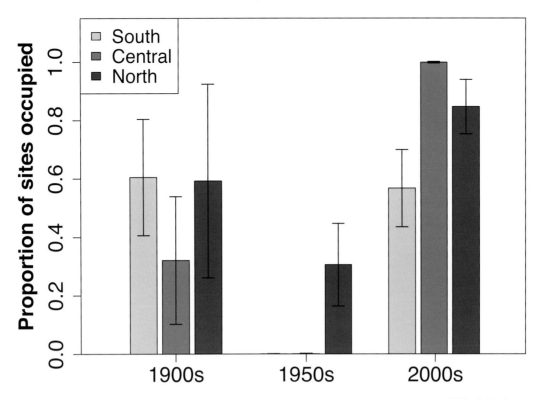

5.137. Occupancy rates of Chipping Sparrows in the northern, central, and southern regions of Illinois in the 1900s, 1950s, and 2000s.

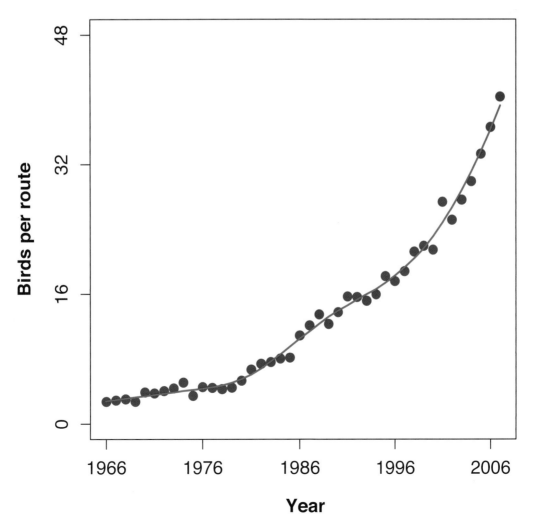

5.138. Abundance of Chipping Sparrows on Breeding Bird Survey routes in Illinois, 1966–2007.

Field Sparrow. The distribution pattern of Field Sparrows (Fig. 5.139) is similar to the Northern Bobwhite: always more common in southern Illinois, but declining in all regions between each survey period (Fig. 5.142.). Field Sparrows are found in a variety of habitats, but are most common in shrublands (Fig. 5.141). Changes in agricultural practices, in particular larger, "cleaner" fields with fewer shrubby edges, and the succession of shrublands into forest, have also had negative effects on Field Sparrows. Breeding Bird Survey data illustrate how the species is declining in Illinois (Fig. 5.143) and across its range (Fig. 5.140), leading many to consider them a conservation priority species. Like meadowlarks, Field Sparrows can still be found in many parts of Illinois and maintain relatively high occupancy rates despite declining density.

Cowbirds frequently parasitize Field Sparrow nests, and Field Sparrows often abandon nests that have been parasitized. Field Sparrows have a long nesting season, often attempting 3rd or 4th nests late into summer after most cowbirds have stopped laying eggs for the season (Carey et al. 2008). This nesting behavior may boost the recruitment of Field Sparrows and explain why their population decline has not been as precipitous as some other shrubland birds. The future is not bright for Field Sparrows, as there is little chance their preferred shrubland habitat will become much more common and they show no signs of adapting to developed areas.

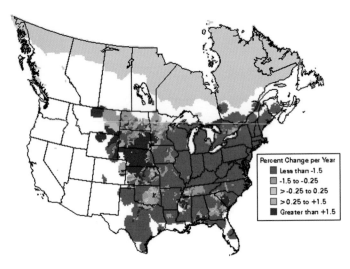

5.140. Geographic pattern of Field Sparrow population trends as represented by Breeding Bird Survey routes, 1966 to 2003 (Sauer et al. 2008).

5.139. Field Sparrows were once one of the most common birds in rural Illinois. While this species is still widespread, Field Sparrows and other shrubland birds are experiencing large declines.

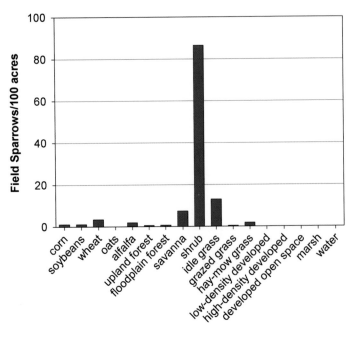

5.141. Average density (birds per 100 acres) of Field Sparrows in various habitats from 2000s transect surveys.

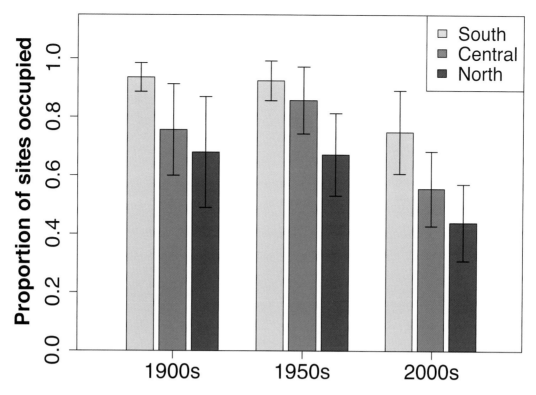

5.142. Occupancy rates of Field Sparrows in the northern, central, and southern regions of Illinois in the 1900s, 1950s, and 2000s.

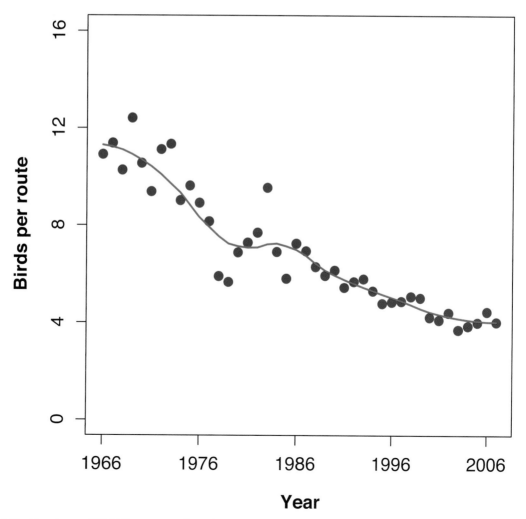

5.143. Abundance of Field Sparrows on Breeding Bird Survey routes in Illinois, 1966–2007.

Grasshopper Sparrow. Just as its close relative, the Henslow's Sparrow, is rebounding (Herkert 2007), Grasshopper Sparrow (Fig. 5.144) abundance is plummeting. Similar to meadowlarks, Grasshopper Sparrows remain broadly distributed across the state (Kleen et al. 2004; Fig. 5.146), but at much lower abundances. The Breeding Bird Survey trend for Grasshopper Sparrows, 6.6% decline per year, represents a cumulative decline of about 95% over the past 40 years (Fig. 5.147). While Henslow's Sparrows prefer the dense cover typical of conservation areas and Conservation Reserve Program grasslands, Grasshopper Sparrows favor the shorter, more open vegetation typical of grazed or hayed grasslands, or even croplands (Fig. 5.145). The highest average density of Grasshopper Sparrows was in unplanted crop fields with annual weeds in southern Illinois (not shown in Fig. 5.145 because of small sample size). Because most of these fields are eventually planted within a season, the Grasshopper Sparrow nests initiated in unplanted fields probably produce few young birds. If Grasshopper Sparrows re-nest or initiate nesting after the fields are planted to no-till soybeans, they may experience much better success. Fields of no-till soybeans with grassy residual vegetation held good numbers of Grasshopper Sparrows, but Grasshopper Sparrows were absent from conventionally-tilled fields. The nesting biology of Grasshopper Sparrows in no-till cropland warrants further study, as it appears to be the best hope for this species to maintain its population in Illinois.

5.144. Grasshopper Sparrows are a difficult bird to see in Illinois due to their cryptic nature and low population levels.

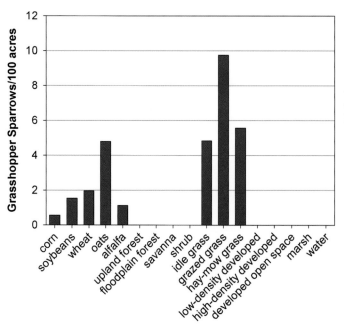

5.145. Average density (birds per 100 acres) of Grasshopper Sparrows in various habitats from 2000s transect surveys.

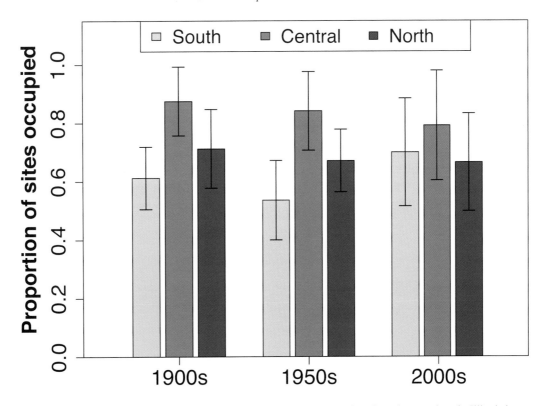

5.146. Occupancy rates of Grasshopper Sparrows in the northern, central, and southern regions in Illinois in the 1900s, 1950s, and 2000s.

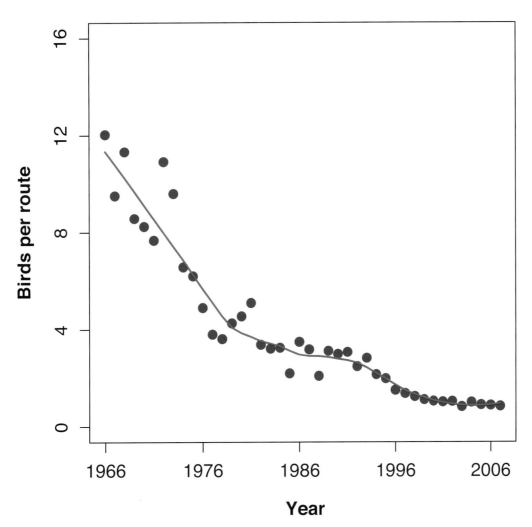

5.147. Abundance of Grasshopper Sparrows on Breeding Bird Survey routes in Illinois, 1966–2007.

Indigo Bunting. When seen with good lighting, the electric blue of a male Indigo Bunting seems to glow (Fig. 5.148). In fact, bunting feathers (like almost all blue feathers on birds) do not contain any blue pigments, and the color is created by the diffraction of light through the structure of the feathers. This colorful bird, while favoring shrublands, has not experienced the same fate as many shrubland species. Indigo Buntings are found in several habitats, including forest edges and canopy openings created by tree falls in forests (Fig. 5.149). Indigo Buntings have notoriously high rates of brood-parasitism by Brown-headed Cowbirds, but they persistently renest into the late summer and early fall, well after cowbirds have stopped laying eggs for the season. The combination of habitat flexibility and reproductive tenacity have served Indigo Buntings well, and they show a stable Breeding Bird Survey trend (Fig. 5.151).

In the 1900s and 1950s, Indigo Buntings were less widespread in northern and central Illinois than they were in the southern region. Today, buntings are ubiquitous throughout the state (Fig. 5.150). Indigo Buntings are expanding their range in all directions as their population continues to grow (Payne 2006, Sauer et al. 2008). Given the species' ability to deal with the loss of shrubland habitat and cowbird parasitism, it is likely Indigo Buntings will continue to flourish into the future.

5.148. Indigo Buntings use a variety of habitats but prefer shrublands. Unlike other shrubland birds, their populations are stable and are expanding north.

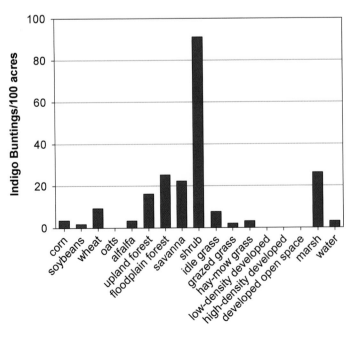

5.149. Average density (birds per 100 acres) of Indigo Buntings in various habitats from 2000s transect surveys.

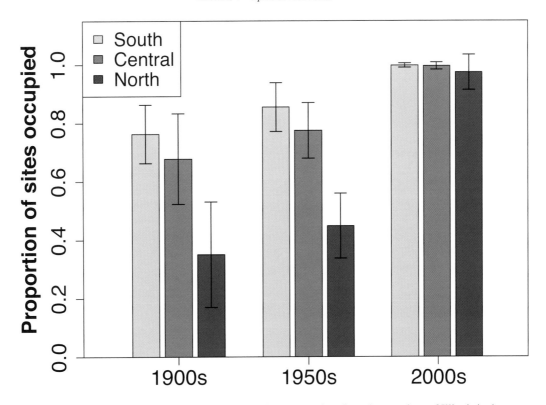

5.150. Occupancy rates of Indigo Buntings in the northern, central, and southern regions of Illinois in the 1900s, 1950s, and 2000s.

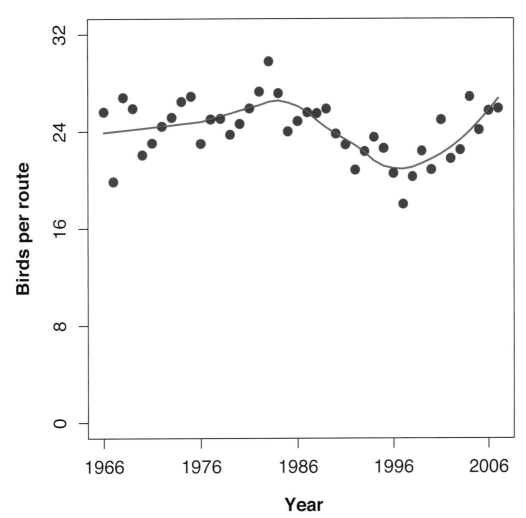

5.151. Abundance of Indigo Buntings on Breeding Bird Survey routes in Illinois, 1966–2007.

Dickcissel. Alfred Gross was fond of Dickcissels (Fig. 5.152), and after moving to Bowdoin College in Maine, he wrote a thorough treatise based on his observations of Dickcissels in Illinois, including during the 1907–1909 surveys (Gross 1921). Gross compiled several interesting statistics and anecdotes. He estimated that a male Dickcissel sings 5,000 times a day, but also condemned him as "a lazy husband and as a father utterly lacking resourcefulness when responsibilities are thrust upon him," because only females incubate eggs and feed nestlings. Based on watching a female Dickcissel bringing grasshopper nymphs to nestlings, he estimated that a million Dickcissels might be saving Illinois farmers $4,680 per day (about $56,000/day in 2010 dollars) by avoiding the destruction of clover fields. "These figures have a meaning which no one can fail to understand," he wrote. "With such a strong popular sentiment already in their favor the Dickcissels are destined to continue their great increase in numbers."

Indeed, the Grabers estimated that the number of Dickcissels nesting in the state had increased between the 1900s and 1950s surveys. Over the next 50 years, occupancy data confirm the species has declined in both central and northern Illinois (Fig. 5.154), as shown by a substantial decline in their abundance on Breeding Bird Survey routes (Fig. 5.155). Like other grassland birds, Dickcissels are faced with a shrinking base of habitat on their nesting grounds in Illinois. Unlike other grassland birds, however, Dickcissels are persecuted as an agricultural pest on their wintering grounds in Venezuela where the "rice birds" (as they are known) are shot, trapped, and sprayed with harmful chemicals (Basili and Temple 1999). Winter flocks may number millions of birds, and they can be a serious economic problem for farmers. However, each flock may also represent a sizable portion of the global population. On their breeding grounds, Dickcissels readily nest in small grassland patches, in roadsides, and in some cropfields (Fig. 5.153), and so are likely to persist in Illinois, even if at lower abundance, provided threats in South America do not become too severe.

5.152. Dickcissel populations, like other grassland birds, have been declining and multiple factors need to be addressed to stabilize their populations.

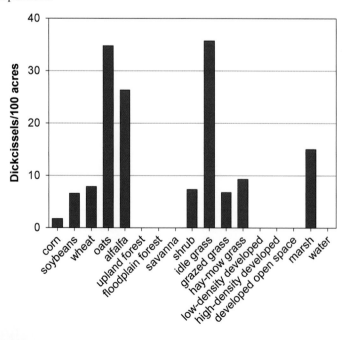

5.153. Average density (birds per 100 acres) of Dickcissels in various habitats from 2000s transect surveys.

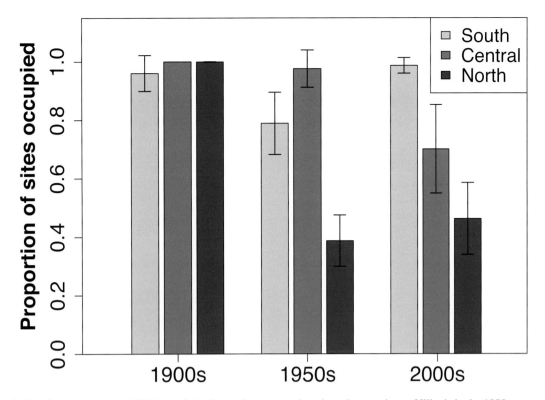

5.154. Occupancy rates of Dickcissels in the northern, central, and southern regions of Illinois in the 1900s, 1950s, and 2000s.

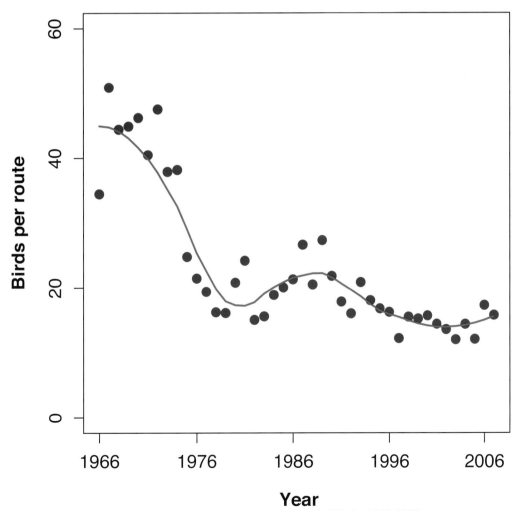

5.155. Abundance of Dickcissels on Breeding Bird Survey routes in Illinois, 1966–2007.

Northern Cardinal. The Northern Cardinal (Fig. 5.156) is the most frequent designee as a state bird, including Illinois and six other states to the south and east. Ridgway (1889) declared the cardinal "truly a glorious bird." Only in recent decades have cardinals become common statewide, however (Fig. 5.158). In a pattern similar to Red-bellied Woodpeckers, cardinals were common throughout southern Illinois, but were not recorded in northern Illinois during the 1900s surveys. By the 1950s, cardinals had expanded to, and saturated much of, the central region. We found them in virtually all suitable habitats statewide in the 2000s. Northern Cardinals are about equally abundant in forests, shrublands, savanna-open woodlands, and low-density developed areas, and about equally common in each of the three regions of Illinois (Figs. 5.157, 5.158).

Today, cardinals are a familiar sight at bird feeders, using their large bills to crush sunflower seeds. That does not seem to have been the case in the 1950s. The Grabers wrote "residential habitat is not so good for cardinals as the natural types, but urbanization, as long as it encroaches on cultivated lands and not on forest, will benefit the cardinal." We found that farther north in Illinois, cardinal populations were more dense in developed habitats and less dense in forests. In winter, these resident birds may need the resources provided by developed habitats in northern Illinois, while the milder climate in the south allows the birds to reside in forests. Halkin and Linville (1999) attributed the cardinal's northerly range expansion at least in part to the availability of bird feeders in winter. Breeding Bird Survey data document a slight increase in cardinal populations in the state since 1966 (Fig. 5.159). Even though Northern Cardinals are a common cowbird host and their nests are often depredated, cardinals thrive in all kinds of forest and in developed areas, and we expect cardinals will maintain or increase their population into the future.

5.156. While the Northern Cardinal is our state bird, the species was largely confined to southern Illinois in the 1900s.

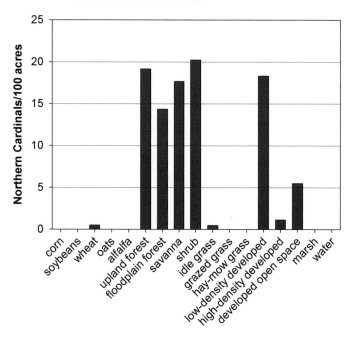

5.157. Average density (birds per 100 acres) of Northern Cardinals in various habitats from 2000s transect surveys.

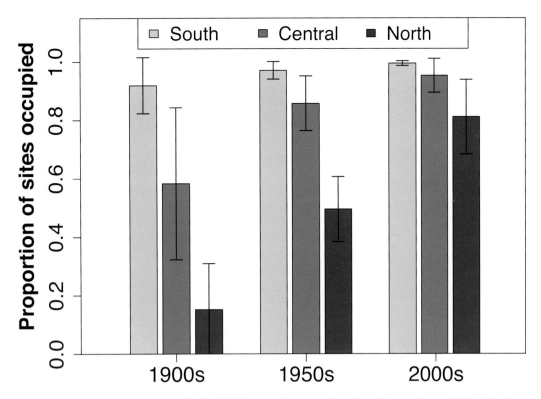

5.158. Occupancy rates of Northern Cardinals in the northern, central, and southern regions of Illinois in the 1900s, 1950s, and 2000s.

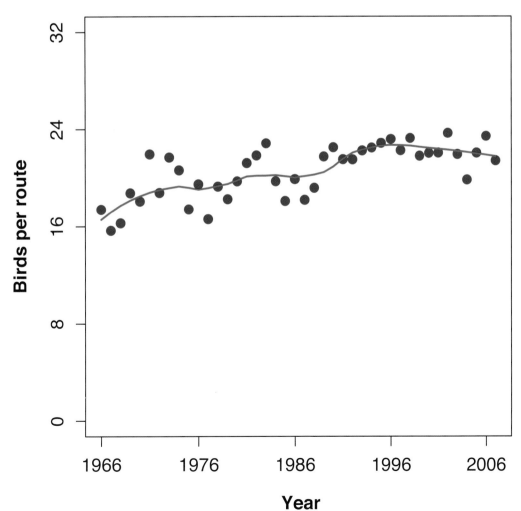

5.159. Abundance of Northern Cardinals on Breeding Bird Survey routes in Illinois, 1966–2007.

House Sparrow.

A certain traveler who knew many continents was asked what he found most remarkable of all. He replied: the ubiquity of sparrows.

-Zagajewski 2002

Though their first successful introduction to North America was in New York in 1851, House Sparrows (Fig. 5.160) were subsequently released in many cities, including Cincinnati, Minneapolis-St. Paul, Salt Lake City, and San Francisco for the purpose of insect control (Lowther and Cink 2006). House Sparrows arrived in Illinois in the 1870s. By the 1880s, House Sparrows were recognized as a pest for consuming livestock feed, competing with native species such as the bluebird, and simply being messy and annoying through their abundance. In 1891, Illinois started a bounty program to aid in their eradication but the program achieved little (Musselman 1921). At the time of the Gross and Ray surveys, House Sparrows were the most abundant bird in the state.

5.160. House Sparrows were probably the most common bird in Illinois in the 1900s. Over the past several decades, their populations have declined.

The shift from horses to motorized transportation in the early twentieth century is seen as a turning point to the detriment of House Sparrows and the benefit of the new invader, European Starlings. Stables, hay, and grain provided perfect nest sites, nesting material, and food for House Sparrows. Our occupancy data (Fig. 5.162) and the Breeding Bird Survey confirm the gradual decline in House Sparrow abundance across Illinois (Fig. 5.163). Although the House Sparrow population may be declining, they remain a very common sight throughout Illinois. House Sparrows were the 5th most frequently counted bird, following Common Grackles, in our 2000s surveys. House Sparrows were about eight times more abundant in developed areas than other habitats (Fig. 5.161).

The House Sparrow is experiencing dramatic declines around the world, and has an "Unfavourable Conservation Status" in Europe (BirdLife International 2004). While the decline of any species is concerning, the drop-off of a species that has adapted to living on every continent except Antarctica and numbering in the hundreds of millions worldwide is particularly alarming. The leading hypothesis for their decline is change in agricultural practices, which might explain why the species is declining in Illinois.

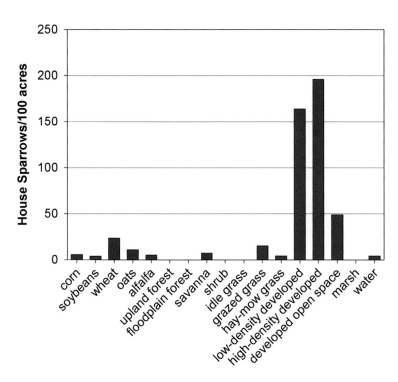

5.161. Average density (birds per 100 acres) of House Sparrows in various habitats from 2000s transect surveys.

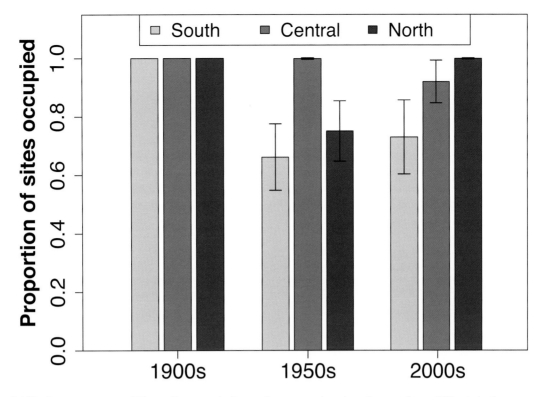

5.162. Occupancy rates of House Sparrows in the northern, central, and southern regions of Illinois in the 1900s, 1950s, and 2000s.

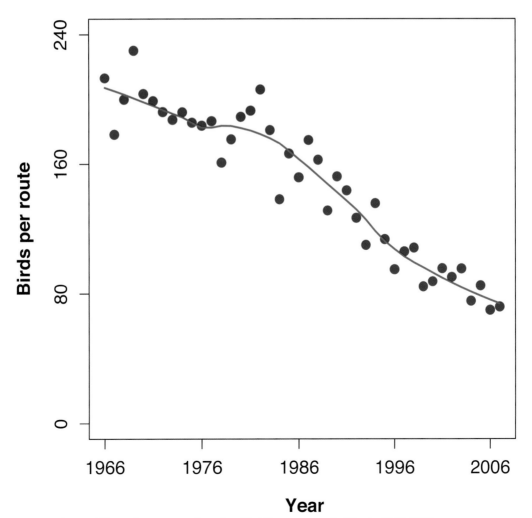

5.163. Abundance of House Sparrows on Breeding Bird Survey routes in Illinois, 1966–2007.

COMMON TRENDS AMONG BIRDS USING SIMILAR HABITATS

Grasslands. Conservationists have long been aware that grassland birds were experiencing the steepest and most widespread declines in abundance of any habitat group. Over the 42-year interval from 1966 to 2007, most grassland birds showed a cumulative loss of 40% to 90% of their population in Illinois (Fig. 5.165). Across the Midwest, declines of grassland birds have closely tracked the availability of hay and pasture (Herkert et al. 1996). The Upland Sandpiper has been virtually extirpated from the Illinois landscape (Fig. 5.167) and is now rarely found outside the few conservation areas in the state. However, most grassland birds (Fig. 5.166), such as meadowlarks, are still widespread though at much lower densities than in the past (Fig. 5.132).

Recently, populations of many grassland birds have stabilized due to a number of factors. Conservation actions,

including the Conservation Reserve Program, have helped; and the most compelling evidence is the case of the Henslow's Sparrow in Illinois (Herkert 2007). Much of the hay and pasture that could be converted to cropland has been converted, so the rate of habitat loss for grassland birds has slowed. Finally, several grassland birds persist at low densities in cropland (Fig. 5.164), but whether the populations of these birds in cropland are self-sustaining is unclear. Grassland birds have received considerable attention, but with reforestation in eastern North America, agricultural intensification in the Midwest and Great Plains, and degradation of western rangelands continuing, grassland and grassland-shrublands birds are expected to be an on-going conservation crisis in the twenty-first century (Brennan and Kuvlesky 2005).

5.164. Grasshopper Sparrows are most common in grasslands but nest in low densities in no-till crops.

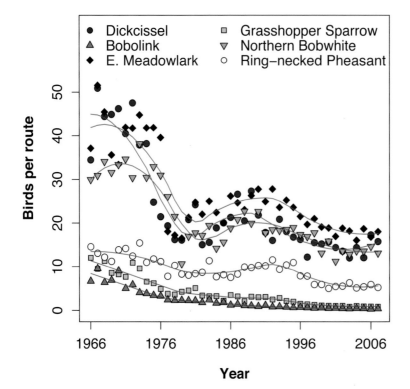

5.165. Abundance of selected grassland birds on Breeding Bird Survey routes in Illinois, 1966–2007. The slight increases in the mid-1980s correspond with the advent of the Farm Bill's Conservation Reserve Program.

5.166. The Grabers estimated there were 200,000 Upland Sandpipers in the state in the 1950s, but today the species is endangered.

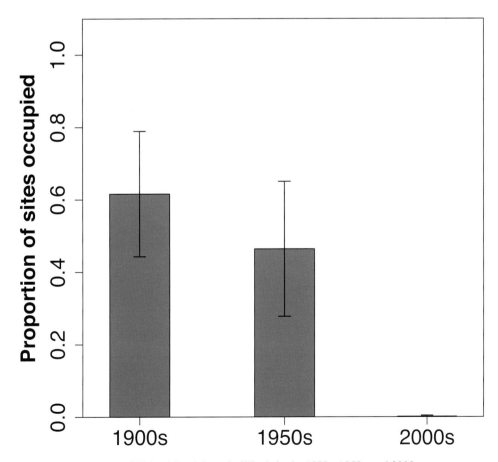

5.167. Occupancy rates of Upland Sandpipers in Illinois in the 1900s, 1950s, and 2000s.

Shrublands and Savannas. Unlike grassland birds, which weathered changes to the Illinois landscape fairly well for the first half of the twentieth century, several shrubland and savanna species appear to have been declining for a century (e.g., Brown Thrashers, Red-headed Woodpeckers, and Field Sparrows, Fig. 5.169). At the time of the 1900s surveys by Gross and Ray, much of the state's forest was probably regenerating shrubland or open woodland because of timber harvesting in the late 1800s (Fig. 5.172). Shrubland and open woodland habitats subsequently declined over the landscape as they recovered into forests over the following decades, as happened all across eastern North America (Askins 2000). The elimination of wooded fence rows and other shrubby habitats, to accommodate larger agricultural fields and development, accelerated in the 1950s (Vance 1976). Today, shrublands, savannas, and their characteristic birds are scarce over much of Illinois (Figs. 5.168, 5.171).

On the other hand, some shrubland and savanna birds are thriving. Indigo Buntings, Northern Cardinals, and Brown-headed Cowbirds are commonly found in forests and other habitats and not narrowly restricted to shrublands or savannas. Chipping Sparrows and Field Sparrows, two closely related and ecologically similar birds, have slightly different habitat preferences and very different population trends. Chipping Sparrows thrive in low-density developed areas and park-like settings and have a rapidly increasing population, whereas Field Sparrows, which are closely tied to shrublands, have a negative population trend (Fig. 5.170). The ability of some birds to use other habitats has enabled them to maintain or increase their populations in spite of reductions in shrublands and savannas.

Unfortunately for the shrubland birds with sharply declining Breeding Bird Survey trends (Fig. 5.169), they have not received the same conservation attention as grassland birds. There has been comparatively little research into managing shrublands, designing reserves for shrubland birds, or developing programs to establish and maintain shrubland habitat as there has been for grasslands, forests, and wetlands.

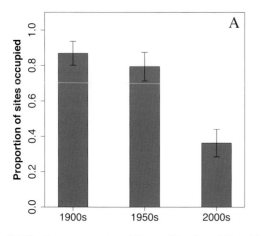
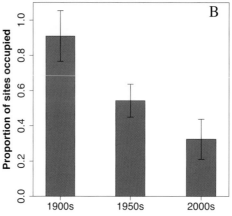

5.168. Occupancy rates of Brown Thrashers (A) and Eastern Towhees (B, C) in the 1900s, 1950s, and 2000s.

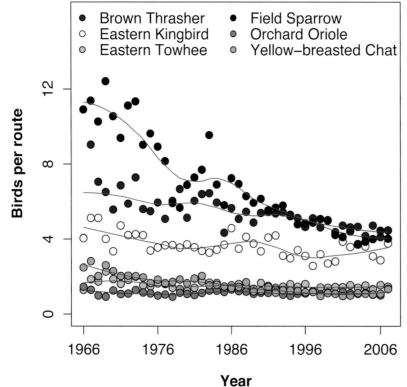

5.169. Abundance of selected shrubland birds on Breeding Bird Survey routes in Illinois, 1966–2007.

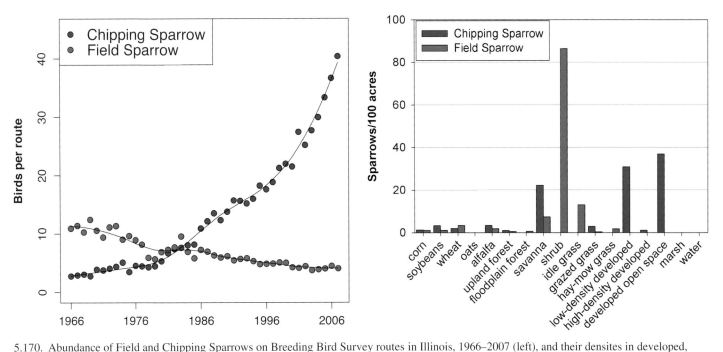

5.170. Abundance of Field and Chipping Sparrows on Breeding Bird Survey routes in Illinois, 1966–2007 (left), and their densites in developed, shrubland, and other habitats (right).

5.171. Black-billed Cuckoos have recently been listed as threatened in the state. This shrubland species is often found in areas with outbreaks of tent caterpillars.

5.172. Gross and Ray ran across many shrublands including habitat they called "sassafras thickets." This photograph was taken two miles northeast of Golconda in Pope County. In the 2000s we very rarely encountered shrublands that were not either on public property or enrolled in the Conservation Reserve Program.

Forests. To some extent, the bad news for birds of savannas and shrublands has been good news for forest birds. Over the past 90 years, the amount of forest in Illinois has been steadily increasing, owing to the gradual maturation of younger shrubby stages with open canopies. These changes in the landscape and forest bird populations were particularly evident between the 1900s and 1950s surveys, as shrub-favoring birds like Field Sparrows and Brown Thrashers gave way to chickadees, vireos, flycatchers, and woodpeckers (Fig. 5.176). Between the Grabers' 1950s surveys and the 2000s, the forest bird community was the least changed of any major habitat type in Illinois. The occupancy pattern and Breeding Bird Survey trend of the Eastern Wood-Pewee epitomize the stability of many forest species (Figs. 5.47, 5.49). On the other hand, Red-bellied Woodpeckers

and several other forest birds have increased in abundance and expanded their ranges northward (Fig. 5.173). Most of these birds are residents or short-distance migrants, and are tolerant of smaller, fragmented forests. By contrast, Wood Thrushes, Cerulean Warblers, and some other Neotropical migratory forest birds are clearly less common now than they were 50 years ago. Overall, the Breeding Bird Survey trends for most resident forest birds are positive (Fig. 5.173) and the trends for migratory species are stable (Fig. 5.174). While forest bird populations are generally in better condition than grassland and shrubland birds, on-going changes in forest composition, such as the gradual decline of oaks and rapid spread of invasive shrubs (Ebinger 1986, Nowacki and Abrams 2008; Fig. 5.177), suggest the next 50 years will see more changes in forest bird populations than the past 50 years.

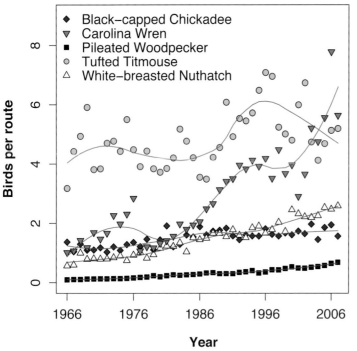

5.173. Abundance of selected resident forest birds on Breeding Bird Survey routes in Illinois, 1966–2007.

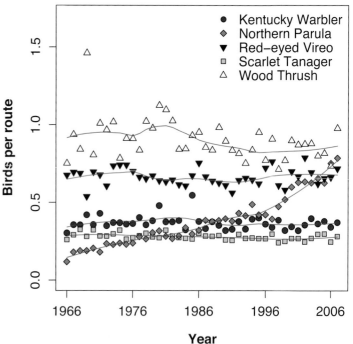

5.174. Abundance of selected migratory forest birds on Breeding Bird Survey routes in Illinois, 1966–2007.

5.175. Forest nesting Mississippi Kites have become more common in Illinois, though not to the same extent as Red-shouldered and Cooper's Hawks.

5.176. The typical forest encountered by Gross and Ray was a young forest and often the understory was rather open. This photograph was ½ mile east of Mulkeytown, Franklin County.

5.177. Many of Illinois's forests are invaded by exotic species. This forest in northern Illinois is choked with buckthorn and honeysuckle. Exotic species such as buckthorn, honeysuckle, and garlic mustard fundamentally alter the structure of the forest floor and have a negative effect on species such as the Ovenbird and Veery.

Wetlands. Several birds of wetlands and open water habitats have increased dramatically in abundance since the 1950s surveys. We encountered herons, egrets, cormorants, and waterfowl far more often while surveying wetland habitats in the 2000s than the Grabers did in the 1950s; these data are supported by the population trends derived from the Breeding Bird Survey (Fig. 5.179). Improvement in water quality attributable to the Clean Water Act was one factor in these recoveries, though Canada Geese, Bald Eagles, Great Blue Herons, and Sandhill Cranes have also proven to be much more adaptable to living near people than imagined a half-century ago (Fig. 5.178). Although stressed by invasive plants, sedimentation, and altered water levels (Spyreas et al. 2004), Illinois has a fairly extensive reserve network of wetlands, particularly along the Illinois and Mississippi rivers. Wetland restoration has partially offset the loss of natural wetlands to development and agriculture, though restored wetlands often do not match the diversity and quality of habitats found in natural wetlands.

5.178. Ring-billed Gulls are one of the many species to have increased due to their ability to adapt to habitat changes and improvements in water quality.

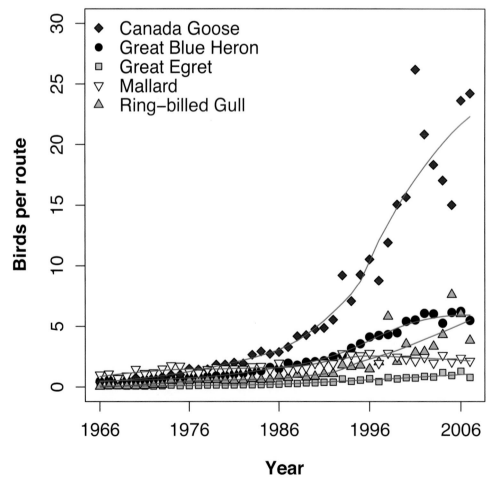

5.179. Abundance of birds of open water on Breeding Bird Survey routes in Illinois, 1966–2007.

Marshes. Shallow wetlands with herbaceous vegetation are rare in Illinois, and the birds found only in marshes appear to have become permanently "conservation reliant" (Scott et al. 2010), Black Terns, King Rails, American Bitterns, and Yellow-headed Blackbirds, all endangered in Illinois, only persist in Illinois through the continued management of a small number of marshes. Although these surveys and the Breeding Bird Survey do not have the resolution to estimate population trends for most wetland birds, the Northeast Illinois Wetland Bird Survey has been monitoring wetland birds for almost 30 years. This survey has found that most wetland birds are declining at alarming rates. Only Mute Swans and Sandhill Cranes have had increasing populations while species such as Common Moorhen, American Coot, Sora, Virginia Rail, Black Tern, and Yellow-headed Blackbird are all declining (Ward et al. 2010a). The most likely reason for this decline is the loss of high-quality wetlands which is likely exacerbated by the altered hydrology often associated with development (Fig 5.181).

5.180. Common Moorhens, while never common in the state, are currently relegated to a handful of wetlands.

5.181. Redwing Slough (the wetland in the center of the map), near Antioch in Lake County, was sampled by both the Grabers in the 1950s and by us in the 2000s. In both time periods, this was one of the best wetlands in the state, and in the 2000s it contained the only Common Moorhens, Least Bitterns, and Black Terns found during the survey. While the wetland remains in good condition, development in the area is a potential threat, as highlighted in these two aerial images (left 1954, right 2007).

Developed Areas. Birds that have adapted to living near people are thriving (Fig. 5.183), with a few exceptions. Common Nighthawks, Chimney Swifts, and House Sparrows are declining, though it is not clear whether changes in their urban habitats are to blame. During this study, we repeatedly found a pattern whereby use of developed habitats by a species was associated with its northward or southward range expansion or overall increase in abundance. House Wrens, found almost exclusively in developed areas in southern Illinois, are expanding their range southward (Fig. 5.66). Northern Cardinals show the same pattern, but from south to north. The dramatic increase in abundance of American Robins since the 1950s coincides with a shift in the highest densities of robins from forests to developed areas (see next section).

Developed areas also may play the same role in the establishment and range expansion of introduced birds. Rock Pigeons (Fig. 5.184), Eurasian Collared-Doves, European Starlings, House Finches, Eurasian Tree Sparrows, and House Sparrows are all most common in developed areas in Illinois. Developed areas have lower bird species diversity than other habitats, though the total number of individual birds in a given area tends to be quite high. Less competition with other species of birds, less severe climate conditions, or the novel resources available in developed areas (e.g., ornamental fruiting trees, bird houses/structures, bird feeders; Fig. 5.182) may be to the advantage of some birds, allowing them to expand their ranges or become established via developed areas. Because the amount of

M. Jeffords

5.182. Feeding birds does not completely explain the increase in certain species in developed areas, primarily because many species were increasing before bird feeding became popular. Bird feeding probably benefits certain species in developed areas.

developed habitats will surely grow in the future (Fig. 5.185), it is important to understand the population dynamics of birds in these habitats. We are already observing how certain species may be maintained in public lands in urban landscapes (e.g., Bobolinks in northeast Illinois grasslands). Conserving birds in an urban context will be more commonplace, as well as more necessary, in the future.

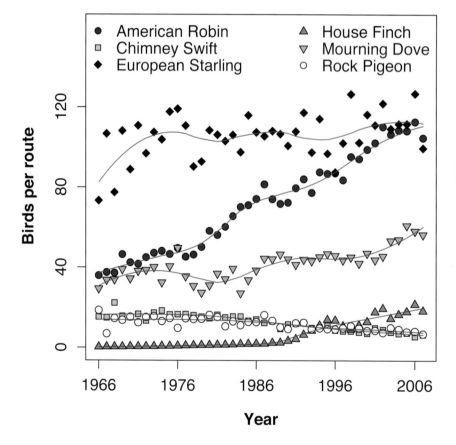

5.183. Abundance of birds of developed areas on Breeding Bird Survey routes in Illinois, 1966–2007.

5.184. Rock Pigeons are a good example of an introduced species closely tied with development.

Elburn 1961

Elburn 2007

0   0.5   1
N   Kilometers

5.185. These images are from Kane County near Elburn. The most dramatic change in Illinois' landscape has been conversion of agricultural land to development in the northern portion of the state. The development of residential areas changes the bird community, and these areas are often dominated by American Robins, Mourning Doves, and other urban species.

5.186. "Expedition" to St. Joseph, along the Salt Fork River. While A. O. Gross considered this an expedition, St. Joseph is only about 15 miles from the INHS bulding, and is currently about a 20 minute automobile ride.

Section VI
LOOKING BACK, MOVING FORWARD: BIRD POPULATIONS AND CONSERVATION IN THE TWENTY-FIRST CENTURY

While Gross and Ray were traversing Illinois, many seminal events in conservation were taking place. Gifford Pinchot, the first Chief of the U.S. Forest Service, was the first to use the term "conservation," meaning the management of natural resources. President Theodore Roosevelt set forth sweeping policies to create the National Wildlife Refuge System and National Forests. This interest in natural resource conservation was largely in response to great abuses to the land and wildlife. In Illinois, birds such as the Eskimo Curlew, Passenger Pigeon, and Carolina Parakeet had recently been extirpated by market hunting and unrestricted persecution. In 1900, the Lacey Act made it illegal to transport wildlife across state lines, essentially ending market hunting. The Migratory Bird Treaty Act of 1918 made it illegal to pursue, hunt, take, capture, kill, or sell migratory birds.

Shortly after the Grabers repeated this survey in the 1950s, Rachel Carson's 1962 book, *Silent Spring,* brought attention to the plight of many birds caused by DDT and other chemicals. The federal Endangered Species Act of 1973 provided additional protection to critically imperiled birds including the Bald Eagle. Given all of these protections and conservation measures, we might expect that bird abundance and diversity in Illinois should have steadily increased since Gross and Ray's surveys to the present.

Without question there have been conservation successes. Only one bird, the Bachman's Sparrow, has been completely extirpated from the state since 1906. One reason why so few species have been lost is the remarkable efforts that have been directed to conserve certain birds. Legal protection and species-specific actions, like nesting platforms and reintroductions, have brought Canada Geese, Wood Ducks, Wild Turkeys, and Bald Eagles back as common nesting birds in Illinois.

Over the past century, conservation organizations such as the Illinois Department of Natural Resources, U.S. Fish and Wildlife Service, The Nature Conservancy, Illinois Audubon Society, and many others have successfully preserved over 1.5 million acres of bird habitat in Illinois (U.S. Geological Survey 2010). These acquisitions have been effective in conserving many birds, such as Greater Prairie-Chickens that now remain in Illinois only on land purchased and managed for them. Several wetland species (e.g., Yellow-headed Blackbirds, Common Moorhens, Black Terns) also are located almost exclusively on dedicated conservation lands. Although it is encouraging that public resources are used to conserve many species, over 95% of the land area in Illinois is privately owned. It is the people of Illinois who will determine the fate of birds in the state over the next century.

Evaluating how Illinois' bird community has changed over the last century is a complex task, but one of the simplest approaches is to look at which birds in Illinois had increasing, decreasing, or stable occupancy rates (Fig. 6.1). We considered a species' occupancy rate to have meaningfully changed if the standard errors of the occupancy rates of the 1900s and the 2000s did not overlap. Because some species had very low sample sizes during certain time periods (and therefore large standard errors), we included other species with occupancy rate changes of more than 20%. Eighty of the 133 species detected were encountered often enough to estimate how their populations changed over the past century. Overall, a third of the 80 species had stable occupancy rates between the 1900s and 2000s, and slightly more species exhibited increases than decreases. The greater proportion of species with increasing occupancy patterns is attributed to introduced species that were either absent or present in low numbers in the 1900s, and the range expansion of several species (e.g., swallows, woodpeckers, Northern Cardinals).

To provide more detail about how different portions of the state faired in terms of species occupancy, we examined changes in occupancy between the 1900s and 2000s for the northern, central, and southern portions of Illinois (Fig. 6.1). While there have been tremendous landscape changes in the northern, central, and southern portions of the state, each region had roughly the same proportion of species with declining occupancy. The northern region exhibited the most stability. The central had the most species with increasing occupancy rates, probably due to northward and southward range expansions. While roughly the same number of species have increased, decreased, and held stable over the past century, we identified some common traits among groups of species that increased, decreased, experienced "dips" (lower occupancy in the 1950s), or were stable (Figs. 6.3-6.5).

WHY DO WE SEE SIMILAR OCCUPANCY PATTERNS FOR GROUPS OF BIRDS?

Although looking at increasing or decreasing occupancy provides some guidance for conservation priorities, it is much more important to understand the underlying causes of population changes over time. This study does not fully resolve what has been driving the changes in all bird populations over the past century, but implicates several factors. We explore how changes in land use, environmental contaminants (e.g., DDT), invasive species, species' behavior, and climate have affected bird populations over the past century.

Land Cover, Land Use Changes. As presented in Section III, the Illinois landscape has changed substantially over time. Using aerial photographs, we were able to quantify changes such as the increase in development and the decline in grasslands. Changes in habitat quality are much more difficult to evaluate over large areas. For instance, we noticed changes in the forest canopy over a 50-year period near Cora (Fig. 3.26), but it would be a substantial effort to try to describe similar changes in quality for forests across Illinois.

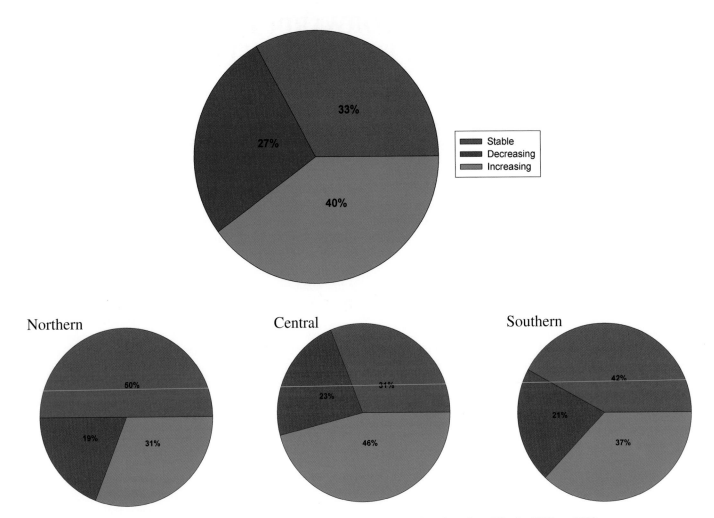

6.1. Changes in occupancy rates for 80 species statewide (top), and in northern, central, and southern Illinois, 1900s to 2000s.

Because of the basic importance of habitat to all species, and the scale of land use change that has occurred in Illinois, the amount or quality of available habitat is the most logical explanation for most bird population changes over the past 100 years. Trends for many bird species simply reflect the trends in their preferred habitat. For example, shrubland birds have been declining over the course of the past century along with reductions in shrubland cover, particularly in central Illinois. Grassland bird populations declined substantially over the past 50 years, when the conversion of grasslands to row crops and developed areas was more dramatic (Warner 1994, Herkert et al. 1996). Forest bird populations increased from the 1900s to 1950s and have been stable since, whereas the state's forests were heavily cut-over in the late 1800s and early 1900s, and have generally matured and increased in area since. Because of the fundamental importance of habitat, it's essential that conservation efforts are focused on protecting existing habitat, maintaining or improving habitat quality, and restoring lost habitats when possible.

One aspect of land use change – habitat fragmentation – has profound ecological effects on birds. The highly fragmented nature of forests and grasslands in Illinois and the Midwest has made our region a natural laboratory for fragmentation research. Habitat fragmentation affects birds and other species in several possible ways: fragmented habitats generally have less total area,

remaining patches have smaller average size, and the amount or proportion of habitat near edges is greater. The effects of less available habitat are clear, but the roles of more edge habitat and smaller patches are not as obvious.

Aldo Leopold (1933) first observed that edges where two types of habitat meet tend to attract a greater diversity of wildlife than found within just one of the habitat types, and maximizing edge habitat became a basic strategy of wildlife management. However, some species either avoid or survive and reproduce poorly near edges. Research has shown that some birds are "area sensitive," meaning they tend to avoid parcels of habitat that are small and seek out larger, more intact patches of suitable habitat. These kinds of area effects have been demonstrated for forest (Temple 1986, Blake and Karr 1984) and grassland birds (Herkert 1994, Winter and Faaborg 1999) in the Midwest. Further, brood parasitism by Brown-headed Cowbirds and nest predation tend to be higher nearer edges or in smaller patches (Gates and Gysel 1978, Robinson 1992, Robinson et al. 1995, Winter et al. 2000, Herkert et al. 2003). Based on our analysis of aerial photos, fragmentation of grasslands may be a factor in the declining abundance of grassland birds. Sites in all three regions of the state tended to lose grassland habitat between the 1950s and the 2000s, and remaining grasslands averaged smaller in northern and central Illinois, but larger in southern Illinois (Table 3.4). For forest birds, increases in the amount of available habitat have been accompanied by larger average forest patches. Forest patches in northern and central Illinois are considerably larger in the 2000s compared to the 1950s (Table 3.5). However, most forests in Illinois remain very small, and habitat fragmentation effects may be contributing to the declines of some birds, including Wood Thrushes and Red-eyed Vireos.

Environmental Contaminants. An unexpected result of this survey is that many birds had much lower occupancy rates in the 1950s than in the 1900s or 2000s. This decline between the 1900s and the 1950s and subsequent recovery between the 1950s and the 2000s, or what we refer to as a "dip," can be viewed as a positive because whatever factors were associated with the initial declines appear to have been remedied in recent decades. Understanding what caused these dips is important for avoiding similar declines in the future. The timing of these declines coincided with the advent and widespread use of synthetic pesticides. The 18 species that displayed these mid-century dips cannot be easily classified into a single habitat-based category, but they share other characteristics: they are primarily insectivorous, and are commonly associated with agricultural or developed areas (Table 6.1).

Table 6.1 Species that experienced dips in occupancy rates during the 1950s.

Killdeer	Orchard Oriole
Eastern Kingbird	Brown-headed Cowbird
Eastern Phoebe	Red-winged Blackbird
Barn Swallow	Common Grackle
American Crow	Dickcissel
Gray Catbird	Song Sparrow
Eastern Bluebird	Savannah Sparrow
American Robin	Chipping Sparrow
Yellow Warbler	House Sparrow

    House Sparrows, Eastern Phoebes, and Barn Swallows commonly nest within barns and sheds on farmsteads. American Robins, Common Grackles, Red-winged Blackbirds, and Brown-headed Cowbirds are often observed feeding in lawns, crop fields, or pastures. All of these human-associated species were positioned to be affected when DDT became a prevalent insecticide in the 1940s (Fig. 6.2). Similarly, sudden declines of Chipping Sparrows in Chicago in the mid-1930s (Ford et al. 1934) coincided with the use of pyrethrum to control mosquitoes (Northshore Mosquito Abatement District 1933). The book *Silent Spring* recounted the effects of DDT and other chemicals on birds, including mass die-offs of robins (Carson 1962). Although pesticides were an important factor in the mid-century declines of many birds, the rebound of many species is a testament to the resiliency of bird populations and the efficacy of environmental regulations.

    While 18 species recovered following declines in the 1950s, 12 species that experienced regional population declines between the 1900s and 1950s have yet to recover. Six birds (American Kestrel, Red-headed Woodpecker, Northern Flicker, Loggerhead Shrike, Blue Jay, and Bewick's Wren) exhibited statewide declines. While the decline of Blue Jays was relatively small, the remaining five birds experienced dramatic declines. Pesticides, in particular DDT, have been implicated in the decline of Loggerhead Shrikes (Pruitt 2000) and American Kestrels

DDT... FOR CONTROL OF HOUSEHOLD PESTS

6.2. This 1947 poster by the U.S. Department of Agriculture and U.S. Public Health Service promoted DDT as a safe and effective means of controlling insect pests.

(Smallwood and Bird 2002). In Illinois, Herkert (2004) found that 90% of the shrike egg samples in 1971–72 had DDT (or its derivatives), while in 1995 only 11% of eggs contained DDT. Because populations of these birds did not recover after DDT was banned, other factors such as habitat changes or competition with other birds may have contributed to their decline and may be inhibiting their recovery.

    The banning of DDT, creation of the Environmental Protection Agency, and passage of the Clean Water Act were significant events in the early 1970s that were instrumental to beginning the recoveries of many raptors and fish-eating birds, but they did not mark an end to the problems that environmental contaminants posed to birds and other wildlife.

    Organophosphates and carbamates, which are more toxic but shorter-lived, have largely replaced persistent organochlorines (like DDT) since the 1970s as agricultural insecticides. The U. S. Fish and Wildlife Service estimates some 672 million birds are exposed to pesticides on agricultural lands each year, and that roughly 10% are killed as a result (U. S. Fish and Wildlife Service 2000). The use of these pesticides can further harm birds and other wildlife by reducing the availability of invertebrates for food (Benton et al. 2002). Similarly, herbicides, which tend to be less toxic to wildlife, affect the availability of weedy habitat and seeds.

    Other environmental contaminants leave a long legacy of toxic effects. The problem of waterfowl dying from ingesting lead shot was researched extensively in Illinois (Sanderson and Bellrose 1986), ultimately leading to the banning of lead for waterfowl hunting in 1991. However, lead is still used for other types of ammunition and in fishing tackle, and birds still consume lead deposited decades ago. PCBs, banned since the 1950s, are still sufficiently concentrated in the fishes of Lake Michigan such that the only colony of Common Terns in Illinois has low reproductive success (Ward et al. 2010b).

INCREASING OCCUPANCY

Rock Pigeon

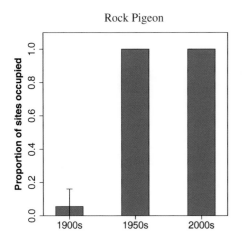

<u>Early Increase (1900s-1950s)</u>

Rock Pigeon
Kentucky Warbler
American Redstart
European Starling
Northern Cardinal

Cliff Swallow

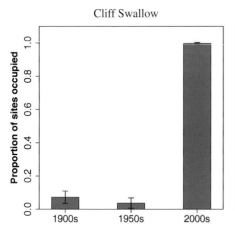

<u>Late Increase (1950s-2000s)</u>

Cliff Swallow
American Robin
White-breasted Nuthatch
Great Blue Heron
Cedar Waxwing

Blue-gray Gnatcatcher

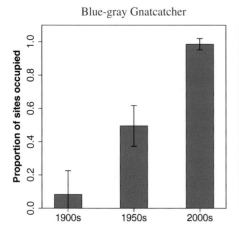

<u>Consistent Increase (1900s-2000s)</u>

Blue-gray Gnatcatcher
Horned Lark
House Wren
Indigo Bunting
Tree Swallow

6.3. Examples of birds with different increasing occupancy patterns between 1900s-1950s, 1950s-2000s, and consistent increases over the past century.

DECREASING OCCUPANCY

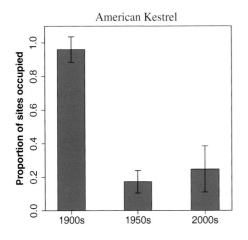

Early Decrease (1900s-1950s)

American Kestrel
Bewick's Wren
Loggerhead Shrike
Northern Flicker
Red-headed Woodpecker

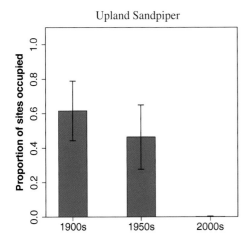

Late Decrease (1950s-2000s)

Upland Sandpiper
Bobolink
Brown Thrasher
Ring-necked Pheasant
Wood Thrush

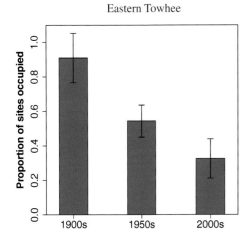

Consistent Decrease (1900s-2000s)

Eastern Towhee
Yellow-billed Cuckoo
Northern Bobwhite
Field Sparrow

6.4. Examples of birds with different decreasing occupancy patterns between 1900s-1950s, 1950s-2000s, and consistent decreases over the past century.

DIPS

Eastern Bluebird

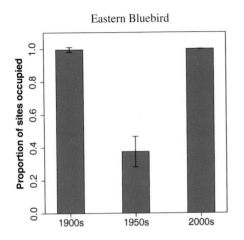

<u>Dip (1900s-1950s-2000s)</u>

Eastern Bluebird
Eastern Kingbird
Eastern Phoebe
Chipping Sparrow
Common Grackle

STABLE

Common Yellowthroat

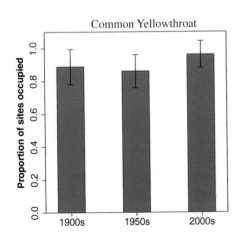

<u>Stable (1900s-1950s-2000s)</u>

Common Yellowthroat
Eastern Wood-Pewee
Acadian Flycatcher
Black-capped & Carolina Chickadee
Mourning Dove

6.5. Examples of birds with a dip (lower occupancy in the 1950s than in the 1900s and 2000s) or stable occupancy patterns.

Introduced Species. In the 1950s, the Grabers suggested that several species had declined due to competition with introduced birds. They thought that competition with House Sparrows had caused the decline of Eastern Bluebirds, while competition with European Starlings led to Northern Flicker declines. While there is some evidence that House Sparrows and European Starlings affected some populations (Cabe 1993, Lowther and Cink 2006), the declines associated with the rapid increase of starlings in Illinois from the 1930s to the 1950s coincided with the use of new pesticides. Competition with introduced species, along with environmental contaminants, may have jointly contributed to these declines.

Eurasian Collared-Doves and House Finches have invaded Illinois in recent decades, and to date there is little evidence these birds have had a significant effect on populations of native birds. While we should avoid the establishment of new exotic birds in Illinois, the conservation impact of established introduced bird species is probably best mitigated by creating high-quality habitat. Except for Ring-necked Pheasants, all of the widely established introduced birds in Illinois (House Sparrow, Eurasian Tree Sparrow, House Finch, European Starling, Rock Pigeon, Eurasian Collared-Dove) thrive in highly altered, often urban, environments and are usually present at low densities in natural habitats.

Invasive plants that fundamentally change the composition and structure of natural habitats are of great concern. Even when conservationists had the best of intentions, they have occasionally made mistakes. Several plants that were initially promoted for properties like erosion control (e.g., kudzu) or wildlife habitat (e.g., autumn olive, multiflora rose) later turned out to be invasive, and ultimately caused more problems than any benefits they provided. The Illinois Critical Trends Assessment Program shows that most of the state's wetlands and grasslands are dominated by non-native plants, and these degraded sites provide suitable habitat for many fewer bird species than higher-quality sites (Critical Trends Assessment Program 2007). Invasive plants are a major concern in forests where understories are being invaded and dominated by honeysuckle and buckthorn.

6.6. View of Grand Tower, Jackson County, from Devils Backbone in 1907 (top) and 2009 (bottom). Many developed areas in Illinois have large trees with extensive canopies creating appropriate habitat for many forest species.

While some species may prefer these exotic shrubs, many species of conservation concern are negatively affected by these invaders (McCusker et al. 2010).

Insects and diseases are other invasive species that can have equally devastating effects on birds and their habitats. After Dutch elm disease killed elms in central Illinois forests, Kendeigh (1982) documented that the newly-created canopy openings, and burrowing insects in standing dead trees, led to a temporary increase in the numbers of Northern Flickers and Red-headed Woodpeckers. Currently, the emerald ash borer is invading Illinois. If ash trees in the state's forests are affected as heavily as elms were by Dutch elm disease, the changes will be reflected in forest bird communities.

The West Nile Virus was first detected in North America in 1999 and reached Illinois in 2001. Birds turned out to be important reservoirs for this mosquito-borne disease. To date, individuals of more than 300 species have been known to have died from the West Nile Virus in North America. Blue Jays, American Crows, and Black-capped Chickadees were among the species whose populations were hardest hit by the virus (Ward et al. 2006, LaDeau et al. 2007).

Behavioral Changes. When considering which species may do well in the future, one approach is to look at the "winners" (bird populations that increased the most) of the recent past and consider whether their strategies could work for other birds. One of the most abundant birds in the state – and perhaps in North America (Yasukawa and Searcy1995) – is the Red-winged Blackbird. The Red-winged Blackbird was a marsh specialist 150 years ago, taking advantage of the large expanses of marshes and wet prairies throughout Illinois (Ridgway 1889). Over 90% of Illinois' wetlands have been lost, and if the Red-winged Blackbird had remained a marsh specialist, it would be rare and perhaps endangered today. Instead, the Red-winged Blackbird invaded upland habitats, and now nests in roadsides, grasslands, small grains, soybeans, and shrublands. Unfortunately, the ability of Red-winged Blackbirds to adapt to other available habitats is not universal among birds, and those species that have not been able to adapt have suffered more because of habitat loss.

The case of two closely-related species, the Field Sparrow and Chipping Sparrow, highlights the difference that slight differences in habitat flexibility can have on population trends. Shrublands and savannas are the natural habitats preferred by both species, but Chipping Sparrows have also begun to utilize savanna-like low-density developed areas and developed open spaces, such as parks and cemeteries (Fig 5.171). While Field Sparrows continue their long-term downward trend (Fig. 5.140) following their preferred habitat, Chipping Sparrows are probably now more abundant in Illinois than at any point over the past century (Fig. 5.136).

In the future, behavioral factors may be a critical determinant of the fate of several species. How well species can adapt to human-modified landscapes has affected past population trends and will undoubtedly affect the future conservation status of many species. American Robins, Northern Cardinals, and Mourning Doves were not urban birds 100 years ago, but now are more abundant in developed areas than in natural habitats. Canada Geese, Mallards, and even Wild Turkeys have demonstrated they are far more adaptable to people and suburban environments than was imagined 50 years ago.

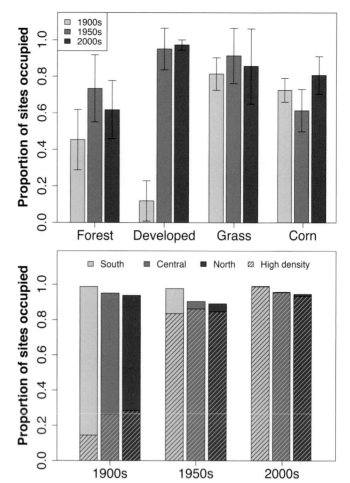

6.7. Mourning Doves are a good example of a species whose populations increased when they moved into developed habitats. (Top) Occupancy rates by habitats where Mourning Doves were found in the 1900s, 1950s, and 2000s. (Bottom) High-density and low-density occupancy rates of Mourning Doves in North, Central, and South locations in the 1900s, 1950s, and 2000s. The shift to high-density occupancy between the 1900s and 1950s coincides with an increased use of developed habitats.

Associated with the increase in developed landscapes since the 1950s has been some improvement in the quality of these habitats for many bird species. Most towns and cities eventually develop a mature forest canopy – a large and increasing habitat resource for the forest birds willing and able to use it (Fig. 6.6). Clearly the threats in developed areas are different: predation from cats and collisions with windows and vehicles are obvious risks, but other predators may be less common. Residential landscaping provides many possible nest sites for forest birds, and flowering landscape plants attract insects and produce fruit. As if shelter and fruit-producing plants were not enough, people consistently provide supplemental food at bird feeders, grain elevators, and garbage dumps. The combination of food and shelter may have provided the ideal situation for population growth and range expansion of several birds. For example, as Northern Cardinals expanded northward, winter food availability could have been less of a limiting factor in developed landscapes. On the coldest and snowiest days, cardinals can remain in neighborhoods visiting one or more bird feeders, increasing their chances of winter survival and enabling continued population growth.

Many birds have shifted towards greater use of developed landscapes (Fig. 6.7), and this behavioral change has been associated with many of the range expansions and population increases observed over the past century. The expansion of the House Wren's range into southern Illinois is best explained by use of residential habitats. In their historic range in central and northern Illinois, House Wrens reach their greatest density in forests, but in southern Illinois they are found nearly exclusively in residential areas (Fig. 5.74).

Conversely, species that either do not acclimate to humans or revert from using developed habitats are likely to experience population declines. The Northern Flicker is the most striking example of a species that reduced its use of developed habitat. In the notes of one of his presentations, A. O. Gross spoke of the adaptability of the "Yellow Hammer" (an old name for Northern Flicker):

The Yellow Hammer is the most versatile of our American birds. If all our other birds should disappear, the Flicker would be the last to go for he is the hardiest of all our feathered residents. He hammers the borers out of the bark with the Red-heads. He confiscates cherries, in season with the catbird. He is found digging grubs in the fields with the meadowlarks. If it ever comes to the survival of the fittest, the Yellow Hammer is bound to stay with us because of his ability to change with surrounding conditions.

Given that Northern Flickers have experienced one of the greatest declines of any species in Illinois, the species was not as adaptable as Gross had suggested. Over the next several decades it will be interesting to see which species take advantage of developed habitats, and by doing so, bolster their populations.

It's not just the behavior of birds that can change, but the behavior of people as well. Bird feeding has become a popular hobby in recent decades, with nearly 70% of respondents to our surveys reporting they had fed birds within the past 3 years. Putting up nest boxes and landscaping for birds and wildlife were also commonly reported, and all of these activities have the potential to benefit certain species.

Historically, hawks, owls, crows, and other species were regarded as vermin and frequently shot when they came in close contact with people. In a presentation on the 1900s surveys, even A. O. Gross showed his contempt for Cooper's Hawks:

All birds are not good, much as we desire to commend them. Some are positively harmful as is this handsome robber now upon the screen (Cooper's Hawk). He is the bane of the poultry yard and so wary and so expert does he become, that those who watch for him with the breech-loader, become disgusted and "give up the ship." Ninety percent of the damage done by Hawks may be properly accredited to him. He is widely distributed in groves, country estates, and timber and with his perverted taste for chicken becomes a menace to the county.

With strict protection and consistent education, attitudes toward hawks and owls have largely been reversed, and without persecution, most species have increasing populations. In our survey of residents, 82% of respondents indicated they would like to see the number of hawks and owls in their area to stay the same or increase.

Changes in Bird Distributions. Our surveys in the northern, central, and southern portions of the state provided the opportunity to investigate range expansion. The scale at which we could detect range expansion ranged from about 150 miles to 300 miles. Eight birds expanded their range south, while eight species expanded their ranges northward (Table 6.2). The birds with ranges extending farther south were open habitat birds, and the birds with northward expansions were forest species. The simplest explanation for these changes is that clearing of forests for agriculture in the late 1800s created suitable habitats for open habitat birds in southern Illinois, and recovery of forests during the 1900s has been most pronounced in northern and central Illinois, enabling birds confined to southern Illinois a century ago to expand northward.

The southward range expansions of several species are supported by observations in other states, as well. At the time of the 1900s surveys, Barn Swallows were absent from Arkansas and Tennessee (James and Neal 1986, Nicholson 1997). Ridgway (1915) reported House Wrens initially reached southern Illinois in the 1870s, and they've gradually extended southward over time, now nesting as far south as Georgia (Johnson 1998). In the past few decades, the Cedar Waxwing's range has exploded from Canada and northern states into the Midwest and southeastern states (Witmer et al. 1997).

Not all forest birds have expanded their ranges, however. Resident forest species were much more likely than migratory species to have expanded their range north over the past century. We had sufficient data to examine regional occupancy patterns for 24 forest species (10 residents and 14 migrants). Of the 10 resident species, two were found statewide

Table 6.2. Species that have expanded their range and the time period over which these changes were observed.

Northward Expansion	Southward Expansion
Turkey Vulture (1900s - 1950s - 2000s)	Red-tailed Hawk (1950s - 2000s)
Downy Woodpecker (1900s - 1950s - 2000s)	Cedar Waxwing (1950s - 2000s)
Hairy Woodpecker (1950s - 2000s)	Barn Swallow (1900s - 1950s)
Red-bellied Woodpecker (1900s - 1950s - 2000s)	Tree Swallow (1900s - 1950s - 2000s)
Blue-gray Gnatcatcher (1900s - 1950s - 2000s)	Horned Lark (1900s - 1950s - 2000s)
Indigo Bunting (1950s - 2000s)	House Wren (1950s - 2000s)
Summer Tanager (1950s - 2000s)	Song Sparrow (1900s - 1950s - 2000s)

in the 1900s (Blue Jay, White-breasted Nuthatch) and four expanded northward (Downy Woodpecker, Hairy Woodpecker, Red-bellied Woodpecker, Northern Cardinal). Black-capped and Carolina Chickadees appear to have formed a relatively stable contact zone across the central portion of the state that may restrict range expansion (Enstrom and Bollinger 2009). The only remaining year-round forest residents that were possible candidates for northward expansion were the Carolina Wren and Tufted Titmouse. While our occupancy models do not show definitive range expansion, we did encounter both species in northern Illinois and other sources, including the Breeding Bird Survey and Christmas Bird Counts, suggesting that the Carolina Wren is expanding north (Fig. 6.8).

Although migratory birds are obviously capable of moving to new locations outside their current range, only three (Blue-gray Gnatcatcher, Indigo Bunting, and Summer Tanager) of the 12 migrant forest species have expanded northward. Kentucky Warblers may be expanding north, but the small number of them that we detected outside of southern Illinois makes it difficult to determine. Five migratory forest birds (Acadian Flycatcher, Eastern Wood-Pewee, Great Crested Flycatcher, Warbling Vireo, and American Redstart) have had consistent occupancy patterns and three species have experienced population declines (Red-eyed Vireo, Yellow-billed Cuckoo, Wood Thrush).

Why are resident forest birds tending to increase while migratory species tend to have stable or declining populations? There are several potential reasons for this disparity. First, migrants are affected by changes in habitat availability and quality not only in Illinois, but also along their migratory path and on their wintering grounds. The Grabers suggested that range expansion of some species was caused by increased densities, and increased competition, in their core range. For example, they suggested that densities of Red-bellied Woodpeckers "level off at five birds per 100 acres…a figure (that) represents a saturation level for the breeding population in this species." By this logic, only when densities exceed the "saturation level" are birds forced to move elsewhere to seek out nesting territories and expand the species' range.

Another possible driver of range expansion for forest residents is that they select habitats differently. Resident species have the opportunity in fall, winter, and spring to explore and assess new potential breeding areas, whereas migratory birds have a tight timeline for establishing a territory, building a nest, raising young, and migrating back to their wintering grounds. Therefore, the time and costs associated with dispersing far from familiar nesting areas may be greater for migrants than for residents. Many questions remain to be answered, including what specific factors influence species range limits. The reasons why certain species have not expanded their ranges are likely to be as interesting as why other species have.

Climate Change. The climate of Illinois, because of its temperate, mid-continental location, is variable over the course of a year. It is normal for temperatures to vary by more than 100° F throughout a year. Periodic cycles of drought and abundant precipitation are normal. However, over the past half century the average annual temperature has increased, there have been more heat waves, fewer cold snaps, snow is melting sooner in the spring and arriving later in the fall, and heavy rains are occurring

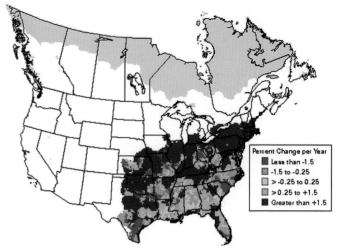

6.8. Map of the geographic pattern of Carolina Wren's population trend as represented by Breeding Bird Survey routes across North America from 1966 to 2003 (Sauer et al. 2008). Notice the blue areas along the northern edge of the species range, suggesting the population is expanding in this area.

about twice as frequently (De Gaetano 2002, Kunkel et al. 1999). These changes are expected to continue into the future (Union of Concerned Scientists 2009).

The northward range expansions we documented for several species fit with a warming trend. Permanent residents or short-distance migrants, like Mourning Doves and American Robins, may benefit more from milder winters (with improved overwinter survival) and longer growing seasons than long-distance migrants. However, five of the eight birds were expanding north early in the century before there were noticeable changes in winter temperatures or growing season length (Fig. 6.9); Hairy Woodpeckers, Indigo Buntings, and Summer Tanagers have moved northward more recently. Additionally, climate change is an unlikely explanation for southward range expansions. While climate certainly affects changes in bird distributions over time, changes in land cover and land use appeared to have a much greater effect. In particular, birds that thrive in developed habitats have had some of the most

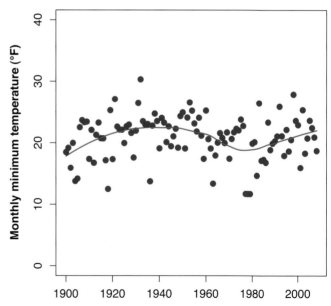

6.9. Mean monthly minimum temperature during winter months (December, January, and February) across Illinois.

noteworthy range shifts over the past 50 years. The 300-mile range expansion of Red-bellied Woodpeckers from southern to northern Illinois likely resulted from habitat changes and possibly an increased reliance on developed areas.

ATTITUDES TOWARD BIRDS AND BIRD HABITAT

Ultimately, understanding which bird species are declining, and why, is only important if the public appreciates nature (Fig. 6.10-12). It is likely that the birds present in Illinois in 2057 will reflect what Illinoisans want the state to look like. Unlike the previous 1900s and 1950s studies, we conducted a survey to determine the attitudes of the general public toward birds and bird habitat. A complex mix of factors determine an individual's support for conservation actions, but we have some indication of how Illinoisans would like to see bird communities in Illinois change in the near future. Previous research has shown that memories beyond five years into the past or aspirations beyond five years into the future are not reliable for these types of surveys, so we did not ask people about changes they had observed (or would like to see) over several decades to more closely match the time span of the bird surveys.

Survey respondents clearly have noticed changes in the birds they see around their homes and in the habitats which support those birds (Figs. 6.10, 6.11). To help guide conservation priorities, we asked respondents how much of a change they would like to see in bird populations and habitat characteristics, and how important those changes were to them. In general, respondents from the northern region felt that improvements in habitat and populations were more important than respondents in other regions. The overall sentiment was that bird habitat has declined over the past five years, and in the future they would like to see more habitat (Fig. 6.10). Respondents in the central region of the state were most satisfied with the number and types of birds they saw, the amount and quality of bird habitat in their area, and felt that improvements in these issues was least important. Respondents from all regions felt that improvements in the number of species seen (diversity) and quality of bird habitat in the area were more important than the amount of habitat or number of individual birds seen.

The three birds that respondents most often identified with increasing populations were cardinals, sparrows, and starlings, while Blue Jays, pheasants, and quail were most often identified as having declined. Most residents would like to see a large increase in the populations of pheasants and quail, which was not surprising given they are popular, recognizable birds, and people were well aware of their ongoing population declines. What was more surprising was that the respondents generally did a good job identifying species that experienced the greatest declines (Fig. 6.11). The results highlight three groups of birds that people thought had declined the most over the past five years: grassland birds, forest birds, and pheasants and quail.

Two of these groups, grassland birds and pheasants and quail, have experienced large declines, whereas forest birds have been generally stable. Fewer residents wanted increases (and thought changes were least important) in populations of ducks and geese in Illinois. While these are important and popular game birds, Canada Geese are perceived by some Illinoisans as a nuisance and this probably influenced responses to this question. Negative interactions with geese and perceptions of

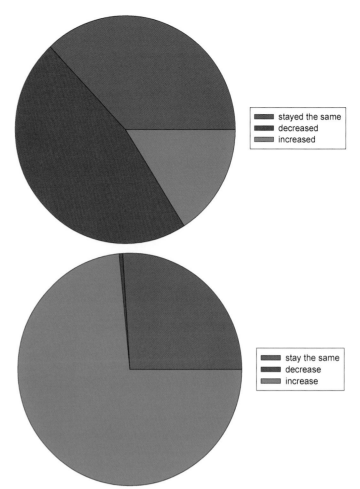

6.10. The response of the general public to how the amount of habitat for birds has changed over the past five years (top), and how they hope the amount of habitat for birds will change in the next five years (bottom).

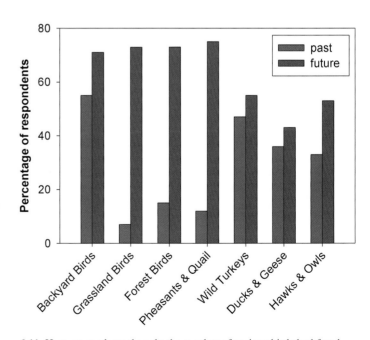

6.11. How respondents thought the number of various birds had fared over the past five years ("past," blue bars) and how they hoped the populations would fare into the future (red bars). Shown as the percentage of respondents reporting they wanted birds to increase.

6.12. While over the past century, few species in Illinois have gone extinct, many are declining and long-lasting conservation can only be achieved by fostering an appreciation of nature in the majority of Illinoisans.

overpopulation of resident geese may have led to the perception that all ducks and geese populations are large enough and have access to sufficient high-quality habitat to sustain them.

The survey did show a mismatch between the public's perception of changes in forests and forest bird populations. Most respondents thought the amount of forest had declined in their area recently, and that they were seeing fewer forest birds. Especially for more familiar forest birds, like woodpeckers, nuthatches, chickadees, and Blue Jays, our findings suggest populations of these species are generally stable or increasing.

While the public appears to have a good understanding of which groups of birds are declining, there was more variation in their responses to the most important factors affecting bird populations (Fig. 6.13). Food availability, nest cover, and winter cover were the three most frequent selections, each receiving similar support. Although each of the factors we presented to respondents seriously affects individual species, it is widely accepted that the amount or quality of habitat limits most bird populations. We are encouraged that the public understands the fundamental importance of habitat, because for large-scale conservation actions to be successful, landowners, policy makers, and conservation organizations must all understand the factors that need to be addressed to sustain bird populations.

THE FUTURE

It is difficult to predict what the future holds for Illinois bird populations. It is likely that some species commonly encountered today will be endangered in 50 years. Conversely, some rare species may become common. Although predicting these trends is challenging, our knowledge of changes in land use, conservation, and environmental policies over the past 100 years can help us make informed statements about what is needed for secure bird populations in Illinois.

Which Birds Deserve the Most Urgent Attention? Two suites of birds are in immediate need of management attention on public and private lands in Illinois: shrubland and grassland birds. Conservationists have been aware of declining grassland bird populations for more than 20 years and have developed strategies to manage these birds. The plight of shrubland birds has received less attention, and research is critically needed to learn how to effectively manage shrublands.

Although Illinois is known as the "Prairie State," prairie habitats in Illinois have been so limited for the past 100 years that they no longer function as meaningful habitats for grassland species. Following conversion of native prairies to

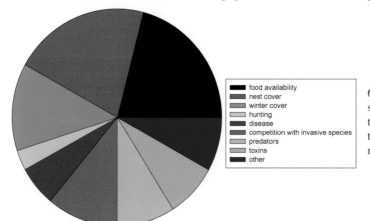

Legend:
- food availability
- nest cover
- winter cover
- hunting
- disease
- competition with invasive species
- predators
- toxins
- other

6.13. Respondents were asked which factors they thought had been responsible for changes they noticed in bird populations in their area over the past five years. The survey contained nine choices, but over half of the respondents answered either food availability (17%), availability of nesting cover (20%), or the availability of winter cover (15%).

agriculture, grassland birds readily adopted hayfields and pastures of introduced grasses as surrogate homes. The limited data on grassland bird populations from soon after the conversion of prairies, and the fact that most grassland birds were common or abundant during the 1900s surveys (Forbes 1908, 1913, Forbes and Gross 1922), suggests that most grassland bird populations remained healthy by using pastures and structurally diverse agricultural fields, which remained common throughout the first half of the twentieth century. When the diverse farms of the 1900s to 1950s were converted to large row-crop monocultures, grassland bird populations began to decline (Warner 1994, Herkert et al. 1996). We found more than half of grassland birds exhibited downward trends over the past 50 years, in close agreement with results from the Breeding Bird Survey. Although difficult to pinpoint, the 1980s appear to be when many grassland bird populations reached their lowest point (Fig. 5.164). The Conservation Reserve Program, a federal program that provides landowners an incentive to remove environmentally sensitive land from annual production and establish grassland or other permanent habitat, has increased the amount of grassland in Illinois, allowing some species to rebound and stabilizing the populations of others. Today, Henslow's Sparrows frequently nest in Conservation Reserve Program grasslands in Illinois (Herkert 2007). This example shows that, while remnant prairies and managed grasslands can maintain bird communities on public lands, programs like the Conservation Reserve Program are needed to sustain populations on large landscapes dominated by private lands.

The loss of grasslands and agricultural practices that benefit grassland birds has resulted in alarming declines, however, there is another suite of birds that are also experiencing dramatic declines. Birds that rely on shrublands and other distrubance-created, early successional habitats (Fig. 6.14), such as Northern Bobwhites, Loggerhead Shrikes, Field Sparrows, and Brown Thrashers, now persist mainly in agricultural areas with low-quality soils. Areas that cannot be profitably farmed are often left idle and provide the weedy and shrubby habitats where these birds thrive. Although many shrubland birds (e.g., Brown Thrashers, Field Sparrows) are still widespread in Illinois, conserving species while they are still relatively common is generally more successful, more cost-effective, and less controversial than waiting until they decline to a point where they become endangered.

Our data suggest that, in general, forest bird populations have improved since the 1900s and have been stable since the 1950s. Nonetheless, several birds within these habitats require conservation action. Some Neotropical migrants, like the Cerulean Warbler and Ovenbird, should be prioritized for conservation to prevent their decline in the next 50 years. Whip-poor-wills also seem to be declining for unknown reasons.

Similar to shrubland birds, birds found in young, regenerating forests, including American Woodcock, Eastern Towhees, and Golden-winged Warblers, are of regional conservation concern. Eastern Towhees, which thrive in small patches of shrubs and young forest, exhibited one of the biggest drops in occupancy. In part, some decline in populations of birds of young forests was inevitable as secondary forests have recovered from the abuses of the late 1800s and early 1900s. Looking forward, the more important consideration for this suite of birds is a process for creating new, young forest habitats. As examples, prescribed fire is little used to maintain open woodlands in Illinois, and the rate of timber harvest (both in total amount and as a proportion of standing timber volume) is low (Bretthauer and Edgington 2002).

Many wetland-dependent birds experienced large declines prior to the 1900s. Since the 1950s surveys, many fish-eating birds, including Ring-billed Gulls, egrets and herons, American White Pelicans, Double-crested Cormorants, Bald Eagles, and Osprey have rebounded in Illinois and neighboring states. By contrast, the rails, bitterns, and terns dependent on wet meadows and emergent marsh vegetation, and are regularly found on only a small number of conservation areas. Some of these small, isolated populations may not be viable for long-term persistence, and meaningful improvements in their populations will require a significant restoration of wetland habitat.

6.14. This reclaimed strip mine, 2 miles northwest of Laura, Peoria County, includes a mix of grazed grassland and shrubs, utilized by Field Sparrows, Brown Thrashers, and Northern Bobwhites. The conversion of marginal farmland to grassland and shrubland habitat through conservation programs benefits these species.

Our View of the Future. Based on recent trends in land use, population projections for the state, and consideration of new and ongoing demands for the state's natural resources, we tried to envision the extent and condition of major habitat types in Illinois, 50 years into the future. Just as land use has been the most important driver of bird population trends over the past century, it likely will be for the next 50 years.

In 50 years, cropland will still be the dominant land use of the state, although covering a smaller total acreage than it does today. Future croplands may not be more intensively cultivated, but are likely to generate higher yields because of improved genetics and new farming methods. We expect cultivation, fertilizer, and pesticides will be used more strategically in fields – both to reduce expenses and to minimize off-field environmental problems like nutrient leaching. No new major crop has emerged in the state since 1920, but as the yield of corn increases there may be "room" on the landscape for other crops, possibly perennial crops used for biofuels.

The suburbanization of Illinois is certain to continue, especially in northeastern Illinois and around other large cities across the state. Whereas suburban developments radiating from urban areas have increased steadily over the past 50 years, exurban development - one or a few non-farming homes in rural areas - is a relatively new phenomenon. Forested areas are especially attractive for this type of development, creating a matrix of mixed residential and forested land cover in many areas of the state. Accompanying these low-density developments will be an increase in green space such as parks and recreation areas embedded within developed landscapes. Low-density developments in suburban and forested areas are likely to provide food and shelter for birds tolerant of human activity, but the disturbance of contiguous forests may have negative effects on certain forest-dwelling species.

Forested areas of the state are likely to cover similar or slightly larger areas in the 2050s than today, but they will be in flux. Some forest will inevitably be lost to development, but other areas will become forested over time, such as abandoned cropland, shrublands, and grasslands. Most of the 130,000 acres of former cropland on floodplain and highly-erodible portions of the Illinois River watershed, which was enrolled in the Conservation Reserve Enhancement Program, will eventually become forested, even if it was initially established as grassland or shallow-water wetland. Today, oaks and hickories are the dominant mature trees in the state's forests, but young oak or hickory trees are scarce. Largely because of fire suppression and an overall reduction in timber harvest, both of which favored oak regeneration, scientists are documenting maple take-over in many forests: as the mature canopy-level oaks die, they are replaced by sugar maples (Ebinger 1986, Nowacki and Abrams 2008). Since 1960, the estimated basal area of maples in Illinois forests has increased 40 times (Bretthauer and Edgington 2002). By 2057, high-quality oak-hickory forests will likely be as rare on the Illinois landscape as high-quality wetlands and prairies are today.

In the future, more engineered wetlands will probably be constructed to mitigate losses of natural wetlands, to abate water flow for flood-water storage, and for nutrient/pollutant filtering and sediment trapping. The track record of constructed wetlands for providing high-quality habitat for birds is mixed. Some of these wetlands are created to perform specific functions, such as removing nitrogen or storing flood water, and designing wetlands

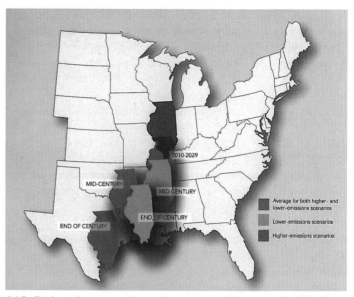

6.15. Projected summer climate changes over this century for Illinois relative to existing average summer temperature and precipitation found throughout the Unites States. For the higher-emissions case, most of Illinois would have a summer climate more like eastern Texas by the end of the century. © Don Wuebbles and Katherine Hayhoe, reprinted from the Illinois Steward magazine.

to maximize these functions may limit their value as wildlife habitat. We will need to build upon the many recent successful wetland restorations (Spunky Bottoms, Nygren Wetlands, Emiquon, Hennipen-Hopper Wetlands, Cache River) in order to recover populations of many wetland-dependent birds.

The potential effects of climate change have received a great deal of attention recently. Looking forward, climate may become a major driver of changes in bird distribution and abundance. By 2050, climate models predict that winters in northern Illinois will average about 5° F warmer, with greater changes in northern and less extreme changes in southern Illinois. Average summer temperatures are expected to increase by approximately 6° F over most of Illinois, giving the state a climate more similar to that in Arkansas today (Fig. 6.15). Projecting out another 50 years to 2100, winters could average 5° F warmer in the south and nearly 10° F warmer in northern Illinois. Summer averages could be about 10° F warmer over the majority of the state. Climate scientists also expect increased variability: more frequent and more extreme heat waves, droughts, and floods.

We should not only consider gradual, predictable northward range shifts as the usual response of birds to climate change. It seems as likely that habitats and bird populations could explode, crash, and jump as much as they "shift." Some analyses, based on anticipated changes in the distribution of tree species and other habitats, project massive changes in the ranges of several species. Bobolink and Sedge Wren breeding ranges may be pushed northward out of Illinois; Bachman's Sparrows and Brown-headed Nuthatches may colonize from the south (Matthews et al. 2004). These types of projections do not fully capture the complexity of the Illinois landscape. How will the fragmented nature of habitats, topography, soils, and human interventions affect the habitats found in an area and the birds that are able to live there? No one knows, but opportunistic and weedy kinds of plants and animals are likely to do best in a rapidly changing and more variable environment. Climate change, the character of the surrounding landscape, and invasive species will all make it harder for conservationists to maintain "time capsules" of forests, savannas, prairies, and wetlands that resemble those habitats of the nineteenth century.

Conservation Lessons. Over the past century, science has revealed much about the life histories of the birds that nest in Illinois. One of the most sobering lessons for conservationists has been that local conservation efforts may set a ceiling for local bird populations, but not a floor. Our efforts may make it possible for more birds, and more types of birds, to live and reproduce in an area, but it is not certain that birds will use the areas that we have preserved or restored. For example, if Bobolinks don't survive the winter in Argentina, no amount of restored prairie in Illinois will bring them back to nest here. Identifying limiting factors for each bird species is challenging, but critical for effectively conserving species of concern. Comprehensive plans for conservation should focus on all parts of the annual cycle of birds, including management of breeding habitat as well as migratory stopover and wintering habitat. Without these connected efforts, resources used in one area may not result in increases or maintenance of species across their range. In 50 years, organizations may be weighing the costs and benefits of purchasing habitat for Wood Thrushes in Pope County, Illinois, compared to Quintana Roo, Mexico.

We expect that more species and habitats will be "conservation-reliant" (Scott et al. 2010), or reliant on conservation intervention to persist in the state. This is the major short coming of conservation to date: we have become fairly good at preventing or delaying extinction, but we are poor at preventing rarity. The North American Waterfowl Management Plan provides a noteworthy counter-example. Motivated by serious declines in waterfowl abundance in the 1980s, stakeholders came together to develop a comprehensive, international framework for conserving waterfowl on their nesting, migratory, and wintering grounds.

Some of the key features of the North American Waterfowl Management Plan's success are the "Joint Venture" framework for prioritizing and delivering conservation, monitoring linked to management decisions (for example, an annual index of population size and number of ponds in the breeding region determine hunting season length), and critically, reliable and consistent funding. This model of conservation is being attempted for land birds (Partners in Flight), "all birds" (North American Bird Conservation Initiative, and for individual species e.g., Northern Bobwhite Conservation Initiative). Additionally, all states have recently developed Wildlife Action Plans, focused on nongame species of greatest conservation need. Whether these newer efforts will be successful remains to be

seen. The science-based foundations of these plans are solid, but marshalling the resources and motivation to implement them will be the real challenge.

The past century has witnessed several successes (e.g., the recovery of Wood Ducks and Wild Turkeys) and failures (e.g., the decline of grassland and shrubland birds). By far, the most difficult conservation challenges have been, and will be, those driven by large-scale land use trends. Although we need to continue to develop information and tools to aid in the conservation and restoration of bird populations, the most important component will be the willingness of the people of Illinois to conserve their natural heritage.

Which Species Will Increase and Decrease Over the Next 50 Years? The classic example of an Illinois bird that changed its ecological strategy is the Red-winged Blackbird, which moved from marshes to uplands. Additionally, grassland birds shifted readily from prairies to pastures and hay fields. Sandhill Cranes and Canada Geese now commonly nest in or near developed areas, but that was not the case 50 years ago. Adaptation can be based on genetics, social cues, and learned behaviors passed among generations.

The recovery of the Sandhill Crane was unexpected after it was extirpated from Illinois. In the 1930s and 1940s, Aldo Leopld and others regarded Sandhill Cranes as birds of wilderness areas. For unknown reasons, the populations in Wisconsin and elsewhere began to recover. Cranes were found nesting in wetlands in close association with people, and commonly started feeding in suburban lawns on their wintering grounds in Florida. Clearly, Sandhill Cranes did not recover solely because of wetland conservation efforts in northeastern Illinois. But would recovery in northeastern Illinois have been possible if wetlands had not been conserved and they had been further destroyed or degraded?

There will always be strong selection pressure on species to use human-modified or human-dominated habitats. Some species that we currently only find in high-quality natural habitats will likely begin to use human-modified habitats, but not all birds will be able to do so. In Illinois and elsewhere, there is some indication that Mississippi Kites are increasingly using developed areas for nesting. By contrast, Bewick's Wrens thrived around human structures in the 1900s, but are rare today. Over the next 50 years a species or two will probably "fall between the cracks" and become extirpated from Illinois.

The factors that conspire to cause large increases or decreases in populations are varied and difficult to predict. We currently do not have the information to accurately predict the population trajectories of species over the course of several decades. To generate discussion, we used our experiences

Table 6.3. The authors' choices for the species likely to be extirpated from Illinois in 50 years, and species whose populations will dramatically increase over the next 50 years.

	Extirpated	Increases
Jeff Walk	Bobolink	Swallow-tailed Kite
Mike Ward	Whip-poor-will	Black-bellied Whistling-Duck
T.J. Benson	Upland Sandpiper	Red-shouldered Hawk
Jill Deppe	Loggerhead Shrike	Trumpeter Swan
Steve Bailey	Common Moorhen	Blue Grosbeak
Jeff Brawn	Red-headed Woodpecker	Fish Crow

and knowledge to make educated guesses about which species may be the next "winners" (dramatic increase in distribution or abundance) and "losers" (species likely to be extirpated from Illinois; Table 6.3).

A few birds, like Bewick's Wrens and Black Rails, are already so scarce in Illinois that we did not consider them. Bobolink and Upland Sandpiper were selected as losing species because of their current low abundance or downward population trend, dependence on large grasslands, and because they are long-distance migrants also experienceing habitat loss on their wintering gounds. Climate change projections suggest northern Illinois will be unsuitable for nesting Bobolinks by the end of century (Matthews et al. 2004). Similarly, Loggerhead Shrikes, Common Moorhen, and Red-headed Woodpeckers are declining and dependent on habitats that are unlikley to become more extensive without significant new conservation efforts. Whip-poor-wills, unlike many forest species, appear to be declining. Invasive shrubs in the forest understory, like bush honeysuckle and buckthorn, likely reduce habitat quality for ground-nesting birds like Whip-poor-wills and Ovenbirds. Another possibility is that reduced abundance of moths, an important food source, are limiting Whip-poor-wills.

The winners that we selected, except for Trumpeter Swan, are all species currently more common to the south of Illinois, and which may be helped northward by climate change. Some other more southerly species that might expand into Illinois included White-winged Doves, Inca Doves, Great-tailed Grackles, and Painted Buntings. Swallow-tailed Kites formerly nested in southern Illinos (Ridgway 1889). Red-shouldered Hawks and Blue Grosbeaks are most common in southern Illinois, and we expect them to expand their range north. Like many other raptors, Swallow-tailed Kites and Red-shouldered Hawks have adapted to developed areas in other parts of their ranges and may become more common in developed areas of Illinois in the future. Fish Crows and Black-bellied Whistling-Ducks are species of riparian habitats, and both are likely to benefit from the ongoing restoration efforts along the major floodplains of the state. Black-bellied Whistling-Ducks have increased rapidly in recent years in the southern U. S., and because they are cavitiy-nesting ducks like Wood Ducks, they may have similar success in Illinois.

Trumpeter Swans have been successfully restored as breeding birds in Minnesota, Wisconsin, and Iowa, and a large portion of the Midwest population winters in southern Illinois. A few Trumpeter Swans have recently nested in northwestern Illinois, and they seem likely to continue expanding their breeding range in Illinois. Though perhaps not as adaptable as Canada Geese, Trumpeter Swans nest at farm ponds and do not seem to require large, high-quality wetlands. One potential limiting factor is competition with introduced Mute Swans, which are established in some wetlands in northeastern Illinois and along the Illinois River.

6.15. To the future scientists that might repeat this survey: all data and information are archived at the Illinois Natural History Survey at the University of Illinois, Urbana-Champaign. Hopefully you won't have to travel by horse and buggy and eat opposum. Good Luck!

6.16. The Greater Prairie-Chicken is an endangered species whose fate in Illinois will likely be determined over the next few decades.

REFERENCES

Anderson, R. C. 1970. Prairies in the prairie state. Transactions of the Illinois State Academy of Science 63:214-221.

Askins, R. A. 2000. Restoring North America's birds: lessons from landscape ecology. Yale University Press, New Haven, Connecticut.

Basili, G. D. and S. A. Temple. 1999. Winter ecology, behavior, and conservation needs of Dickcissels in Venezuela. Studies in Avian Biology 19:289-299.

Bellrose, F. C. 1976. The comeback of the Wood Duck. Wildlife Society Bulletin 4:107-110.

Bellrose, F. C. 1980. Ducks, geese and swans of North America. Third edition. Stackpole Books, Harrisburg, Pennsylvania.

Bent, A. C. 1950. Life histories of North American wagtails, shrikes, vireos, and their allies. U.S. National Museum Bulletin 197:182-214.

Benton, T. G., D. M. Bryant, L. Cole, and H. Q. P. Crick. 2002. Linking agricultural practice to insect and bird populations: a historical study over 3 decades. Journal of Applied Ecology 39:673-687.

Best, L. B. 1974. Breeding ecology of the Field Sparrow. Ph.D. Thesis. University of Illinois, Urbana.

Bibby, C. J., N. D. Bugess, and D. A. Hill. 1992. Bird census techniques. Academic Press. Toronto, Ontario.

Bibby, C. J., N. D. Burgess, D. A. Hill, and S. H. Mustoe. 2000. Bird census techniques. Second Edition. Academic Press.

BirdLife International. 2004. Birds in Europe: population estimates, trends and conservation status. BirdLife Conservation Series No. 12. BirdLife International, Cambridge, U. K.

Blake, J. G., and J. R. Karr. 1984. Species composition of bird communities and the conservation benefit of large versus small forests. Biological Conservation 30:173-187.

Bohlen, H. D. 1989. Birds of Illinois. Indiana University Press, Bloomington.

Bollinger, E. K., P. B. Bollinger, and T. A. Gavin. 1990. Effects of hay-cropping on eastern populations of the Bobolink. Wildlife Society Bulletin 18:142-150.

Brennan, L. A., and W. P. Kuvlesky, Jr.. 2005. North American grassland birds: an unfolding conservation crisis? Journal of Wildlife Management 69:1-13.

Bretthauer, S. M., and J. M. Edgington. 2002. The forest resources of Illinois: 2002. Department of Natural Resources and Environmental Sciences, University of Illinois, Urbana-Champaign.

Brown, C. R. and M. Bomberger Brown. 1999. Barn Swallow (*Hirundo rustica*). The Birds of North America Online. A. Poole, editor. Cornell Lab of Ornithology, Ithaca, New York. http://bna.birds.cornell.edu.bnaproxy.birds.cornell.edu/bna/species/452

Bryan, G. G., Best, L. B., 1991. Bird abundance and species richness in grassed waterways in Iowa rowcrop fields. American Midland Naturalist 126:90-102.

Bryan, G. G., and L. B. Best. 1994. Avian nest density and success in grassed waterways in Iowa rowcrop fields. Wildlife Society Bulletin 22: 583-592.

Cabe, P. R. 1993. European Starling (*Sturnus vulgaris*). The Birds of North America Online. A. Poole, editor. Cornell Lab of Ornithology, Ithaca, New York. http://bna.birds.cornell.edu. bnaproxy.birds.cornell.edu/bna/species/048

Camp, M., and L. B. Best. 1993. Bird abundance and species richness in roadsides adjacent to Iowa rowcrop fields. Wildlife Society Bulletin 21:315-325.

Camp, M., and L. B. Best. 1994. Nest density and nesting success of birds in roadsides adjacent to rowcrop fields. American Midland Naturalist 131: 347-358.

Carey, M., M. Carey, D. E. Burhans and D. A. Nelson. 2008. Field Sparrow (*Spizella pusilla*). The Birds of North America Online. A. Poole, editor. Cornell Lab of Ornithology, Ithaca, New York. http://bna.birds.cornell.edu.bnaproxy.birds.cornell.edu/bna/species/103

Carson, R. 1962. Silent spring. Houghton Mifflin.

Cavitt, J. F., and C. A. Haas. 2000. Brown Thrasher (*Toxostoma rufum*). The Birds of North America Online. A. Poole, editor. Cornell Lab of Ornithology, Ithaca, New York. http://bna.birds. cornell.edu.bnaproxy.birds.cornell.edu/bna/species/557

Chapa-Vargas, L., and S. K. Robinson. 2007. Nesting success of Acadian Flycatchers (*Empidonax virescens*) in floodplain forest corridors. Auk 124:1267-1280.

Cimprich, D. A., F. R. Moore, and M. P. Guilfoyle. 2000. Red-eyed Vireo (*Vireo olivaceus*). The Birds of North America Online. A. Poole, editor. Cornell Lab of Ornithology, Ithaca, New York. http://bna.birds.cornell.edu.bnaproxy.birds.cornell.edu/bna/species/527

Cink, C. L., and C. T. Collins. 2002. Chimney Swift (*Chaetura pelagica*), The Birds of North America Online. A. Poole, editor. Cornell Lab of Ornithology, Ithaca, New York. http://bna.birds. cornell.edu.bnaproxy.birds.cornell.edu/bna/species/646

Collins, J. A. 1996. Breeding and wintering ecology of the Loggerhead Shrike in southern Illinois. M.S. thesis, Southern Illinois University, Carbondale.

Cooke, W. W. 1915. Preliminary census of the birds of the United States. U. S. Department of Agriculture Bulletin 187.

Cooke, W. W. 1916. Second annual report of bird counts in the United States, with discussion of results. U. S. Department of Agriculture Bulletin 396.

Critical Trends Assessment Program. 2007. Keeping an eye on Illinois habitats. Illinois Natural History Survey, Champaign.

Crocker, S. J., E. C. Leatherberry, G. J. Brand, and D. C. Little. 2006. Illinois' forest resources in 2004. Resource Bulletin NC-260. U. S. Forest Service, North Central Research Station, Minneapolis, Minnesota.

DeGaetano, A. T. 2002. Trends in twentieth-century temperature extremes across the United States. Journal of Climate 15:3188–3205.

Dillman, D. A. 2000. Mail and Internet Surveys: The Tailored Design Method. John Wiley and Sons, Inc. New York.

Ebinger, J. 1986. Sugar maple, a management problem in Illinois forests? Transactions of the Illinois State Academy of Science 79:25-30.

Efford, M. G., and D. K. Dawson. 2009. Effect of distance-related heterogeneity on population size estimates from point counts. Auk 126:100-111.

Enstrom, P. C., and E. K. Bollinger. 2009. Stability in distributions of Black-capped, Carolina, and aberrant chickadee song types in Illinois. Wilson Journal of Ornithology 121:265-272.

Errington, P. L. 1934. Vulnerability of bob-white populations to predation. Ecology 15:110–127.

Essex, B. L. and D. A. Gansner. 1965. Illinois' timber resources. Resource Bulletin LS-3. U. S. Forest Service, St. Paul, Minnesota.

Evans, K. O., W. Burger, M. D. Smith, S. Riffell. 2008. Conservation Reserve Program CP33–Habitat Buffers for Upland Birds. Bird Monitoring and Evaluation Plan, 2006–2008 Final Report. Mississippi State University.

Forbes, S. A. 1907. An ornithological cross-section of Illinois in autumn. Illinois Laboratory of Natural History Bulletin 7:305-335.

Forbes, S. A. 1908. The mid-summer bird life of Illinois: a statistical study. American Naturalist 42:505-519.

Forbes, S. A. 1913. The midsummer bird life of Illinois: a statistical study. Illinois Laboratory of Natural History Bulletin 9:373-385.

Forbes, S. A., and A. O. Gross. 1921. The orchard birds of an Illinois summer. Illinois Natural History Survey Bulletin 14:1-8 + plates I-VI.

Forbes, S. A., and A. O. Gross. 1922. The number and local distribution in summer of Illinois land birds of the open country. Illinois Natural History Survey Bulleting 14:187-218 + plates XXXV-LXX.

Forbes, S. A., and A. O. Gross. 1923. On the numbers and local distribution of Illinois land birds of the open country in winter, spring and fall. Illinois Natural History Survey Bulletin 14:397-453.

Ford, E. R., C. C. Sanborn, and C. B. Coursen. 1934. Birds of the Chicago region. Program Activities of the Chicago Academy of Science 5, Numbers 2-3. Chicago, Illinois.

Ford, E. R. 1956. Birds of the Chicago region. Chicago Academy of Sciences Special Publication 12.

Frawley, B. J., and L. B. Best. 1991. Effects of mowing on breeding bird abundance and species composition in alfalfa fields. Wildlife Society Bulletin 19:135-142.

Gates, J. E., and L. W. Gysel. 1978. Avian nest dispersion and fledging success in field-forest ecotones. Ecology 59:871-883.

Graber, R. R., and J. W. Graber. 1963. A comparative study of bird populations in Illinois, 1906-1909 and 1956-1958. Illinois Natural History Survey Bulletin 28:378-528.

Gross, A. 1921. The Dickcissel of the Illinois prairies. Auk 38: 163-184.

Haggerty, T. M., and E. S. Morton. 1995. Carolina Wren (*Thryothorus ludovicianus*). The Birds of North America Online. A. Poole, editor. Cornell Lab of Ornithology, Ithaca, New York. http://bna.birds.cornell.edu.bnaproxy.birds.cornell.edu/bna/species/188

Hahn, J. T. 1987. Illinois forest statistics, 1985. Resource Bulletin NC-103. U. S. Forest Service, North Central Research Station, St. Paul, Minnesota.

Halkin, S. L., and S. U. Linville. 1999. Northern Cardinal (*Cardinalis cardinalis*). The Birds of North America Online. A. Poole, editor. Cornell Lab of Ornithology, Ithaca, New York. http://bna.birds.cornell.edu.bnaproxy.birds.cornell.edu/bna/species/440

Hanson, H. C. 1997. The Canada Goose. Revised edition. Southern Illinois University Press, Carbondale.

Havera, S. P. 1999. Waterfowl of Illinois: status and management. Illinois Natural History Survey Special Publication 21.

Henningsen, J. C., and L. B. Best. 2005. Grassland bird use of riparian filter strips in southeast Iowa. Journal of Wildlife Management 69:198-210.

Herkert, J. R. 1991. An ecological study of the breeding birds of grassland habitats within Illinois. Ph.D. Thesis, University of Illinois, Urbana.

Herkert, J. R. 1994. The effects of habitat fragmentation on Midwestern grassland bird communities. Ecological Applications 4:461-471.

Herkert, J. R. 2004. Organochlorine pesticides are not implicated in the decline of the Loggerhead Shrike. Condor 106:702-705.

Herkert, J. R. 2007. Evidence for a recent Henslow's Sparrow population increase in Illinois. Journal of Wildlife Management 71:1229-1233.

Herkert, J. R., D. L. Reinking, D. A. Wiedenfeld, M. Winter, J. L. Zimmerman, W. E. Jensen, E. J. Finck, R. R. Koford, D. H. Wolfe, S. K. Sherrod, M. A. Jenkins, J. Faaborg, and S. K. Robinson. 2003. Effects of prairie fragmentation on the nest success of breeding birds in the midcontinental United States. Conservation Biology 17:587–594.

Herkert, J. R., D. W. Sample, and R. E. Warner. 1996. Management of Midwestern grassland landscapes for the conservation of migratory birds. Pages 89–116 in Managing Midwestern Landscapes for the Conservation of Neotropical Migratory Birds (F. R.Thompson III, Ed.). U.S. Department of Agriculture, Forest Service General Technical Report NC-187.

Herkert, J. R., R. E. Szafoni, V. M. Kleen, and J. E. Schwegman. 1993. Habitat establishment, enhancement and management for forest and grassland birds in Illinois. Natural Heritage Technical Publication 1. Illinois Department of Conservation, Springfield.

Hickey, J. J. 1981. Estimating relative abundance (Part 1). Studies in Avian Biology 6:11.

Hoover J. P., and S. K. Robinson. 2007. Retaliatory mafia behavior by a parasitic cowbird favors host acceptance of parasitic eggs. Proceedings of the National Academy of Sciences 104:4479-4483.

Hoover, J. P., T. H. Tear, and M. E. Baltz. 2006. Edge effects reduce the nesting success of Acadian Flycatchers in a moderately fragmented forest. Journal of Field Ornithology 77:425-436.

Igl, L. D., and D. H. Johnson. 2005. A Retrospective Perspective: Evaluating Population Changes by Repeating Historic Bird Surveys. Pages 817-830 in C. J. Ralph and T. D. Rich, eds. Bird conservation implementation and integration in the Americas: proceedings of the third international Partners in Flight conference, March 20-24, 2002; Asilomar, California. General Technical Report PSW; PSW-GTR-191. U.S. Forest Service, Pacific Southwest Research Station, Albany, California.

Illinois Department of Agriculture. 2001. Land cover of Illinois 1999-2000. http://www.agr.state.il.us/gis/landcover99-00.html

Illinois Endangered Species Protection Board. 2009. Checklist of endangered and threatened animals and plants of Illinois. http://dnr.state.il.us/espb/

Ingold, D. J. 1989. Nesting phenology and competition for nest sites among Red-headed and Red-bellied woodpeckers and European Starlings. Auk 106:208-217.

Jackson, L. S., C. A. Thompson, and J. J. Dinsmore. 1996. The Iowa breeding bird atlas. University of Iowa Press, Iowa City.

James, D. A., and J. C. Neal. 1986. Arkansas birds: their distribution and abundance. University of Arkansas Press, Fayetteville.

Johnson, L. S. 1998. House Wren (*Troglodytes aedon*). The Birds of North America Online. A. Poole, editor. Cornell Lab of Ornithology, Ithaca, New York. http://bna.birds.cornell.edu.bnaproxy.birds.cornell.edu/bna/species/380

Kammin, L. 2003. Conservation buffer filter strips as habitat for grassland birds in Illinois. M.S. thesis, University of Illinois, Urbana-Champaign.

Kendeigh, S. C. 1982. Bird populations in east-central Illinois: fluctuations, variations, and development over a half-century. Illinois Biological Monograph Number 52.

Kennedy, E. D., and D. W. White. 1997. Bewick's Wren (*Thryomanes bewickii*). The Birds of North America Online. A. Poole, editor. Cornell Lab of Ornithology, Ithaca, New York. http://bna.birds.cornell.edu.bnaproxy.birds.cornell.edu/bna/species/315

Kleen, V. M., L. Cordle, and R. A. Montgomery. 2004. The Illinois breeding bird atlas. Illinois Natural History Survey Special Publication 26.

Kunkel, K., K. Andsager, and D. Easterling. 1999. Long-term trends in extreme precipitation events over the conterminous United States and Canada. Journal of Climate 12:2515-2527.

LaDeau, S. L., A. M. Kilpatrick, and P. P. Marra. 2007. Continental declines in bird populations and the emergence of West Nile virus. Nature 447:710-714.

Leopold. A. 1933. Game management. Charles Scribner's Sons, London, UK, and University of Wisconsin Press, Madison.

Linz, G. M., H. J. Homan, S. M. Gaukler, L. B. Penry, and W. J. Bleier. 2007. The European Starling: a review of an invasive species with far-reaching impacts. Pages 379-386 in Managing Vertebrate Invasive Species: Proceedings of an International Symposium. G. W. Witmer, W. C. Pitt, and K. A. Fagerstone, editors. U. S. Department of Agriculture APHIS/Wildlife Services, National Wildlife Research Center, Fort Collins, Colorado.

Lowther, P. E. 1993. Brown-headed Cowbird (*Molothrus ater*). The Birds of North America Online. A. Poole, editor. Cornell Lab of Ornithology, Ithaca, New York. http://bna.birds.cornell.edu. bnaproxy.birds.cornell.edu/bna/species/047

Lowther, P. E., and C. L. Cink. 2006. House Sparrow (*Passer domesticus*), The Birds of North America Online. A. Poole, Editor. Cornell Lab of Ornithology, Ithaca, New York. http://bna.birds.cornell.edu/bna/species/012

Luman, D., M. Joselyn, and L. Suloway. 1996. Critical trends assessment land cover database of Illinois, 1991–1995: IDNR GIS database. Illinois Department of Natural Resources, Champaign.

McGarigal, K., S. A. Cushman, M. C. Neel, and E. Ene. 2002. FRAGSTATS: Spatial Pattern Analysis Program for Categorical Maps. Computer software program produced by the authors at the University of Massachusetts, Amherst. www.umass.edu/landeco/research/fragstats/fragstats.html

MacKenzie, D. I., J. D. Nichols, J. A. Royle, K. H. Pollock, L. L. Bailey, and J. E. Hines. 2006. Occupancy estimation and modeling. Academic Press.

Martin, S. G., and T. A. Gavin. 1995. Bobolink (*Dolichonyx oryzivorus*). The Birds of North America Online. A. Poole, editor. Cornell Lab of Ornithology, Ithaca, New York. http://bna.birds.cornell.edu.bnaproxy.birds.cornell.edu/bna/species/176

Matthews, S., R. O'Connor, L. R. Iverson, and A. M. Prasad. 2004. Atlas of climate change effects in 150 bird species of the eastern United States. General Technical Report NE-318. U. S. Forest Service, Northeast Research Station, Newtown Square, Pennsylvania.

McCusker, C. E., M. P. Ward, and J. D. Brawn. 2010. Seasononal responses of avian communities to invasive bush honeysuckles (*Lonicera* spp.). Biological Invasions 12:2459-2470.

Mengel, R. M. 1965. The birds of Kentucky. Ornithological Monographs No. 3.

Merritt, H. C. 1904. The shadow of a gun. F. T. Peterson Company, Chicago.

Middleton, A. L. 1998. Chipping Sparrow (*Spizella passerina*). The Birds of North America Onlin. A. Poole, editor. Cornell Lab of Ornithology, Ithaca, New York. http://bna.birds.cornell.edu. bnaproxy.birds.cornell.edu/bna/species/334

Musselman, T. E. 1921. A history of the birds of Illinois. Journal of the Illinois State Historical Society 14:1-73.

National Audubon Society. 2002. The Christmas Bird Count Historical Results [Online]. http://www.audubon.org/bird/cbc

Nicholson, C. P. 1997. Atlas of the breeding birds of Tennessee. University of Tennessee Press, Knoxville.

Niven, D. K., G. S. Butcher, and G. T. Bancroft. 2009. Christmas Bird Counts and Climate Change: Northward Shifts in Early Winter Abundance. American Birds 63:10-15.

Northshore Mosquito Abatement District. 1933. Annual Report. Evanston, Illinois.

Nowacki, G. J. and M. D. Abrams. 2008. The demise of fire and "mesophication" of forests in the eastern United States. BioScience 58:123-138.

Nuzzo, V. 1985. Extent and status of Midwest oak savanna: Presettlement and 1985. Natural Areas Journal 6:6-36.

Payne, R. B. 2006. Indigo Bunting (*Passerina cyanea*). The Birds of North America Online. A. Poole, editor. Cornell Lab of Ornithology, Ithaca, New York. http://bna.birds.cornell.edu. bnaproxy.birds.cornell.edu/bna/species/004

Peterjohn, B. G., J. R. Sauer, and C. S. Robbins. 1995. Population trends from the North American Breeding Bird Survey. Pages 3-39 in T. E. Martin and D. M. Finch, editors. Ecology and Management of Neotropical Migratory Birds, Oxford University Press, New York.

Peterjohn, B. G., and J. R. Sauer. 1999. Population status of North American grassland birds from the North American Breeding Bird Survey. Pages 27-44 in P. D. Vickery and J. R. Herkert, editors. Ecology and conservation of grassland birds of the western hemisphere. Studies in Avian Biology 19.

Pruitt, L. 2000. Loggerhead Shrike. Status Assessment, U.S. Fish and Wildlife Service, Fort Snelling, Minnesota.

Raftovich, R.V., K.A. Wilkins, K.D. Richkus, S.S. Williams, and H.L. Spriggs. 2009. Migratory bird hunting activity and harvest during the 2007 and 2008 hunting seasons. U.S. Fish and Wildlife Service, Laurel, Maryland, USA.

Ridgway, R. 1889. The ornithology of Illinois, Volume 1. State Laboratory of Natural History, Champaign.

Ridgway, R. 1915. Bird-life in southern Illinois. Bird-Lore 17:191-198.

Ridgway, R. 1920. Notes from Bird Haven, Olney, Illinois. Illinois Audubon Society Bulletin 11:20.

Robbins, M. B., and D. A. Easterla. 1992. Birds of Missouri: their distribution and abundance. University of Missouri Press, Columbia.

Robertson, R. J., B. J. Stutchbury, and R. R. Cohen. 1992. Tree Swallow (*Tachycineta bicolor*). The Birds of North America Online. A. Poole, editor. Cornell Lab of Ornithology, Ithaca, New York. http://bna.birds.cornell.edu.bnaproxy.birds.cornell.edu/bna/species/011

Robinson, S. K. 1992. Population dynamics of breeding Neotropical migrants in a fragmented Illinois landscape. Pages 408-418 in J.M. Hagan and D.W. Johnson, editors. Ecology and Conservation of Neotropical Migrant Landbirds. Smithsonian Institution Press, Washington D.C.

Robinson, S. K., F. R. Thompson III, T. M. Donovan, D. R.Whitehead, and J. Faaborg. 1995. Regional forest fragmentation and the nesting success of migratory birds. Science 267:1987-1990.

Roseberry, J. L., and J. Cole. 2006. The bobwhite in Illinois: Its past, present and future. Illinois Department of Natural Resources, Springfield.

Sallabanks, R., and F. C. James. 1999. American Robin (*Turdus migratorius*). The Birds of North America Online. A. Poole, editor. Cornell Lab of Ornithology, Ithaca, New York. http://bna. birds.cornell.edu.bnaproxy.birds.cornell.edu/bna/species/462

Sanderson, G. C., and F. C. Bellrose. 1986. A review of the problem of lead poisoning in waterfowl. Illinois Natural History Survey Special Publication 4.

Sauer, J. R. 2000. Combining information from monitoring programs: complications associated with indices and geographic scale. Pages 124-126 in R. Bonney, D. N. Pashley, R. J. Cooper, and L. Niles, editors. Strategies of bird conservation: The Partners in Flight planning process. Forest Service Proceedings RMRS-P-16. U.S. Department of Agriculture.

Sauer, J. R., J. E. Hines, and J. Fallon. 2008. The North American Breeding Bird Survey, Results and Analysis 1966 - 2007. Version 5.15.2008. USGS Patuxent Wildlife Research Center, Laurel, Maryland.

Schmidt, T. L., M. H. Hansen, and J. A. Solomakos. 2000. Illinois' forests in 1998. Resource Bulletin NC-198. U. S. Forest Service, North Central Research Station, St. Paul, Minnesota.

Scott, J. M., D. D. Goble, A. M. Haines, J. A. Wiens, and M. C. Neel. 2010. Conservation-reliant species and the future of conservation. Conservation Letters 3:91-97.

Smallwood, J. A., and D. M. Bird. 2002. American Kestrel (*Falco sparverius*). The Birds of North America Online. A. Poole, editor. Cornell Lab of Ornithology, Ithaca, New York. http://bna.birds. cornell.edu.bnaproxy.birds.cornell.edu/bna/species/602

Smith, K. G., J. H. Withgott, and P. G. Rodewald. 2000. Red-headed Woodpecker (*Melanerpes erythrocephalus*). The Birds of North America Online. A. Poole, editor. Cornell Lab of Ornithology, Ithaca, New York. http://bna.birds.cornell.edu. bnaproxy.birds.cornell.edu/bna/species/518

Spyreas, G., J. Ellis, C. Carroll, B. Molano-Flores. 2004. Non-native plant commonness and dominance in the forests, wetlands, and grasslands of Illinois, USA. Natural Areas Journal 24:290-299.

Telford, C. J. 1926. Third report of a forest survey of Illinois. Illinois Natural History Survey Bulletin 16:1-102.

Temple, S. A. 1986. Predicting impacts of habitat fragmentation on forest birds: A comparison of two models. Pages 301-304 in J. Verner, M. L. Morrison and C. J. Ralph, editors. Wildlife 2000: Modeling habitat relationships of terrestrial vertebrates. University of Wisconsin Press, Madison.

Thomas, L., S. T. Buckland, E. A. Rexstad, J. L. Laake, S. Strindberg, S. L. Hedley, J. R. B. Bishop, T. A. Marques, and K. P. Burnham. 2010. Distance software: design and analysis of distance sampling surveys for estimating population size. Journal of Applied Ecology 47:5-14.

U.S. Census Bureau. [Source of state and county population information, including the 10-year United States Census.] http://www.census.gov/

U.S. Department of Agriculture. National Agricultural Statistics Service. [Source of state and county statistics on agriculture and land use, including periodic Censuses of Agriculture.] http://www.nass.usda.gov/

U. S. Fish and Wildlife Service. 2000. Pesticides and birds. Office of Migratory Bird Management.

U.S. Forest Service. 1949. Forest resources of Illinois. Forest Survey Release 7. U.S. Forest Service, Central States Forest Experiment Station, Columbus, Ohio.

U. S. Geological Survey. 2010. Protected Areas Database of the United States (PAD-US), Version 1.1. National Biological Information Infrastructure, Gap Analysis Program. http://www.nbii.gov/portal/server.pt/community/gap_home/1482

Union of Concerned Scientists. 2009. Confronting climate change in the U. S. Midwest: Illinois. www.ucsusa.org/mwclimate

Vance, D. R. 1976. Changes in land use and wildlife populations in southeastern Illinois. Wildlife Society Bulletin 4:11-15.

Walk, J. W., and T. L. Esker. 2001. Coming soon to a town near you…Eurasian Collared-doves are showing up in towns throughout Illinois. Illinois Audubon, Summer 2001:4-7

Walk, J. W., E. L. Kershner, and R. E. Warner. 2006. Low nesting success of Loggerhead Shrikes in an agricultural landscape. Wilson Journal of Ornithology 118:70-74.

Ward, M. P., A. Raim, S. Yaremych, and R. Novak. 2006. Does the roosting behavior of birds affect transmission dynamics of West Nile Virus? American Journal of Tropical Medicine and Hygiene 75:350-355.

Ward, M. P., B. Semel, and J. Herkert. 2010a. Long-term declines of wetland-dependent birds in a rapidly developing landscape. Biodiversity and Conservation 19: 3287-3300.

Ward, M. P., C. Jablonski, B. Semel, and D. Soucek. 2010b. The biological pathway and effect of PCBs on common terns in Lake Michigan. Ecotoxicology (in press).

Warner, R. E. 1992. Nest ecology of grassland passerines on road rights-of-way in central Illinois. Biological Conservation 59: 1-7.

Warner, R. E. 1994. Agricultural land use and grassland habitat in Illinois: future shock for Midwestern birds? Conservation Biology 8:147-156.

Warner, R. E., and S. L. Etter. 1989. Hay cutting and survival of pheasants: a long-term perspective. Journal of Wildlife Management 53:455-461.

Westemeier, R. L. 1985. The history of prairie-chickens and their management in Illinois. Pages 17-27 in R. W. McCluggage, editor. Selected Papers in Illinois History 1983. Fourth Annual Symposium of the Illinois State Historical Society, Springfield.

Wiebe, K. L., and W. S. Moore. 2008. Northern Flicker (*Colaptes auratus*). The Birds of North America Online. A. Poole, editor. Cornell Lab of Ornithology, Ithaca, New York. http://bna.birds. cornell.edu.bnaproxy.birds.cornell.edu/bna/species/166a

Wiemeyer, S. N. and J. L. Lincer. 1987. The use of kestrels in toxicology. Pages 165-178 in The ancestral kestrel. Bird, D. M. and R. Bowman, editors. Raptor Research Report 6.

Winter, M., and J. Faaborg. 1999. Patterns of area sensitivity in grassland-nesting birds. Conservation Biology 13:1424-1436.

Winter, M., D. H. Johnson, and J. Faaborg. 2000. Evidence for edge effects on multiple levels in tallgrass prairie. Condor 102:256–266.

Witmer, M. C., D. J. Mountjoy, and L. Elliot. 1997. Cedar Waxwing (*Bombycilla cedrorum*). The Birds of North America Online. A. Poole, editor. Cornell Lab of Ornithology, Ithaca, New York. http://bna.birds.cornell.edu.bnaproxy.birds.cornell.edu/bna/species/309

Yasukawa, K., and W. A. Searcy. 1995. Red-winged Blackbird (*Agelaius phoeniceus*). The Birds of North America Online. A. Poole, editor. Cornell Lab of Ornithology, Ithaca, New York. http://bna.birds.cornell.edu.bnaproxy.birds.cornell.edu/bna/species/184

Yosef, R. 1996. Loggerhead Shrike (*Lanius ludovicianus*). The Birds of North America Online. A. Poole, editor. Cornell Lab of Ornithology, Ithaca. http://bna.birds.cornell.edu.bnaproxy.birds.cornell.edu/bna/species/231

Zagajewski, A. 2002. Another Beauty. University of Georgia Press, Athens.

Appendix I. Descriptions of approximate locations of sites surveyed for birds in the 2000s. Precise locations (UTM coordinates) were recorded for all transects and point counts.

Region	County(ies)	Nearest Landmark(s)
North	Boone	Poplar Grove
North	Carroll	Savanna, Ayers Sand Prairie
North	Cook	Chicago, Northerly Island
North	Dekalb	Creston, Malta
North	DeKalb	Sycamore
North	Jo Daviess	Apple River Canyon State
North	Jo Daviess	Scales Mound
North	Jo Daviess	Stockton
North	Kane	Elburn
North	Kane	Hampshire
North	Lake	Chain O' Lakes State Park
North	Lake	Long Lake
North	Lake	Lake Villa
North	McHenry	Harvard
North	McHenry	Marengo
North	McHenry	McHenry
North	Ogle	Baileyville
North	Ogle	Flagg Center, Kyte River
North	Ogle	Polo, White Pines State Park
North	Stephenson	Cedarville
North	Stephenson	Freeport
North	Stephenson	Lena
North	Winnebago	Harrison, Sugar River
North	Winnebago	Rockford
North	Winnebago	Pecatonica
Central	Champaign	Champaign
Central	Champaign	Urbana, Meadowbrook Park
Central	Champaign	Royal
Central	DeWitt	Clinton
Central	DeWitt	Parnell, Clinton Lake State Recreation Area
Central	Ford	Sibley, Sibley Grove
Central	Fulton	Ipava
Central	Fulton	Lewistown
Central	Hancock	Carthage, LaMoine River
Central	Hancock	Nauvoo
Central	Logan	Lincoln, Railsplitter State
Central	Logan	Beason
Central	Logan	New Holland
Central	Macon	Argenta
Central	Mason	Havana, Topeka
Central	Mason	Easton
Central	McDonough	Argyl Lake State Park
Central	McDonough	Adair, Table Grove
Central	McLean	Heyworth
Central	Piatt	Allerton Park
Central	Piatt	Lodge Park, Sangamon River
Central	Piatt, Seymour	Seymour

Region	County(ies)	Nearest Landmark(s)
Central	Vermillion	Kickapoo State Park, Middle Fork State Fish and Wildlife Area
Central	Vermillion	Oakwood
Central	Vermillion	Henning
South	Alexander	Cario
South	Alexander, Pulaski	Mounds
South	Edwards	Bone Gap
South	Franklin	Benton
South	Gallatin, White	Omaha
South	Hardin	Karber's Ridge
South	Jackson	Cora, Crain
South	Jackson	Elkville
South	Jackson	Pomona
South	Jackson	Vergennes
South	Jackson	Gorham, Fountain Bluff, Oakwood Bottoms
South	Jefferson	Mt. Vernon
South	Jefferson, Franklin	Ina
South	Johnson, Williamson	Goreville
South	Massac	Metropolis
South	Perry	Pyramid State Recreation Area, Pyatts
South	Pope, Saline	Delwood, Mitchellsville
South	Randolph	Sparta
South	Randolph	Steeleville
South	Saline	Harrisburg
South	Union	Anna
South	Wabash	Allendale
South	Wayne	Fairfield
South	White	Burnt Prairie
South	Williamson	Crab Orchard

Appendix II. Land cover classification and analysis from aerial imagery.

We used aerial imagery from the 1950s or early 1960s and 2007 to describe the landscapes encountered by birds during the two time periods in the three regions of the state (North, Central, and South). In each of the three regions we randomly selected seven sites that were surveyed by the Grabers in the 1950s and INHS researchers in the 2000s (Fig. 2.3). We created land cover maps by manually digitizing aerial images collected between 1954 to1961 and in 2007.

For 2007 we used natural color, or RGB, images from the USDA Farm Service Agency National Agriculture Imagery Program (NAIP). NAIP images have a 1 m ground sample distance with a 6 m horizontal accuracy (i.e., inspected locations fall within 6m of matched locations on the photographs) and are delivered as compressed county mosaics created by compressing digital ortho quarter quads (DOQQs). All NAIP images were taken during leaf-on conditions.

Black-and-white aerial photographs from the 1950s and 1960s were taken by the U. S. Department of Agriculture at a scale of 1:20,000, and the photographs for this time period were acquired from the University of Illinois at Urbana-Champaign Maps and Geography Library. Photographs were not available for 13 sites in 1957 or 1958, so for those sites we acquired photographs that were as close as possible to the Grabers' survey period. Aerial photographs of all 21 sites were taken between 1954 to 1961: 1954 (3 sites), 1955 (1), 1956 (1), 1957 (4), 1958 (4), 1959 (6), 1960 (1), and 1961 (1). Aerial photographs during 1954-1961 were taken in September and October, with the exception of seven sites whose photographs were taken in May, June, and July. Aerial photographs from the 1950s and early 1960s were orthorectified using ERDAS Imagine; NAIP 2007 images were used as our horizontal reference layer during orthorectification, and a 30 m resolution digital elevation map of Illinois (created by Donald Lumen, Illinois State Geological Survey) was used as our vertical reference layer.

We classified land cover in a 6 km by 6 km (14 square miles or 36 square kilometers) area centered on the starting locations of the 1957-58 and 2006-08 bird survey transects. We manually digitized orthorectified images in ArcGIS 9.3 (ESRI©), and polygons were assigned to one of 16 land cover classes. We used these original 16 land cover classes in our analyses of landscape richness and diversity, but for our assessment of landscape change we aggregated land cover types to produce the 11 major land cover types listed in Table 2.1 and described in Table A1. Images from the two time periods differed in color and quality, so we constrained our land cover classification to visual cues that were available during both time periods to achieve consistency in our classification. For each site we only had images from a single date each year, rather than a series of photographs taken throughout the growing season; this prevented us from identifying specific crop types and agricultural land uses. Because we were unable to identify specific crop types, our land cover classes at the landscape scale deviated from the habitat types used to classify bird habitat in the field.

Once land cover maps were created for each site during the two time periods, they were checked for errors and consistency. We calculated several landscape metrics for each site; some metrics were calculated for each land cover type in the 36 km^2 area (number of habitat patches, mean patch size, and percent cover of land cover type in the 36 km^2 study site), whereas others were calculated for the landscape as a whole, taking into account all land cover classes simultaneously, including land cover richness, land cover diversity (Shannon Diversity Index), and land cover evenness (Shannon Evenness Index). We calculated landscape metrics using Patch Analyst 4.0 implemented in ArcGIS (R. Rempel; http://flash.lakeheadu.ca/~rrempel/patch/index.html) and Fragstats 3.3 (McGarigal et al. 2002). Landscape metrics were calculated for each site and then averaged for the three regions of the state (North, Central, and South) for both time periods. We used the 16 original land cover classes in our evaluation of landscape richness and diversity, and we used the 11 major land cover types listed in Table A1 to calculate all other landscape metrics and to assess landscape change over the past 50 years and regional patterns.

We assessed land cover change in the 21 selected sites in two ways. First, we calculated change in each land cover class by subtracting its percent cover in the 1950s/1960s from its percent cover in the 2007. Positive values represent net gains in land cover, whereas negative values represent a net loss; values are reported as percent cover of the 36 km^2 area. For example, if forest cover was 50% in the 1950s and 80% in 2007, there was a net gain of 30% forest cover in the 36 km^2 area over the 50-year time period.

Second, we calculated the percentage of the landscape (36 km^2 area) that shifted from one land cover type to another between the two time periods; we did this for all 256 possible transition types among the 16 original land cover classes. These shifts include changes from one land cover type to another and vice versa; for example, forest to cropland and cropland to forest. Thus, they do not necessarily reflect net changes in any single land cover type, since one habitat patch can shift from cropland to forest while an adjacent patch of equal size shifts from forest to cropland, resulting in a 100% shift in land cover but no net change in the amount of either land cover type. Such changes are insightful because they highlight the spatially dynamic nature of the landscape over time, especially in instances where there are no net changes in the absolute percent cover of land cover types in the landscape. These transitions were used to interpret the net gains and losses in land cover types in the landscape.

Table A1. Major land cover types identified in aerial images from 1950s and 2007.

Land cover type	Description
Barren	Exposed soil, sand, or rock; includes active strip mines, quarries, and gravel pits; non-vegetated barren lands along margins of lakes and rivers
Cropland[1]	Row crops, continuous crops (e.g., legumes), and hayed grass; tilled fields or recently harvested fields without vegetation
Orchard	Orchards, groves, vineyards, and plant nurseries
Developed	Areas used for industrial, commercial, and residential purposes, including rural, suburban, and urban zones and areas occupied by transportation, power, and communications facilities; roads with an average width $\geq$ 10m
Forest	Mature and older second growth forest, bottomland and upland forest, riparian forest, forestry plots; savannas with tree density greater than 66%; linear forests and small forest patches with an average width or diameter of 10-40 m were classified as linear forests
Linear forest[2]	Linear forests, shelterbelts, and hedgerows with an average width of 10 to 40m; small forest patches with diameter between 10 and 40 m
Grassland	Natural grasslands (e.g., prairies), human-created or modified grasslands, (e.g., pastures), savannas with tree density less than 33%; patches of trees embedded within grasslands were only digitized separately and classified as forest or linear forest if tree density was $\geq$ 66%; linear grasslands and small grassland patches with an average width or diameter of 10 to 40 m were classified as linear grasslands
Linear grassland[2]	Grassy waterways, filter strips, field margins, and grassy ditches with an average width of 10-40 m; small grassland patches with a diameter between 10 and 40 m
Shrubland	Areas dominated by shrubs and saplings (but possibly with scattered trees); areas with a density of shrubs, samplings, and trees > 33% and a visibly shorter average height than forests
Wetland	Wet meadows, marshes, bogs, swamps and visually wet woodlands (the latter usually along edges of rivers where presence of water below canopy was visually apparent in aerial images)
Water	Lakes, ponds, reservoirs, rivers, streams, open water with little or no emergent vegetation; rivers were delineated if their average width was $\geq$ 10 m

[1] Cropland was classified into two types, cropland with and without trees in their interior. These two cropland types were aggregated into a single class for our landscape change evaluation.

[2] Linear forests and linear grasslands were classified into three types based on their average width. Thin linear forests and grasslands had an average width of 10 to 20 m, medium linear forests and grasslands had an average width of 21 to 30 m, and wide linear forests and grasslands had an average width of 31 to 40 m. These original land cover classifications were used in our analysis of landscape richness, diversity and evenness, but they were aggregated into linear forest and linear grassland for our evaluation of landscape change.

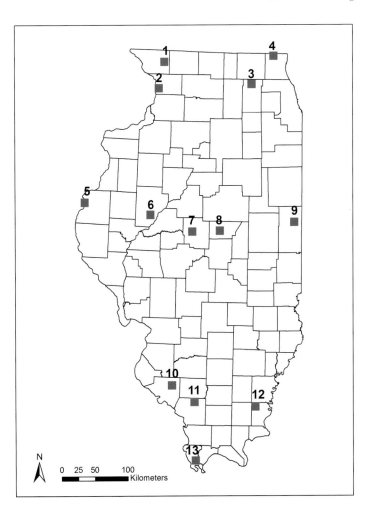

Eight of 21 sites where we assessed land cover/land use changes with aerial photography were featured in Section III. The 13 additional locations were:

1. Stockton, Jo Daviess County
2. Seven miles south-southeast of Savanna, Carroll County
3. Elburn, Kane County
4. Antioch, Lake County
5. Five miles south-southeast of Nauvoo, Hancock County
6. Duncan Mills, Fulton County
7. Four miles west of Lincoln, Logan County
8. Clinton, DeWitt County
9. Ten miles north of Danville, Vermillion County
10. Sparta, Randolph County
11. Vergennes, Jackson County
12. South of Omaha, Gallatin County
13. Five miles west-northwest of Mounds, Alexander County

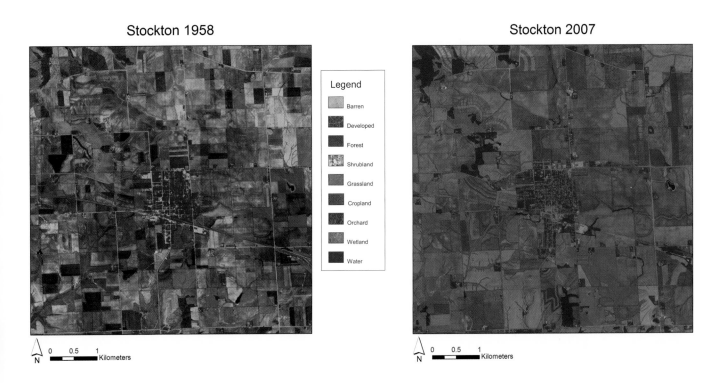

Stockton 1958

Stockton 2007

Legend

Barren
Developed
Forest
Shrubland
Grassland
Cropland
Orchard
Wetland
Water

South of Savanna 1958

South of Savanna 2007

North of Elburn 1961

North of Elburn 2007

Legend

Barren	
Developed	
Forest	
Shrubland	
Grassland	
Cropland	
Orchard	
Wetland	
Water	

Antioch 1954

Antioch 2007

South of Nauvoo 1957

South of Nauvoo 2007

Duncan Mills 1957

Legend

	Barren
	Developed
	Forest
	Shrubland
	Grassland
	Cropland
	Orchard
	Wetland
	Water

Duncan Mills 2007

West of Lincoln 1957

West of Lincoln 2007

Clinton 1960

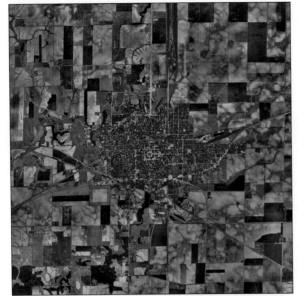

Clinton 2007

North of Danville 1954

North of Danville 2007

Legend

Barren

Developed

Forest

Shrubland

Grassland

Cropland

Orchard

Wetland

Water

Sparta 1959

Sparta 2007

Vergennes 1959

Vergennes 2007

South of Omaha 1959

South of Omaha 2007

Legend

Barren

Developed

Forest

Shrubland

Grassland

Cropland

Orchard

Wetland

Water

West of Mounds 1956

West of Mounds 2007

Appendix III. Survey of residents about birds and habitat, with summarized results. The survey was given to 1,596 households from May to August 2007, and 652 completed surveys were returned (41% response rate).

Conserving wild birds in Illinois:
a survey of your views
Results Summary

THANK YOU FOR YOUR COOPERATION!
All of your responses will be kept confidential.
Please return this survey in the postage-paid return envelope provided.

Illinois Department of Natural Resources

Division of Wildlife Resources
and
Illinois Natural History Survey

ILLINOIS
NATURAL
HISTORY
SURVEY

The Department of Natural Resources is requesting disclosure of information that is necessary to accomplish the statutory purpose as outlined under the Illinois Compiled Statutes, The Wildlife Code, Chapter 520. Disclosure of information is voluntary. This study is funded by the federal Wildlife Restoration Fund through the purchase of hunting arms and ammunition.

Conserving wild birds in Illinois:
A survey of your views

This questionnaire is part of a study to help wildlife professionals make better decisions about the management of grassland, upland, and backyard birds and their habitats in Illinois. Your views are important and give a better understanding of how people feel about management of these species in Illinois. Please keep in mind that we are interested in <u>everyone's responses</u>, not just hunters or farmers!

In order to collect the most complete information, please have the person in your household who typically makes decisions about how you use your land fill out this questionnaire. Please complete the questionnaire at your earliest convenience, seal it in the postage-paid envelope provided and drop it in any mailbox. There are 34 questions in the survey. It should take about 20 minutes to complete. We realize that many Illinoisans visit other parts of the state, however, we are particularly interested in your views about birds and their habitats in the county in which you live. Therefore, **please *only* refer to your experiences in your county of residence or the immediately adjacent counties when answering these questions.** The final question provides you with an opportunity to share any other comments you may have about birds and their management in Illinois.

**Your responses will remain confidential
and will never be associated with your name.**

If you have any questions or comments about this study, please contact Linda Campbell, Survey Administrator, at (217) 244-5121 or write her at the Illinois Natural History Survey, 1816 S. Oak St., Champaign, IL, 61820.

THANK YOU FOR YOUR ASSISTANCE!

If you choose not to complete the questionnaire, please return it with a note on Question 34 on the inside back cover. Simply seal it in the postage-paid envelope and drop it in a mailbox.

Wildlife and You

1. The following are some ways that Illinoisans interact with birds and other wildlife. Have you participated in these activities in the past 3 years? *(Please check one for each item.)*

	n	**Yes**	**No**
a. Read about birds or other wildlife	576	80.6%	19.4%
b. Photographed birds or other wildlife	556	59.4%	40.6%
c. Closely observed or tried to identify birds	583	79.2%	20.8%
d. Closely observed or tried to identify other wildlife	572	76.7%	23.3%
d. Grew food or flowers in a garden	585	88.9%	11.1%
e. Worked on a farm	552	42.2%	57.8%
f. Fed birds on a regular basis	575	67.5%	32.5%
g. Fed other wildlife on a regular basis	538	23.2%	76.8%
h. Hunted game birds	540	20.9%	79.1%
i. Hunted wildlife other than game birds	541	27.9%	72.1%
k. Other *(Please specify.* _____ *)*	44	100%	

2. How many acres of the land <u>you own</u> in this or an adjacent county are used in the following ways? *(Please indicate the <u>number of acres</u>.)*

     a. (*n*=525) **1,938** Home, buildings (including barns, lawn, gardens, etc.)

     b. (*n*=132) **4,627** Hay and livestock pasture (including alfalfa, orchard grass, etc.)

     c. (*n*=66) **1,980** Land in conservation programs (including CRP, Acres for Wildlife, etc.)

     d. (*n*=141) **27,461** Corn and/or soybean fields

     e. (*n*=23) **1,140** Other agricultural fields *(Crop grown?* _____ *)*

     f. (*n*=175) **3,743** Wood lots

     g. (*n*=97) **503** Wetlands, Ponds

     h. (*n*=68) **99** Orchards, fruit trees/plants

     i. (*n*=22) **305** Other *(Please specify.* _____ *)*

     ----

     j. 41,796 TOTAL ACRES

3. In the past 10 years, how has the amount of <u>your land</u> you use in the following ways changed? *(Please check one for each item.)*

	n	I don't use my land in this way.	Increased	Stayed the same	Decreased	I am not sure.
a. Home, buildings (including barns, lawn, gardens, etc.)	548	3.3%	15.3%	77.4%	2.0%	2.0%
b. Hay and livestock pasture (including alfalfa, orchard grass, etc.)	494	58.1%	2.8%	31.2%	5.7%	2.2%
c. Land in conservation programs (including CRP, Acres for Wildlife, etc.)	486	68.5%	6.2%	19.8%	2.3%	3.3%
d. Corn and/or soybean fields	494	60.9%	4.0%	27.9%	5.1%	2.0%
e. Other agricultural fields *(Crop grown? _____)*	16	0.0%	31.3%	62.5%	6.3%	0.0%
f. Wood lots	490	51.0%	4.1%	41.2%	1.0%	2.7%
g. Wetlands, ponds	470	64.3%	4.5%	26.8%	1.7%	2.8%
h. Orchards, fruit trees/plants	470	59.1%	7.7%	28.5%	1.9%	2.8%
i. Other *(Please specify. _____)*	11	0.0%	54.5%	36.4%	9.1%	0.0%

4. In the past 10 years, how do you feel the amount of land <u>in this county and the adjacent counties</u> used in the following ways has changed? *(Please check one for each item.)*

	n	Increased	Stayed the same	Decreased	I am not sure.
a. Home, buildings (including barns, lawn, gardens, etc.)	555	70.1%	14.1%	8.1%	7.7%
b. Hay and livestock pasture (including alfalfa, timothy, orchard grass, etc.)	534	4.5%	25.3%	48.3%	21.9%
c. Land in conservation programs (including CRP, Acres for Wildlife, etc.)	533	25.1%	26.1%	15.6%	33.2%
d. Corn and/or soybean fields	528	18.9%	31.8%	30.7%	18.6%
e. Other agricultural fields *(Crop grown? _____)*	9	44.4%	33.3%	22.2%	0.0%
f. Wood lots	520	2.3%	25.2%	47.5%	25.0%
g. Wetlands, ponds	518	13.5%	31.3%	22.6%	32.6%
h. Orchards, fruit trees/plants	517	6.6%	30.2%	29.0%	34.2%
i. Other *(Please specify. _____)*	5	100%			

5. Do you manage any of your land specifically for birds or other wildlife? *For example: Feeding birds, planting plants for wildlife, letting trees grow, etc.* ***n = 566***

> **50.4%** Yes   **49.6%** No *(Please skip to question 8.)*

6. If yes, for which of the following kinds of birds or other wildlife do you manage? *(Please check all that apply.)* ***n = 758***

> **35.2%** Song birds (cardinals, bluebirds, etc.)
> **14.6%** Upland game birds (wild turkey, pheasant, quail, doves, etc.)
> **5.4%** Waterfowl (ducks and geese)
> **13.3%** White-tailed deer
> **18.6%** Other mammals (rabbits, squirrels, etc.)
> **5.8%** Fish (bluegill, bass, etc.)
> **5.5%** Reptiles and amphibians (snakes, frogs, etc.)
> **1.5%** Other *(Please specify._____)*

7. What actions do you take specifically for the benefit of birds or other wildlife on your land? *(Please check all that apply.)* ***n = 895***

> **21.1%** Plant trees, shrubs or grasses specifically for wildlife cover
> **9.6%** Cut trees or shrubs to improve wildlife cover
> **6.9%** Maintain ponds or wetlands for wildlife cover
> **17.9%** Provide boxes, platforms or others areas for wildlife nesting and/or rearing
> **9.6%** Delay mowing or haying until after nesting/rearing season is over
> **25.4%** Provide seeds, corn or other food for wildlife
> **8.3%** Plant food plots specifically for wildlife
> **1.2%** Other *(Please specify. _____)*

8. Do you allow other people access to your property to hunt any species of birds or other wildlife? ***n = 575***

> **21.6%** Yes   **78.4%** No *(Please skip to question 10.)*

9. If you do allow others access to your land to hunt, who are they? *(Please check all that apply.)* ***n = 208***

> **31.3%** No one
> **17.8%** Only myself and my immediate family
> **41.3%** Only friends and family who ask permission to access my land
> **4.8%** Anyone who asks permission to access my land
> **2.9%** Lessees who pay me for access to my land
> **1.0%** Anyone; I allow open, public access to my land.
> **1.0%** Other *(Please specify. _____)*

The Birds Around You

10. How many kinds (species) of birds you see in this area could you identify by song or sight? *n = 597*

> **2.7%** 0 kinds of birds
> **59.3%** 1-10 kinds of birds
> **23.6%** 11-20 kinds of birds
> **11.6%** 21-50 kinds of birds
> **2.8%** 51 or more kinds of birds

11. Which 1-3 kinds (species) of birds do you see or hear most commonly in this area? *(Please write in below or check the box provided.)* ***3 most common***

1. **Cardinals**
2. **Robins**
3. **Sparrows**

ₗ[ ] I do not know.

12. Which 1-3 kinds (species) of birds do you think have <u>increased</u> the most in total number in this area over the past 5 years? ***3 increased most***

1. **Cardinals**
2. **Sparrows**
3. **Starlings**

ₗ[ ] I do not know.

13. Which 1-3 kinds (species) of birds do you think have <u>decreased</u> the most in total number in this area over the past 5 years? ***3 decreased most***

1. **Blue jays**
2. **Quail**
3. **Pheasant**

ₗ[ ] I do not know.

14. How do you think the following items have changed in this area over the past 5 years? *(Please check one for each item.)*

	n	increased greatly.	increased somewhat.	stayed the same.	decreased somewhat.	decreased greatly.	I am not sure.
a. The amount of habitat for birds has…	584	2.6%	13.5%	24.5%	35.1%	12.0%	12.3%
b. The quality of habitat for birds has…	579	2.2%	14.2%	26.9%	30.1%	12.4%	14.2%
c. The number of kinds of birds I see has…	583	1.9%	28.1%	34.1%	21.6%	3.3%	11.0%
d. The total number of birds I see has…	582	2.7%	28.4%	38.8%	18.2%	2.9%	8.9%
e. The number of backyard birds (cardinals, robins, etc.) I see has…	587	3.2%	33.0%	39.4%	16.5%	1.7%	6.1%
f. The number of grassland birds (meadowlarks, bobolink, etc.) I see has…	586	0.5%	6.8%	26.6%	20.6%	10.4%	35.0%
g. The number of forest birds (woodpeckers, orioles, etc.) I see has…	585	1.0%	14.4%	33.2%	22.2%	9.2%	20.0%
h. The number of pheasants and quail I see has…	584	1.7%	10.8%	19.2%	21.2%	24.7%	22.4%
i. The number of wild turkeys I see has…	576	18.2%	28.5%	18.6%	8.2%	6.3%	20.3%
j. The number of ducks and geese I see has…	585	11.1%	25.3%	32.1%	12.1%	3.6%	15.7%
k. The number of hawks and owls I see has…	587	6.0%	26.9%	35.9%	13.3%	4.4%	13.5%

15. How would you like to see the following items change in the next 5 years? *(Please check one for each item.)*

I would like...	*n*	increase greatly.	increase somewhat.	stay the same.	decrease somewhat.	decrease greatly.	I am not sure.
a. the amount of habitat for birds to…	585	25.6%	47.5%	20.5%	0.3%	0.2%	5.8%
b. the quality of habitat for birds to…	582	28.4%	49.0%	16.0%	0.3%	0.2%	6.2%
c. the number of kinds of birds I see to…	585	29.9%	50.1%	15.0%	0.7%	0.2%	4.1%
d. the total number of birds I see to…	573	22.9%	51.0%	20.8%	1.2%	0.2%	4.0%
e. the number of backyard birds (cardinals, robins, etc.) I see to…	588	24.3%	46.4%	24.8%	0.9%	0.3%	3.2%
f. the number of grassland birds (meadowlarks, bobolink, etc.) I see to…	582	25.6%	47.6%	16.7%	0.3%	0.2%	9.6%
g. the number of forest birds (woodpeckers, orioles, etc.) I see to…	583	28.1%	44.9%	19.6%	0.9%	0.2%	6.3%
h. the number of pheasants and quail I see to…	584	34.2%	40.6%	15.8%	0.5%	0.0%	8.9%
i. the number of wild turkeys I see to…	580	20.0%	34.8%	27.8%	4.3%	1.9%	11.2%
j. the number of ducks and geese I see to…	582	16.2%	26.5%	36.4%	8.6%	3.1%	9.3%
k. the number of hawks and owls I see to…	584	19.2%	33.4%	29.6%	5.5%	3.4%	8.9%

16. How important to you are the following items? *(Please check one for each item.)*

	n	Very important	Somewhat important	Not at all important	I am not sure.
a. The amount of habitat for birds in this area	581	47.8%	46.1%	2.2%	3.8%
b. The quality of habitat for birds in this area	580	51.9%	42.8%	1.7%	3.6%
c. The number of kinds of birds I see in this area	576	48.4%	46.4%	2.4%	2.8%
d. The total number of birds I see in this area	579	43.9%	49.2%	3.5%	3.5%
e. The number of backyard birds (cardinals, robins, etc.) I see in this area	586	50.5%	44.7%	2.9%	1.9%
f. The number of grassland birds (meadowlarks, bobolink, etc.) I see in this area	580	40.9%	47.1%	4.7%	7.4%
g. The number of forest birds (woodpeckers, orioles, etc.) I see in this area	580	44.1%	47.4%	4.7%	3.8%
h. The number of pheasants and quail I see in this area	578	43.4%	43.4%	6.1%	7.1%
i. The number of wild turkeys I see in this area	581	32.4%	45.1%	14.8%	7.7%
j. The number of ducks and geese I see in this area	574	27.0%	47.7%	17.6%	7.7%
k. The number of hawks and owls I see in this area	580	36.2%	47.4%	9.1%	7.2%

17. Which of the following factors do you think has the greatest effect on the number and type of birds you see in this area? *n = 1,200*

    20.9% Food availability
    20.7% Availability and quality of nesting cover
    13.0% Availability and quality of winter cover
    3.4% Hunting
    5.7% Diseases and parasites
    11.2% Competition with invasive, pest birds (starlings, house sparrows, etc.)
    8.5% Predators
    8.2% Pollution or toxins in the environment
    3.7% Other *(Please specify)*_____
    4.7% I am not sure.

18. Which of the following factors do you think has been responsible for changes you have noticed in bird populations in this area over the past 5 years? *n = 1,620*

16.7% Food availability

19.5% Availability and quality of nesting cover

15.3% Availability and quality of winter cover

4.4% Hunting

6.6% Diseases and parasites

11.8% Competition with invasive, pest birds (starlings, house sparrows, etc.)

9.6% Predators

8.9% Pollution or toxins in the environment

2.2% Other *(Please specify)*_____

5.0% I am not sure.

Your Land in Illinois

19. How important to you were the following factors when you decided to purchase land in this or an adjacent county? *(Please check one for each item.)*

	n	Very important	Somewhat important	Not at all important	I am not sure.
a. This area is close to my place of employment.	519	41.2%	32.8%	23.5%	2.5%
b. This area is close to my family and friends.	530	46.8%	34.0%	16.8%	2.5%
c. I grew up in this area.	526	41.8%	20.5%	33.5%	4.2%
d. This area provides the quality of life I want.	543	72.0%	23.4%	2.2%	2.4%
e. This area is close to other towns and amenities I want to access.	526	36.1%	41.4%	20.0%	2.5%
f. This area has a reasonable cost of living.	528	50.8%	38.8%	6.6%	3.8%
g. This area seems safe.	534	68.0%	27.0%	3.0%	2.1%
h. This area seems natural to me and I want to live in a natural area.	541	59.7%	31.1%	6.1%	3.1%
i. This area is close to areas where I can hunt, fish, watch wildlife, camp, etc.	528	34.3%	25.0%	37.5%	3.2%
j. Other *(Please specify.* _____ *)*	8	100%			

20. How important to you are the following benefits that may result from owning or managing land in this county or the adjacent counties? *(Please check one for each item.)*

	n	Very important	Somewhat important	Not at all important	I am not sure.
a. Providing a place for you and your family to live	561	86.3%	11.8%	0.9%	1.1%
b. Maintaining ownership of the land in your family	554	55.6%	26.2%	14.8%	3.4%
c. Appreciation of the land as a real estate investment	552	43.3%	36.2%	16.8%	3.6%
d. Crops you are able to produce and sell from this land	538	21.6%	14.1%	57.6%	6.7%
e. Gas, oil, gravel, coal or other minerals you are able to extract from the land	531	3.0%	5.1%	81.5%	10.4%
f. Timber you are able to produce and sell from this land.	534	3.9%	10.5%	76.4%	9.2%
g. Your ability to subdivide this land and re-sell or lease it for commercial or residential development	534	3.0%	6.7%	83.7%	6.6%
h. Your ability to use the land for recreation	535	30.5%	34.8%	30.3%	4.5%
i. Providing habitat for birds and other wildlife	546	39.0%	48.9%	8.4%	3.7%
j. Other *(Please specify.)*	7	100%			

21. How would you rate the quality of the land in this area as a place for wildlife to live?
   n = 584

        18.5% Excellent
        38.9% Above average
        32.7% Average
        5.0% Below average
        1.4% Poor
        3.6% I am not sure.

22. How would you rate the quality of the land in this area as a place for people to live?
   n = 585

        27.2% Excellent
        38.3% Above average
        30.4% Average
        1.9% Below average
        0.9% Poor
        1.4% I am not sure.

23. When you decide how to use land that you own or manage, how important to you are the following factors? *(Please check one for each item.)*

	n	Very important	Somewhat important	Not at all important	I am not sure.
a. Income you could gain from the action	552	25.5%	25.2%	42.6%	6.7%
b. Cost of the action	542	34.9%	37.1%	19.9%	8.1%
c. Time and effort you will have to invest	542	30.4%	40.6%	21.4%	7.6%
d. Your familiarity with the action	534	27.3%	42.9%	18.9%	10.9%
e. Availability of expert assistance	536	23.5%	40.7%	25.0%	10.8%
f. Opinions of your neighbors or community	544	14.3%	43.0%	34.9%	7.7%
g. Recommendations of conservation organizations (Pheasants Forever, Audubon Society, etc.)	542	19.0%	45.0%	25.1%	10.9%
h. Your ability to use the land for recreation	539	28.0%	39.0%	24.9%	8.2%
i. The effect of the action on wildlife habitat and numbers	541	38.3%	46.0%	8.5%	7.2%
j. The effect of the action on bird habitat and numbers	545	38.5%	45.9%	7.5%	8.1%
k. The aesthetics or beauty of the land	546	58.8%	33.3%	3.7%	4.2%

24. If you wanted to do something for wildlife on your land, where would you go for assistance or information? *(Please check all that apply)* **n = 1,498**

4.8% I would not contact any organization for assistance.

6.0% U.S. Department of Agriculture

9.3% Illinois Department of Agriculture

18.1% Illinois Department of Natural Resources

10.5% Illinois Farm Bureau

15.1% University of Illinois Extension Services

13.4% Wildlife conservation organizations (Pheasants Forever, Audubon Society, etc.)

3.8% Local or municipal government

16.6% Friends, family and neighbors

2.4% Other *(Please specify._____)*

Background Information

25. In what year were you born? *n* = **587** **Ave.** 19_52_

26. For how many years have you lived in this area? *n* = **588** _35_ years

27. What is your occupation? **n** = **576**_____

28. Are you   **48.3%** male or   **51.7%** female? *n* = **592**

29. What is your highest level of education? *n* = **589**
   4.2% Less than high school diploma
   28.2% High school graduate or GED
   6.1% Vocational or trade school
   18.0% Some college
   8.1% Associate's Degree (2 year)
   19.4% Bachelor's Degree (4 year)
   16.0% Graduate/Professional Degree

30. How would you describe the area where you currently live? *n* = **590**
   29.2% Rural setting, on a farm
   39.7% Rural setting, <u>not</u> on a farm
   6.1% Rural subdivision
   4.4% Suburban area on the edge of a town or city
   14.6% Within a small town (Population less than 25,000)
   5.4% Within an urban area (Population between 25,000 and 500,000)
   0.7% Within a metropolitan area (Population more than 500,000)

31. How would you describe the area where you lived during most or all of your childhood? *(Please check only one.)* **n = 574**

> **35.4%** Rural setting, on a farm
> **16.9%** Rural setting, not on a farm
> **3.0%** Rural subdivision
> **5.9%** Suburban area on the edge of a town or city
> **21.8%** Within a small town (Population less than 25,000)
> **11.1%** Within an urban area (Population between 25,000 and 500,000)
> **5.9%** Within a metropolitan area (Population more than 500,000)

32. Please list the names of any wildlife, conservation or hunting organizations to which you belong.

> **n = 214**

33. What is your approximate annual household income? **n = 480**

> **5.2%** Less than $20,000 per year
> **19.0%** $20,000 to $39,999 per year
> **25.2%** $40,000 to $59,999 per year
> **20.0%** $60,000 to $79,999 per year
> **14.6%** $80,000 to $99,999 per year
> **10.4%** $100,000 to $149,999 per year
> **5.6%** Over $150,000 per year

34. Please use the space below to write any additional comments or observations you would like
to share.

n = 116

THANK YOU VERY MUCH FOR YOUR PARTICIPATION!
Please return this survey in the postage-paid envelope provided.

A summary of the study findings will be available at:
www.inhs.uiuc.edu/cwpe/hd.

THANK YOU FOR YOUR TIME AND ASSISTANCE!
Please return this survey in the postage-paid envelope provided.

Appendix IV. List of all species , by time period and region, during summer bird surveys in Illinois. An "x" indicates species recorded during transect surveys; an "o" marks species observed during field work, but not recorded on transects (e.g., recorded on point counts or beyond the boundaries of a transect). Scientific and common names follow the American Ornithologists' Union "Checklist of North American Birds," 7th edition, 50th supplement.

Common Name	Scientific Name	1900s North	1900s Central	1900s South	1950s North	1950s Central	1950s South	2000s North	2000s Central	2000s South
Black-bellied Whistling Duck	Dendrocygna autumnalis									o
Canada Goose	Branta canadensis						o	x	x	x
Mute Swan	Cygnus olor							x	o	
Trumpeter Swan	Cygnus buccinator							o		
Wood Duck	Aix sponsa					o		x	x	x
Mallard	Anas platyrhynchos				x		o	x	x	x
Blue-winged Teal	Anas discors				x	x		x	o	
Hooded Merganser	Lophodytes cucullatus									o
Gray Partridge	Perdix perdix				x					
Ring-necked Pheasant	Phasianus colchicus				x	x		x	x	o
Greater Prairie-Chicken	Tympanuchus cupido	x	x							
Wild Turkey	Meleagris gallopavo							x	x	o
Northern Bobwhite	Colinus virginianus	x	x	x	x	x	x	x	x	x
Pied-billed Grebe	Podilymbus podiceps							o		
Horned Grebe	Podiceps auritus				x					
American White Pelican	Pelecanus erythrorhynchos								o	
Double-crested Cormorant	Phalacrocorax auritus							x		o
American Bittern	Botaurus lentiginosus				x					
Least Bittern	Ixobrychus exilis				x		x			
Great Blue Heron	Ardea herodias		o	x	x		x	x	x	x
Great Egret	Ardea alba						x	x	x	x
Snowy Egret	Egretta thula									o
Little Blue Heron	Egretta caerulea						o			x
Green Heron	Butorides virescens		x	x	x	x	x	x	x	x
Black-crowned Night-Heron	Nycticorax nycticorax	x			x	x	o			
Yellow-crowned Night-Heron	Nyctanassa violacea									x
Ibis spp.	Plegadis spp.									x
Black Vulture	Coragyps atratus									x
Turkey Vulture	Cathartes aura		o	x		x	x	x	x	x
Mississippi Kite	Ictinia mississippiensis									o
Bald Eagle	Haliaeetus leucocephalus							x		x
Northern Harrier	Circus cyaneus	x			x	o				
Cooper's Hawk	Accipiter cooperii				x			x	x	x
Red-shouldered Hawk	Buteo lineatus		x			o	x	o	o	x
Broad-winged Hawk	Buteo platypterus				o					
Swainson's Hawk	Buteo swainsoni							o		
Red-tailed Hawk	Buteo jamaicensis		x	x	x	x	x	x	x	x
American Kestrel	Falco sparverius	x	x	x	x	x	o	x	x	x
King Rail	Rallus elegans	o			x					o
Virginia Rail	Rallus limicola				x			x		
Sora	Porzana carolina		x					o		
Common Moorhen	Gallinula chloropus				o			x		
American Coot	Fulica americana				x		o	o		o
Sandhill Crane	Grus canadensis							x		
Killdeer	Charadrius vociferus	x	x	x	x	x	x	x	x	x

Common Name	Scientific Name	1900s			1950s			2000s		
		North	Central	South	North	Central	South	North	Central	South
Spotted Sandpiper	Actitis macularia		x	x	x		o	x	x	
Upland Sandpiper	Bartramia longicauda	x	x	x	x	x	x	o	o	
Wilson's Snipe	Gallinago delicata				x					
American Woodcock	Scolopax minor			x					o	
Ring-billed Gull	Larus delawarensis							x	o	
Herring Gull	Larus argentatus							x		
Least Tern	Sternula antillarum									o
Caspian Tern	Hydroprogne caspia							x		
Black Tern	Chlidonias niger				x			x		
Forster's Tern	Sterna forsteri							x		
Rock Pigeon	Columba livia				x	x	x	x	x	x
Eurasian Collared-Dove	Streptopelia decaocto								x	x
Mourning Dove	Zenaida macroura	x	x	x	x	x	x	x	x	x
Yellow-billed Cuckoo	Coccyzus americanus	x	x	x	x	x	x	x	x	x
Black-billed Cuckoo	Coccyzus erythropthalmus		x	x	x	o	x	x		
Great Horned Owl	Bubo virginianus				o	x		x	x	
Barred Owl	Strix varia			x			x		x	x
Common Nighthawk	Chordeiles minor		x	x	o	o	x	x	o	o
Whip-poor-will	Caprimulgus vociferus						x			
Chimney Swift	Chaetura pelagica	x	x	x	x	x	x	x	x	x
Ruby-throated Hummingbird	Archilochus colubris		x	x	x	x	x	x	x	x
Belted Kingfisher	Megaceryle alcyon		x	x	x	x	o	o	x	
Red-headed Woodpecker	Melanerpes erythrocephalus	x	x	x	x	x	x	o	x	x
Red-bellied Woodpecker	Melanerpes carolinus		x	o	x	x	x	x	x	x
Downy Woodpecker	Picoides pubescens	o	o	x	x	x	x	x	x	x
Hairy Woodpecker	Picoides villosus		x	x	o	x	x	x	x	x
Northern Flicker	Colaptes auratus	x	x	x	x	x	x	x	x	x
Pileated Woodpecker	Dryocopus pileatus						x	o	x	x
Olive-sided Flycatcher	Contopus cooperi									o
Eastern Wood-Pewee	Contopus virens	x	o	x	x	x	x	x	x	x
Acadian Flycatcher	Empidonax virescens			x	x	x	x	x	x	x
Alder Flycatcher	Empidonax alnorum							o	o	
Willow Flycatcher	Empidonax traillii		x	x	x	x	x	x	x	x
Least Flycatcher	Empidonax minimus		x					o		
Yellow-bellied Flycatcher	Empidonax flaviventris		x							
Eastern Phoebe	Sayornis phoebe	x	x	x	x	o	x	x	x	x
Great Crested Flycatcher	Myiarchus crinitus	o	x	x	x	x	x	x	x	x
Eastern Kingbird	Tyrannus tyrannus	x	x	x	x	x	x	x	x	x
Loggerhead Shrike	Lanius ludovicianus	x	x	x	x	x	x		x	o
White-eyed Vireo	Vireo griseus			x			x	o	x	x
Bell's Vireo	Vireo bellii					x	x	x	x	x
Yellow-throated Vireo	Vireo flavifrons				x	x	x	x	o	x
Warbling Vireo	Vireo gilvus	x		x	x	x	x	x	x	x
Red-eyed Vireo	Vireo olivaceus	x	x	x	x	x	x	x	x	x
Blue Jay	Cyanocitta cristata	x	x	x	x	x	x	x	x	x
American Crow	Corvus brachyrhynchos	x	x	x	x	x	x	x	x	x
Fish Crow	Corvus ossifragus									x
Horned Lark	Eremophila alpestris	x	x	x	x	x	x	x	x	x
Purple Martin	Progne subis		x	x	x	x	x	x	x	x

Common Name	Scientific Name	1900s			1950s			2000s		
		North	Central	South	North	Central	South	North	Central	South
Tree Swallow	Tachycineta bicolor				x	x		x	x	x
Northern Rough-winged Swallow	Stelgidopteryx serripennis				x	x	x	x	x	x
Bank Swallow	Riparia riparia	x	x	x	x	x		x	x	
Cliff Swallow	Petrochelidon pyrrhonota		x	x	x		o	x	x	x
Barn Swallow	Hirundo rustica	x	x	x	x	x	x	x	x	x
Carolina Chickadee	Poecile carolinensis		o	x		x	x		x	x
Black-capped Chickadee	Poecile atricapillus				x			x	x	
Tufted Titmouse	Baeolophus bicolor			x	x	x	x	x	x	x
Red-breasted Nuthatch	Sitta canadensis								o	
White-breasted Nuthatch	Sitta carolinensis		x		x	x	x	x	x	x
Brown Creeper	Certhia americana							o	x	
Carolina Wren	Thryothorus ludovicianus			x		x	x	o	x	x
Bewick's Wren	Thryomanes bewickii		o	x			x			
House Wren	Troglodytes aedon	o	x	x	x	x	x	x	x	x
Sedge Wren	Cistothorus platensis				x	o	x	x	x	x
Marsh Wren	Cistothorus palustris				x			x	o	
Blue-gray Gnatcatcher	Polioptila caerulea				x	x	x	x	x	x
Eastern Bluebird	Sialia sialis	x	x	x	x	x	x	x	x	x
Veery	Catharus fuscescens								o	
Swainson's Thrush	Catharus ustulatus		x							
Wood Thrush	Hylocichla mustelina		o	x		x	x	o	x	x
American Robin	Turdus migratorius	x	x	x	x	x	x	x	x	x
Gray Catbird	Dumetella carolinensis	x	x	x	x	x	x	x	x	x
Northern Mockingbird	Mimus polyglottos		x	x		x	x	o	x	x
Brown Thrasher	Toxostoma rufum	x	x	x	x	x	x	x	x	x
European Starling	Sturnus vulgaris				x	x	x	x	x	x
Cedar Waxwing	Bombycilla cedrorum					o		x	x	x
Northern Parula	Parula americana		x				x	o	o	o
Yellow Warbler	Dendroica petechia	x		x		x	x	x	x	x
Chestnut-sided Warbler	Dendroica pensylvanica		x							
Magnolia Warbler	Dendroica magnolia		x							
Yellow-throated Warbler	Dendroica dominica						o	x	o	x
Pine Warbler	Dendroica pinus						o	o	o	x
Prairie Warbler	Dendroica discolor						x			x
Cerulean Warbler	Dendroica cerulea				x	x	x	o		o
Palm Warbler	Dendroica palmarum		x							
Black-and-white Warbler	Mniotilta varia			o			x		o	
American Redstart	Setophaga ruticilla		x	x	x	x	x	x	x	x
Prothonotary Warbler	Protonotaria citrea			x			x	x	o	x
Worm-eating Warbler	Helmitheros vermivorus						x	o		x
Swainson's Warbler	Limnothlypis swainsonii			x						
Ovenbird	Seiurus aurocapillus				x	x		o	o	x
Louisiana Waterthrush	Seiurus motacilla			x	x		x		o	x
Kentucky Warbler	Oporornis formosus					x	x	o	x	x
Mourning Warbler	Oporornis philadelphia									x
Common Yellowthroat	Geothlypis trichas	x	x	x	x	x	x	x	x	x
Hooded Warbler	Wilsonia citrina						x	o		o
Yellow-breasted Chat	Icteria virens		o	x		x	x	o	x	x
Summer Tanager	Piranga rubra		o	x			x	o	x	x

Common Name	Scientific Name	1900s			1950s			2000s		
		North	Central	South	North	Central	South	North	Central	South
Scarlet Tanager	Piranga olivacea		x	x	x	o	x	x	o	x
Eastern Towhee	Pipilo erythrophthalmus	x	x	x	x	x	x	x	x	x
Bachman's Sparrow	Aimophila aestivalis			x			x			
Chipping Sparrow	Spizella passerina	x	x	x	x		x	x	x	x
Field Sparrow	Spizella pusilla	x	x	x	x	x	x	x	x	x
Vesper Sparrow	Pooecetes gramineus	x	x		x	x	x	x	x	o
Lark Sparrow	Chondestes grammacus	x	x	x	x	x		o	x	x
Savannah Sparrow	Passerculus sandwichensis	x	x		x			x	x	
Grasshopper Sparrow	Ammodramus savannarum	x	x	x	x	x	x	x	x	x
Henslow's Sparrow	Ammodramus henslowii		x		o	x			x	x
Song Sparrow	Melospiza melodia	x	x		x	x	x	x	x	x
Swamp Sparrow	Melospiza georgiana	x		o	x		o	x		
White-throated Sparrow	Zonotrichia albicollis								x	
Northern Cardinal	Cardinalis cardinalis		x	x	x	x	x	x	x	x
Rose-breasted Grosbeak	Pheucticus ludovicianus	x	x		x	x		x	x	o
Blue Grosbeak	Passerina caerulea				o	x		o	x	x
Indigo Bunting	Passerina cyanea	x	x	x	x	x	x	x	x	x
Dickcissel	Spiza americana	x	x	x	x	x	x	x	x	x
Bobolink	Dolichonyx oryzivorus	x	x		x	x		x	x	x
Red-winged Blackbird	Agelaius phoeniceus	x	x	x	x	x	x	x	x	x
Eastern Meadowlark	Sturnella magna	x	x	x	x	x	x	x	x	x
Western Meadowlark	Sturnella neglecta				x	x		x	o	o
Yellow-headed Blackbird	Xanthocephalus xanthocephalus				x			o		
Brewer's Blackbird	Euphagus cyanocephalus				x					
Common Grackle	Quiscalus quiscula	x	x	x	x	x	x	x	x	x
Brown-headed Cowbird	Molothrus ater	x	x	x	x	x	x	x	x	x
Orchard Oriole	Icterus spurius	x	x	x	x	x	x	x	x	x
Baltimore Oriole	Icterus galbula	x	x	x	x	x	x	x	x	x
House Finch	Carpodacus mexicanus							x	x	x
American Goldfinch	Carduelis tristis	x	x	x	x	x	x	x	x	x
House Sparrow	Passer domesticus	x	x	x	x	x	x	x	x	x
Eurasian Tree Sparrow	Passer montanus								x	

Appendix V. Scientific names of plant species mentioned by common name in this report.

Common name	Scientific name
alfalfa	Medicago sativa
apple	malus sp.
ash	Fraxinus sp.
green ash	Fraxinus pennsylvanica
autumn olive	Elaeagnus umbellata
bald cypress	Taxodium distichum
barley	Hordeum vulgare
big bluestem	Andropogon gerardii
black locust	Robinia pseudoacacia
black willow	Salix nigra
blackberry	Rubus sp.
blue spruce	Picea glauca
blueberry	Vaccinium sp.
bluegrass	Poa sp.
broom sedge	Andropogon virginicus
buckthorn	Rhamnus cathartica
bulrushes	Scirpus sp.
bush honeysuckle	Lonicera sp.
cattail	Typha sp.
corn	Zea mays
cottonwood	Populus deltoides
eastern red cedar	Juniperus virginiana
elm	Ulmus sp.
garlic mustard	Alliaria petiolata
gooseberry	Ribes sp.
green beans	Phaseolus vulgaris
green peppers	Capsicum annuum
hackberry	Celtis occidentalis
hickories	Carya sp.
honey locust	Gleditsia triacanthos
Indian grass	Sorghastrum nutans
Japanese stilt grass	Microstegium vimineum
kudzu	Pueraria montana var. lobata
little bluestem	Schizachyrium scoparium
maples	Acer sp.
silver maple	Acer saccharinum
sugar maple	Acer sacarrum
mare's tail	Conyza canadensis
multiflora rose	Rosa multiflora
oaks	Quercus sp.
black oak	Quercus velutina
burr oak	Quercus macrocarpa
white oak	Quercus alba
oats	Avena sativa
orchard grass	Dactylis glomerata

Common name	Scientific name
Osage orange	Maclura pomifera
pecan	Carya illinoinensis
phragmites	Phragmites australis
pines	Pinus sp.
poison ivy	Toxicodendron radicans
potatoes	Solanum tuberosum
purple loosestrife	Lythrum salicaria
ragweed	Ambrosia sp.
raspberry	Rubus sp.
red clover	Trifolium pratense
reed canarygrass	Phalaris arundinacea
rushes	Juncus sp.
rye	Secale cereale
sassafras	Sassafras albidum
sedges	Carex spp.
sericea lespedeza	Lespedeza cuneata
smooth brome	Bromus inermis
sorghum	Sorghum bicolor
soybeans	Glycine max
spruces	Picea sp.
sunflower	Helianthus annuus
sweet clover	Melilotus sp.
yellow sweet clover	Melilotus officinalis
switchgrass	Panicum virgatum
sycamore	Platanus occidentalis
tall fescue	Festuca arundinacea
timothy	Phleum pratense
wheat	Triticum aestivum

Index of Bird Common Names